FIRE BY NIGHT

An autobiography by
Richard and Sara Michalski

A saga of God's Sovereign leading from Soviet lands
through Communist China to FREEDOM

Cover Art by Adam Lubanski
adam@l42.com

First Edition   April, 2012

FIRE BY NIGHT

Library of Congress Control Number 2011938482
Trade Edition ISBN 978-0-9657661-2-8

DEDICATION

Sara and I would like to dedicate this book to Michael & Nadejda Ilyin, whose legacy of faith has challenged and encouraged their family and the family of Faith.

It is our desire that the saga of this historic exodus would be life changing in your relationship with the Lord, Jesus Christ.

APPRECIATION

We would like to acknowledge the following individuals whose tireless help and dedication made this book possible:

Preliminary editing by Jackie Vick of Stevensville, Montana
Primary editing by Professor Jeff Pope from Northwest University, Kirkland, WA.
Final Editing by Robin Lommori,
Formatting & picture development by Jesse Lopienski, Vernon, British Columbia, Canada
Cover & graphics by Adam Lubanski, Bellevue, WA.
Surround Media Inc. (website: www.surroundmedia.com)
Compulation & Print brokerage by Al Dager of Spotlight Media, Issaquah, WA.

We personally thank Dr. Marilyn Hickey for the writing of our foreword and for her support of our mission over many years and believing in the miracles of God.

TABLE OF CONTENTS

FOREWORD

Fire by Night is a very exciting book because it reveals how God makes Himself a pillar of fire for us in the most unusual situations even by sending great angelic help. It is encouraging to know that God was at work in communistic times way beyond what we could imagine or expect. It is encouraging to read about those who experienced unusual duress and came out victoriously. This book will be a pillar of fire in your spirit and will lead you in the dark times of your circumstances, and will encourage and help you to no end.

Dr. Marilyn Hickey
Marilyn Hickey Ministries

PREFACE

AS THE HOURGLASS of time shifts its sands of decades and nations, God has faithfully proven Himself by keeping covenant with His people. From the Old Testament passages of antiquity, the Sovereign God of all the ages has delivered His people from Egypt and from bondage with His mighty outstretched arm. God hardened Pharaoh's heart to display His power to the ends of the earth and from generation to generation.

The God that vanquished Pharaoh, Egypt's former glory and all her gods is the unchanging Ancient of Days and still sets His people free. God establishes kings and kingdoms and removes them by a breath of His word, but He keeps covenant with His righteous seed throughout all generations.

This story is of the sons of Abraham hearing and heeding the God of the Old Testament in a New Testament relationship and dramatic deliverance. Couched deep in the setting of the peasant farmers' rich, dark soil of southern Ukraine unfolds an exquisite tapestry of God's leading and guarding by His prophetic Word.

This is about people of today, no different from the people of ages past who wandered in unbelief until they came to know the voice of God and in knowing Him sealed their faith. His prophetic promise declared that their seed would return to the lands that they once fled and would establish a myriad of churches in the end of time.

This book chronicles the process of God's powerful arm raised against His enemies and His tender, caring hand on those who put their trust in Jesus Christ. Walk with us through the journey that covers the circumference of the earth—a journey of failure and, most of all, a journey displaying the unfaltering favor of God.

10 Fire By Night

Rest assured that all the participants in this epic are made of clay, but also be assured that the Master Potter can mold the most unlikely into vessels of honor for His Name's sake. This story takes us back to the 1920s and eventually brings us to testimonies that have exploded on the horizon of the present time.

As you take this journey with us, it is our sincere desire that we all learn to hear the Master's voice better and follow Him with a greater sense of destiny so that His great Name may be heralded and glorified among the nations that do not yet know God. It is our prayer that from every tribe, kindred and tongue, knees by the millions will bow in adoration and worship to our Lord Jesus Christ who changes not, who still speaks to His own. As He was the fourth man in the fire of Shadrach, Meshach and Abednego, so let Him be a pillar of fire in the darkness of this final age, a fire that consumes the dross and refines the soul—a fire that brings forth your life and mine to shine like gold, reflecting His image in us by God's purifying fire.

Let His fire be a terror to His enemies and a sense of warm, clear directive to His followers. May your faith be stirred to trust Jesus for more, believe in Him more deeply, and then walk out your journey, declaring His glory.

At every turn, whether through tragedy or triumph, Christ is displayed in this book as Faithful and True—whether it be in the provision of water out of the desert sand or in the slaying of enemies that plotted against His people or in a communist government bowing before the Lord's desire to let His people go. This story is true because the One Who wrote it on the hearts of His people is called Faithful and True. He is forever the unchanging Christ.

Chapter One
ANGELS WATCHING OVER ME

"Surely He shall deliver you from the snare of the fowler" (Psalm 91:3a).

I N A DAY and an hour when the supernatural of God is rare and mocked in the land, in a season where it is vogue to embrace the vain and the flagrant, this accounting by contrast is a true testimony of the power of God. The reason the miraculous is so rare in our lives is because few are the times when our crisis is so acute that it demands Christ's intervention. To the ardent believer, the pattern seems to be the deeper and darker the valley of our trial, the greater the opportunity for God's light and glory to be shown. With this as a backdrop, let us begin our story displaying how God's grace intervened to the sparing of our lives once again.

Sara, my wife and I have a Czech friend whose name is Zamek. His name in the Czech language and Polish language means *Lock*. God has unlocked many revelations and true treasures to our dear brother; however, the first time I met him, I thought the man had eaten too much garlic sausage. He was always seeing angels. In a time frame when few have had an angelic visitation over a lifetime, our young brother was seemingly encountering the angelic on a regular basis. I was immediately suspect of these numerous angelic visitations, but because of the intensity with which he related the incident to us, we began to believe his accounting.

It wasn't, however, until our own experience with an angelic encounter that the reality of God's covering and mercy was understood by our hearts. One day, Paul Zamek astounded me with the revelation that two large war angels follow Sara and me because of the uniqueness of our calling and the countries of our leading. Heaven seems to think that we need this special envoy to cover and guard our steps.

Upon first hearing this from Paul, I tried to subdue the sarcasm in my voice and asked him if he could describe these war angels assigned for our protection. Paul began to describe that one of them was over eight-feet tall with blonde hair and blue eyes and the other angel being of darker complexion, but of the same height. Both of them manifested a strong physical build. They were well suited to their calling of angels of war and had been assigned to our care by the Commander of Heaven, Jesus Christ.

Paul gave us added revelation that these angelic beings often stood behind us at the ready, especially when we were ministering the Word of God. This again came as an overwhelming revelation to us. Before anything more is said, let it be known that what we are about to share is not for the exaltation of angels, but rather to the glorification of our Great Captain and Head of the Church, our Lord and Savior, Jesus Christ. He alone is worthy of worship. He not only commands the Heavenly host but is Lord of our lives, and before Him alone we humbly bow in adoration. Angels are merely messengers fulfilling Christ's bidding on behalf of the heirs of salvation.

The time frame of our story begins in the 1970s with communism arising to its pyramid peak of terror and tyranny over the nations of Eastern Europe. Winston Churchill rightfully called it what it was: an Iron Curtain that had come down over a major part of Europe and Asia. The Soviets, by design, loved to do everything on a three-tier basis. Their outer perimeters and buffer zones of nations, such as East Germany, Czechoslovakia, Hungary and Poland, all followed this multi-tier pattern.

Each border nation played a peculiar function and role predetermined by its Soviet conquerors. The buffer nations on the outer fringes were often the most severe because their position placed them as an immediate affront to the West. The purpose of their existence was to cause fear and intimidation to Western guests who in their democracies knew nothing but individual rights and basked in the warm sun of personal freedom.

The border between East Germany and West Germany was perhaps the most severe in its time with over 375 miles of razor wire, mine fields, and dog runs fortified by electronic sensors and shrapnel grenades, presenting itself as an impregnable zone of fear. The razor wire and barb configuration were often pointing inward, making the statement to Eastern European citizens that they were trapped with no escape from this grandiose experiment of social engineering called communism. Looming above the minefields and barbed wire, silhouetted against the dark sky every several hundred yards, were tall guard towers manned with automatic weapons just in case their primary barriers failed in any capacity.

As it had been our pattern for over 40 years of active ministry in the Soviet Block, we took teams with us whenever we could. This established accountability for us and eyewitnesses to the miraculous demonstration of God's supernatural deliverances. This particular trip did not deviate from our normal pattern in that we were delivering back to the West a team that had traveled with us in a huge circle which had encompassed many nations in Eastern Europe.

Having begun in Frankfurt, Germany, our team set out from the south to the nation of Austria, on to Hungary and Yugoslavia, cutting up through the spine of Romania and into the underbelly of Moldavia and the Ukraine. Poland was our last stop in an Eastern European nation before transiting through East Germany and delivering our team back to Frankfurt where their journey had begun. This entire trip of over a month's duration would end by their returning to the United States and Canada from where our team members had originated. This team was made up of some wonderful people:

Becky Arneson, the daughter of Pastor Ted and Lola Arneson, our pastors at that time and personal friends of ours to this day. Becky's sweet spirit is something that Sara and I dearly cherish.

Linda Boekel, a Y.W.A.M. graduate who after her DTS (Discipleship Training School) had taken on this missions trip with us to fulfill her burden for Eastern Europe. This would be her first and last trip into the Eastern Block because she died in less than a year after her return home due to a mysterious illness that took her to her Heavenly Home of her reward.

Michael Chirkoff, whose joyous disposition, Australian accent, and Canadian residence put him close enough to our family that eventually his younger brother, Paul, married Sara's younger sister, Elizabeth.

Helen Fokin hails from Sara's first church on American soil (Russian Full Gospel Temple in San Francisco, California), and she is active in that church to the present time.

Sergey Golin was the youngest in our group and hailed from the Vernon, British Columbia area where Sara's parents eventually settled in their latter years. Sergey, would often do his own thing, in contrast of our instructions. After being reprimanded he would ask for forgiveness. Some years later he became a pastor in Eastern Canada and a strong field representative for missions.

Eileen Hendrickson was a good friend of Becky Arneson and the daughter of one of the elders of Lynnwood Assembly of God church. Her outgoing, gregarious personality was unmistakable in the crowd.

Roger and Gayle Jacobson were relatively new converts in Christ whom we met at Redmond Assembly of God. We had great fellowship and friendship with them over many years until Roger's "home-going" some short years ago.

Paul McGowan was the only son of our British directors Rev. Hugh and Iris McGowan, and notably had a call of God on his life which was evident on this trip and the years that followed.

Nida Pustobaeff came from the Seattle area and had become more closely related to us through her sister, Vera, marrying Walter, Sara's older brother. Her quiet shell was broken on this trip, and we found sweetness in her that we've cherished over the years.

Sara in Hebrew is the equivalent of "Princess" and truly, God had gifted me with this precious princess as a wife and missions partner to the nations. God would often lead us into troubled areas where souls had been made ready through strife and conflict for the hearing of the Gospel.

Sara and I remained in Europe and took on a personal assignment that would take us deep into the heart of Siberia. These deep penetrations into the Soviet heartland were deemed too risky for outside team members. The necessity of these infiltrations into the Soviet Union was such an urgent matter that they had to be effected immediately. The task of gaining distribution feedback of how deep our Bibles had penetrated and adding new legs of distribution to our smuggling operation of Scriptures could only be risked by Sara and me.

To maximize our time and effort, Sara and I contrived an ill-conceived plan of dividing and conquering. While I remained back in Poland, arranging visas for Siberia, Sara was to take the ten team members back through the precarious barriers and borders of Poland and East Germany, delivering the team safely to the Frankfurt airport. The plan was made with the sincere hope that our years of experience and knowledge of the languages of the Eastern Block would assist this team back to the airport and to their connections to their homelands of Canada and the United States.

My little bride, Sara, took diligently to her task without hesitation or reservation. As she saw the last team member off the train and to their gate at the Frankfurt *Flughafen* (Airport), she immediately caught the outgoing train back through West Germany that wound its way through East Germany and on to Poland. Her dedication meant that she would snatch a few moments of sleep while sitting up in her car compartment. In her diligence to return, she had forgotten to stop long enough to take nourishment in the form of a meal.

It wasn't until years after this event that Sara related to me how much fear and trepidation she endured in making this return leg back to Poland on her own. We always had been together, and in our unified agreement in God, we had formed a three-stranded cord that could not be easily broken. Now for the first time in her life—without her Godly parents beside her, without friends or family, and even without her husband—she would make this journey alone and find a secret in Christ: that we are never alone.

16 Fire By Night

The departure from the Warsaw Central train station with the gregarious team of ten went smoothly enough all the way to Frankfurt, West Germany; however, the return leg of the trip would prove to be a life-changing experience and one that forever would mark Sara's relationship with God and gratefully endear her to the myriad of intercessors that God has brought sovereignly into our lives.

Chapter Two
OUT OF THE JAWS OF DEATH

THE RETURN LEG of Sara's train trip was not plotted or planned with the best of strategy, nor were the pitfalls and dangers considered. Our human weaknesses and poor planning often give divine opportunity for Heavenly intervention, especially when we call on God in our hour of need.

In our youth, what we lacked in wisdom, God often compensated for because of our zeal for Him and our tenacious clinging to Him and His promises. After a day of visiting consulate offices and doing a horrendous amount of paperwork in preparation for our journey to Siberia, I collapsed in a rickety single bed on the top floor of the Warsaw Bible School in Poland. The accommodations were not luxurious, but they were clean and reasonable. Despite the weariness of my body, that entire night, sleep eluded me. I was thankful that I was the only one on that floor as the rickety bedsprings sang their own song throughout the night as I fitfully rolled back and forth, trying to sleep and yet filling every waking moment with fervent prayer. I sensed something ominous had gone wrong and that Sara was in great danger, but without revelation as to what that danger was, I didn't know how to pray effectively. In the frailty of my limitations, I agreed with the Scripture that declares, "...*for we do not know what we should pray for as we ought, but the Spirit Himself makes intercession for us with groanings which cannot be uttered*" (Romans 8:26).

Hundreds of kilometers away, my bride was going through the testing of her lifetime. With no cell phones in that era or any means of communication, all I could do was cry and groan out my anguish to the heavens, knowing that the God Who called us is faithful to hear and answer prayer and protect His own.

What will the morning light bring? What news would this fitful night of wrestling with God produce? These questions and a million more went through my mind and my spirit. The one constant that filled my life with any peace was the knowledge that He Who called us was faithful and true and what He had begun in us, He would oversee to the finish—and that the name of Jesus Christ would be glorified in the end.

Sara and I had not planned how quickly her turnaround would be undertaken. I assumed that she had found accommodations in Frankfurt, Germany, at the Ernzhausen Bible School where we had stayed many times before, or perhaps with some Christian friends in Frankfurt. I had no idea that she was walking in a deep, dark valley on her own and there was none to hold her hand except our Lord Jesus Christ. My spirit man understood the distress of her heart and carried her anguish before the throne of God. It seemed like an eternity past that our jovial team had been with us.

We were like sheep before wolves, innocence before wickedness, but thank the Lord for the Good Shepherd, Jesus Christ, who goes before His Sheep and calls us each by name. The comfort of friends had fleeted far into the back of our memories. The fervency of the hour now loomed before us.

As the clickety-clack of the train brought Sara ever closer to the foreboding border between East and West Germany, the consequences of our rash decisions were now beginning to materialize. As the train wound through the gentle rolling hills, it was coming up to the East zone. Anyone with any spiritual discernment would feel it was like piercing a wall of dreadful darkness. It hung in the air like a heavy mist and lingered over the land as a heavy and oppressive burden over the millions of souls trapped on the wrong side of freedom's wall.

The screech of train brakes against rails now permeated the air as the train gradually came to a stop. The doors of the train suddenly opened, and a platoon of gray-uniformed customs officers with green braiding on their shoulders and black bill caps crested with a gold insignia of a hammer and sickle appeared by the dozens on each train car. Their abrasive manner and their demanding passports and visas made one aware that they were no longer basking in the freedom of the West, but the train had crossed the barrier into the East zone of communist tyranny. Their harsh demanding would strike terror in the hearts of the young and the elderly, but their hardened hearts showed no mercy for the tears they would often invoke.

Sara's lip began to tremble and her knees began to shake as the full realization of what she was facing settled upon her spirit. These brutal beasts without the milk of human kindness screamed their demands at their captives: *"Papier!"*(Paper-work). If you looked affluent, their demands always centered on the ploy of some fictitious form that you did not have that would cost you a sizeable amount of Deutschmarks. Extortion and bullying was the name of their game, and they played it well.

These guards were fluent in several languages. The most common among them, of course, was the German language; Russian and some English were also spoken. Sara, hoping to disarm their harsh verbiage, asked politely in Russian for her guard's assistance in transferring between trains when this particular leg of the train trip ended in Berlin. The guards assured Sara that they would inform her when it was time to transfer to another train for her continuing leg to Warsaw, Poland.

Believing their answer settled Sara momentarily until the train pulled out of its gray, dilapidated station. Half of the military officers and customs officers had left the train, evident by the sound of their heavy black military knee-high boots tromping their way to the nearest exit. The doors finally shut, the departure whistle blew, and the train began to travel several hundred kilometers toward the heart of Eastern Germany and to the dividing city of East Berlin.

What seemed like an eternity later had now repeated itself with the train screeching to a halt at its last stop in West Berlin. With the halting of the train, all its passengers hurriedly grabbed their belongings and scurried to their exits. Many of them gave a sigh of relief, having just transited through East Germany to the little isle of freedom called West Berlin. This city was entirely circumferenced by barbed-wire barriers and divided down the middle by the infamous Berlin Wall. Those getting off the train had escaped the crushing boot heel of "Big Brother" one more time.

Sara assumed that with everybody vacating the train, this was her point of departure as well. After having grabbed her meager bag and following the crowd toward the exit, she was suddenly stopped and restrained by a heavy hand upon her shoulder. A rough hand whirled Sara around, and the gruff voice from an East German customs officer chided her for her mistrust and not waiting for his releasing her at the transfer point. It was a long, eerie walk down the corridors of the train with all the compartment doors being open, but not a soul remaining in her car.

Sara sat down fearfully in the compartment she had vacated some moments before and breathed a prayer Heaven-ward, asking God for His protection and for His peace. Her silent prayer was shattered as the train lurched forward and the pounding of military boots toward her brought three East German guards who glared at her contrite and broken figure cowering in the corner of her compartment. The demands were fast and furious: "Who are your contacts in East Germany?" "You are a spy!" "Tell us the truth. We will break you, and then you will tell us the truth—and all the truth!" "Give us all the money you have, and we will make it easier on you, but be assured that you cannot escape us."

Their barrage of words was not having the desired effect of striking paralyzing fear into Sara's heart, so one of the guards lunged forward to where she sat and picked her up by the shoulders. With one jerking motion, he threw her into the air, and she was caught by another guard who in turn threw her to the third guard. In Sara's own words, she had a Belshazzar experience: her knees were "having fellowship with one another." With great fear and trembling, one knee "smote against" the other, and her heart began to pound in rhythm with the level of fear now pervading her body.

Just as suddenly as the train had lurched forward, it screeched to a stop. Now the part that the train played in this game was over. Heavy hands on Sara's shoulders and others grabbing her arms behind her back pushed her down the aisle of the train toward the far door that was now open. The three officers that had treated her so brutally conferred among themselves, stating, "It takes so much of our government's money to break these Westerners. Let's show her who really is in charge. We saw her praying. Let's show her how strong her God is." All three guards agreed.

She was pushed out of the train onto the deserted platform, and one of the three guards broke from the ranks and ran to an adjacent platform, opening a cage and releasing a penned-up, very large and angry German shepherd. As the dog lurched, angrily straining at the short leash that restrained him, the trainee reached down and removed the muzzle that had, up until this moment, covered his face. With this new freedom, the dog anticipated an assignment that dogs like him greatly enjoyed.

Let me take a moment and give you a brief background of why these German shepherds were used at the borders of the communist frontier. These dogs are extremely intelligent, and the East Germans had bred a version of the German shepherd that was stocky, powerful and muscularly built, renowned throughout the security industry. Their jaw pressure was nearly half that of a mature alligator. I have personally seen shepherd dogs like these take a femur bone of a cow, which is the largest and most dense bone in a skeleton of a cow, and snap it like a dried twig. The East Germans took the German shepherd dog and trained it to a level unheard of in intensity of loyalty and viciousness.

The dog's first full year of training was conducted in a warehouse or airplane hangar with no natural light. In the process of this first year, something snapped in the dog's mind, and the only two people he would trust were his trainer and his back-up trainer that fed him. He would without hesitation, on command, attack a machine gun, and dogs that would not follow through on such commands were shot to death and removed from further training. Needless to say, these were not house pets but a fearsome tool to continue the process of terrorizing and intimidating the populous wherever the dogs appeared.

To compound this matter even worse, as Sara stood there helplessly on the train platform held by the East German guards, her mind for a fleeting moment went back to her childhood in Australia. There, as a young girl of eleven, she was invited to go to the neighborhood grocery store by her best friend, Richard Tula, in Adelaide. At that time Sara's family had just emigrated from China some short years before. This immigrant family of five children couldn't afford their own bicycle, so Richard Tula graciously invited Sara, her friend from church, to ride the short distance to the local grocery store. Rounding the corner out of nowhere *lunged* a large German shepherd dog who's growling and fury cut off their line of travel and caused the bicycle to skid on its side, throwing off its two passengers.

As Sara was on the ground, backing away from the oncoming dog, he caught Sara's foot in his jaws. Quickly, Richard Tula used the bike as a wedge between Sara and the attacking dog. Fending off the dog with the use of the bike and a stick, Sara and Richard limped back home to be greeted by her brothers and sister. Tearful and trembling, Sara's words spilled out like a fountain as she described the ordeal.

Like a flash, those scenes in her mind faded away, and the harsh reality of the present now faced her. She heard the East German trainer give the dog a command to attack in Sara's native language of Russian. *"Vzyat'!"* (Attack!) Without hesitation, the dog bolted from the platform. Its face was contorted into a snarl, revealing long white fangs dripping with saliva. In anticipation of the command, the dog uttered a deep guttural growl. It seemed like the whole world went into slow motion for Sara. There was no room for "Plan B." Either God came through or it was over for Sara at that moment.

To Sara's own surprise, she felt a stirring deep within her spirit and the following words catapulted from her lips: **"In the Name of Jesus Christ of Nazareth, I command you to STOP!"** The dog had bolted and was running at full speed to leap and grab her by the throat. With the sound of her command piercing the air, it seemed as if an invisible wall went up just as the dog reached her, and he dropped to a sitting position, just inches before her, reduced to just growling.

The trainer who had never seen his dog disobey his command, turned ashen white and altered his original command again in the Russian language: *"Ubey!"* (Kill). The dog, however, would not budge an inch. The three border guards now stood there in disbelief. The terrorists of a few moments before were now being terrorized by an unseen presence against which they had no training and had no power to resist.

With the dog in check, the Word began to flow profusely out of Sara's mouth in a river of Scripture after Scripture. The Word declares, *"But when they arrest you and deliver you up, do not worry beforehand or premeditate what you will speak. But whatever is given you in that hour, speak that, for it is not you who speak, but the Holy Spirit"* (Mark 13:11). God's Word shuts the gainsayers' mouths. 1 John 4: 4 says: *"You are of God, little children, and have overcome them, because He who is in you is greater than he who is in the world."* Those Scriptures were now alive in Sara as the words of salvation poured forth from her lips.

Chapter Three
DIVINE INTERVENTION FROM HEAVEN

WHAT WAS REALISTICALLY only about 30 minutes' time seemed much longer due to this intense impasse with Sara standing on the platform, declaring the Word to her peculiar audience of one German shepherd and three fear-filled communist guards. Terror was evident on their faces. Would this wisp of a young lady who had such a command with her God turn the treachery and trickery of the communists upon their own heads, or would this icy standoff end some other way?

The answer to their question came suddenly in the form of a tall, lean, blond officer with blue eyes. When he approached the platform he drew the immediate attention of all the participants on this stage of God's intervention. He was in a light blue uniform, never seen by us in all of our travels in all of Eastern Europe, and the three subordinate officers in their gray garb saluted this approaching superior officer. As they stood there rigidly at attention, the superior officer's gentle gaze settled upon Sara.

Approaching Sara, he whispered in her ear, "Have no fear. God has sent me to deliver you out of your troubles." With that assuring word resonating in her spirit, the officer gently took her by the arm and walked away from the scene behind them that was seemingly frozen in time. The last thing Sara recalled in looking over her shoulder was the three guards standing at rigid attention and the dog obediently sitting on the platform where she had left them.

The questions began to flood into Sara's heart and mind like Niagara Falls. Unable to constrain her heart, Sara inquired of this kind, gentle officer: "Who are you?" His reply, though strange, rang with directness and clarity. "It is not important for you to know who I am." That did not satisfy the query of Sara's heart, so she framed her question in different terms by asking, "What is your name?" Again the reply came, "That's not important for you to know."

The conversation continued with Sara asking, "Are you one of our couriers?" To this there was no reply, but rather a rebuttal in the form of a statement that only God could have known. This messenger responded by saying, "You haven't eaten for 48 hours. Sit here while I get you something to eat. "

Dozens of platforms away from her original encounter with the dog and the guards, Sara sat quietly as her rescuer came back moments later with a tray full of warm food and a four-course meal. The fragrance wafting into Sara's nostrils blotted out all of her questions such as where this officer had obtained the food in such a late hour in a deserted East German railroad spur.

Sara felt a peace that passed all understanding, and as she bowed her head to bless the food that was given to her, she heard the assuring "Amen" of the blond-headed officer sitting across from her in an adjacent bench. While Sara ate, the officer spoke of the great love of God that was manifested in Christ, how Jesus personally loved her and cared for her so deeply that no one could snatch her from the hollow of God's hand. He spoke of how God had heard the prayers and cries of His people.

When she finished eating, she was escorted by her rescue officer several platforms farther away and was placed on the correct train destined from East Germany's Schönfeld Station to Warsaw, Poland. The officer helped her with her bag, put her on the right train in her own compartment, and handed her the tickets for her continued travels. It was only when Sara received the tickets that she realized across the top of the ticket were the words *Ersta Klassa* (First Class). To Sara's shock and amazement, she declared to her friend that she had not paid for this ticket, to which he replied, "It has been paid for you in full, far in advance."

In placing her luggage in the overhead compartment, the officer bid her farewell and exited the train. Standing just outside her window, his final comments through the open glass were, "Be faithful to your Lord and Savior Jesus Christ, for He will be faithful to you unto the end. You will still face many testing's and trials, but the Lord will never leave you nor forsake you. He loves you with an everlasting love and is coming soon for those that love and await His appearing."

With those words ending, the rescuer vanished before Sara's eyes. She lowered the window even farther as the train now began to chug slowly out of its station. Looking to the right and to the left, she called, "Brother, where are you?" "Brother, where did you go?" There was no sound or sight of him, only the train gaining speed into the night.

Tears flooded her eyes as she sat back in her compartment alone—and yet not alone. The presence of the Lord filled that compartment, and an awesome awareness came over her, punctuated by the Scriptures in Psalm 91 that declare, *"He shall give angels charge over you..."* Sara felt so humbled and so insignificant in the grand scheme of the entire universe, and yet the Creator of the Universe had protected her life and saved her out of the snare of the fowler.

Rehearsing through her heart and spirit continually was the entirety of the 91st Psalm. Hot, salty tears coursed down her cheeks as she reflected on God's faithfulness. She couldn't believe that God would personally dispatch a messenger of Heaven to rescue her out of her troubles. That kind of caring and love is more than words could describe.

The little compartment in the train became a sanctuary, electrified by the power and presence of God as the train's wheels turned and the tears of gratitude flowed. God had made a "house call" out of eternity and into time to rescue one of His little hand-maidens. The Word kept on coming back to her heart as the Psalmist declared:

He who dwells in the secret place of the Most High shall abide under the shadow of the Almighty. I will say of the Lord, "He is my refuge and my fortress; My God, in Him I will trust." Surely He shall deliver you from the snare of the fowler and from the perilous pestilence. He shall cover you with His feathers, and under His wings you shall take refuge; His truth shall be your buckler. You shall not be afraid of the terror by night, nor of the arrow that flies by day, nor of the pestilence that walks in darkness, nor of the *destruction that lays waste at noonday. A thousand may fall at your side, and ten thousand at your right hand; but it shall not come near you. Only with your eyes shall you look, and see the reward of the wicked. Because you have made the Lord who is my refuge Even the Most High, your dwelling place, no evil shall befall you, nor shall any plague come near your dwelling; <u>For He shall give His angels charge over you, to keep you in all your ways.</u> In their hands they shall bear you up, lest you dash your foot against a stone. You shall tread upon the lion and the cobra, the young lion and the serpent you shall trample underfoot. Because he has set his love upon Me, therefore I will deliver him; I will set him on high, because he has known My name. He shall call upon Me, and I will answer him; I will be with him in trouble; I will deliver him and honor him. With long life I will satisfy him, and show him My salvation* (Psalms 91: 1-16).

We are all aware that this is a Messianic Psalm promised to our Savior and Lord Jesus Christ, but we are in Him and accept the promise and principle of the same covering due to the covenant of Calvary.

Chapter Four
FROM THE FRYING PAN INTO THE FIRE

WITH THE ORDEAL of this moment behind her, there was a sigh of relief and easing of the tension in Sara's spirit. There was no urgent agenda on her plate except that of making her way to Warsaw, Poland, and rendezvousing with her husband. Tilting her seat back to a reclining position, Sara rehearsed the events of her recent hours. It was still hard to believe, although the comfort of her first-class ticket and compartment remained as a constant reminder of God's special care.

Charged through her dreams that night in the reclining train seat, her heart was filled with reflections of God's faithfulness over a lifetime, culminating in the current events of the present. A deep rest settled upon her. It was God's gift, again manifesting His mercy to her.

A new awareness now dawned on her life as the first rays of the sun breaking the horizon from the east filled her train compartment dancing in radiance. It was hard to believe that it was already morning and that she had begun her long trek by rail and was already in Poland.

What punctuated the clarity of her understanding was the conductor in the aisle announcing "Herbata" (Tea Time). His warm and gracious smile was such a contrast to the East German border experience. Sara assured the steward standing before her in his dark blue uniform that she would certainly enjoy a cup of Polish hot tea. Minutes later, a tray was placed before her with a beautiful crystal cup in an ornate silver-crafted cup holder accompanied by a warm breakfast roll. The selection of crackers and cookies bountifully filled the rest of the tray. Truly the Lord had prepared a table in the presence of His enemies, and God had made provision by His mighty arm.

Looking out the train window, Sara saw a blurry patchwork of fields passing by in squares of grain and grass. On occasion, the color of the passing fields was illuminated with bright greens and yellows as seemingly endless kilometers of sunflowers lifted their beautiful yellow heads toward the heavens in adoration of the God Who made them grow.

It was easy to join with this symphony of praise with all creation taking its part. On the higher elevations, groves of pine trees would, on occasion, punctuate the horizon. As the train slowly meandered its way through the cultivated countryside, it stopped now and again in industrial cities and small town villages where it picked up goods and products to be ushered towards the capital of the nation and from there to the markets of the land.

Sometimes during the scheduled journey of the train, additional passengers were added; and to Sara's delight and joy, a little Polish lady and her young daughter joined her compartment. The conversation in Polish opened up to numerous themes, but Sara's heart was to turn the focus on the Lord and His work of salvation. The little mother and daughter openly listened to the sincerity of Sara's heart. Seeds of faith were sown, and on occasion Sara was reminded to water her sowing with tears. This gracious little mother not only shared conversation with Sara but gladly shared her prepared lunch. Polish rye bread, sausage, and cheese accompanied by hot, dilled new potatoes and cucumbers were the fare for the day. Again, God had effected another day of provision in the day of blessing from the bounty of Heaven.

The train trip from East German borders to the Central Station of Warsaw, Poland, would take an entire night and a major part of the next day, arriving late in the evening. The train chugged in to its destination at the Central Warsaw station, its final stop at ten o'clock in the evening. At long last, Sara's journey was over. Taking her one meager suitcase, Sara made her way to the platform and up two flights of stairs to the main street in front of the station. She then looked in each direction to find a taxi.

To her chagrin, none was in sight. She walked a half a block around the corner of the station and found the last taxi available at that late hour. The Russian Volga in its customary black color had a taxi driver in the driver's seat who had temporarily dozed off. When Sara tapped on the window of the taxi, the startled driver jerked as if coming out of a deep sleep. She gave the address of Zagorna 10, and the reluctant driver opened the back door so that Sara and her suitcase could sit in the backseat. As the clunker of a car made its way from the curbside, the cobblestone streets near the train station glistened in the street lights reflecting residue from a passing rain cloud.

Zagorna means "beyond the hill." As the taxi made its way from the urban heart of downtown Warsaw, it took one of its winding arterials down the hill towards the Wisla River, which transits throughout the entirety of the land of Poland. Its headwaters originate high in the Carpathian Mountains bordering the Czech and Ukrainian Republics. As the river approaches Warsaw, it still has several hundred kilometers to go before emptying itself into the Baltic. This river cuts through the middle of Warsaw and is spanned by scores of bridges and parks on either side of its banks.

The Bible school that was Sara's destination that night was on the west bank, near a long avenue that paralleled the shore. The park along the river's edge was filled with World War II monuments and relics and was often the place where couples walked in the warm summer evening. Sara tried to make light conversation with the taxi driver and assured him that she was going to meet her husband.

As he glared in the rearview mirror, his eyes became darkened with lust and a treacherous plan of violating Sara. He insisted on stopping at the park to carry out his plan and made several stops with the taxi, insisting Sara get out of the vehicle with him. As Sara continually refused, his stops and his persistence became more violent.

Had Sara escaped the East German border crossing only to find herself thrown into the fire of this treacherous man's advances? In the midst of their heated conversation, tears coursed down Sara's cheeks as her spirit cried out to the Lord of Heaven. God had not spared her to have her ravaged by this servant of Satan.

Finally, after numerous stops, she was at last delivered to the address she had given the driver. The ordeal was over, or so she thought. As she took her suitcase from the taxi and paid the few zloty for her fare that had been taken from an old envelope deep within her coat pocket, she made her way up to the front steps of the Bible school. The coach lights on each side of the door provided a dim lighting for the double glass doors.

Sara rang the doorbell, hoping that would awaken the caretaker within and deliver her from the lust-filled, lingering driver at the curbside. After frantically ringing the doorbell brought no response, she now pounded on the glass panes of the door, hoping desperately to awaken somebody, but to no avail.

The taxi driver now got out of his car and from the passenger side of the vehicle stood on the sidewalk, urging Sara to return to the taxi. His mannerism was animated and his voice loud as he spoke in mocking tones, "You have no husband. Come back with me to my house." Sara's response was, "Yes, I do have a husband." She continued knocking on the glass door, this time adding to her frantic pounding the element of prayer.

At last, out of deep slumber, the Christian caretaker appeared from within, apparently sleepwalking across the foyer of the inside entrance. When he heard the pounding on the door, it was then, and only then, that he awakened in response to its urgency. Unlocking several bolts from within, the door finally opened to Sara's great relief. Sara explained who she was and about her relief of being in the Bible school building. She could have almost hugged this little grandpa figure standing before her in his plaid pajamas. This precious little brother was the answer to her prayers. In his sleepy-eyed state, he gave Sara the room number where I was residing, and she began to make her way up to the seventh floor near the rafters of the roof, up the winding staircase, and to our room.

A feeble little knock on the door startled me from a fitful night and day that I had just gone through. My mind and thoughts started to have questions of "Who could be knocking on my door at nearly the midnight hour?" For that matter, who knew that I was here in this little obscure Bible school in the middle of Poland? In making my way to the door, my mind considered several options. Perhaps it was the caretaker, or perhaps it was some other official from the Bible school who had to talk with me that night on a very urgent matter.

When I unlocked the door from within and it opened wide in the dim light of the hallway, I saw my little wife trembling with the mixed emotions of fear and gratitude. She leaped into my arms, and I responded by hugging her strongly. We closed the door and dropped to our knees in prayer. As we called on the Name of Jesus, we felt the assurance of a multitude of prayer warriors who had joined us in this crisis of our faith. Peace settled warmly over us—that peace that truly passes all understanding. It became our portion as we pondered the faithfulness of our God.

God had spared my little wife, Sara, from the jaws of death of a vicious police dog and then from the fiendish plan of ravaging and rape. As we both sat on the single bed with its lumpy mattress, Sara began to share with uncontrollable sobbing the details of the night and day that she had just experienced. It was only then that we realized how great the deliverance of our Lord Jesus Christ had been in Sara's life.

We did not perceive the full dimension of God's deliverance until after we had returned from Siberia to our beloved home in Seattle many months later. While sharing our testimony in some of the churches in the Seattle, Washington, area, Kay Oas came up to us with tear-filled eyes, asking us if we had received her letter in Germany.

John and Kay Oas had been a part of our lives even before we were married. Our friendship continued into the area of ministry long after we had said our wedding vows. I had traveled with John Oas for over a year in a mission agency that we had created called, "Missions Possible." John played the piano and sang, and I was given the privilege of preaching the Word.

Through many crusades and churches, John's impassioned ministry in music and my powerful presentation of missions were the joint theme of our hearts. When John married his childhood sweetheart, Kay, it was evident that there had come a time of settling and redirection in their lives.

Although they had never lost the burden for frontier missions, their front, however, would be that of the urban heart of Seattle. For decades, John pioneered one of America's first airport chaplaincy working in crisis counseling directly with The Port of Seattle Police Department. Their ministry base expanded to ministry among singles and their need for Christian fellowship and discipleship. It was from the rich heritage of this foundation that Kay was raised up by the Lord to be a powerful intercessor and helpmate in John's ministry.

Kay's letter arrived to our address in Neugraben, Germany, weeks after our return from Siberia. This letter portrayed the picture of God awakening Kay early one morning with a heavy burden of intercessory prayer. Not knowing how to handle this burden, Kay removed herself from her bed to her knees where she groaned in her spirit, praying after the will of her Heavenly Father for Sara's safety. As Kay deeply interceded in God, a vision passed through her spirit of train platforms and Sara's life being in jeopardy. She saw God sending a messenger, an angel in the form of a military officer, whose tall, muscular frame was accentuated by a head of beautiful blond hair with blue eyes and a light blue uniform. She continued groaning in the agony of prayer until her burden had lifted, and Kay knew that Sara no longer was in a life-and-death struggle for her very being. At five o'clock in the morning, the urgency at last lifted, and the peace of God returned her to a deep and comforting sleep.

Later in our journals, we found the time frame that God had awakened Kay to intercede in prayer for Sara was the exact time frame of Sara's attack at the East German border by the vehement police dog and by the customs officials' brutality and interrogation.

How many others had joined this chorus in prayer? Who else had our Lord and Savior stirred to call on His Name on behalf of God's missionary envoys? Whenever God puts a face or a name upon your heart, PLEASE PRAY! Your prayers may make the difference between life and death in someone's crisis. Prayer is our calling upon the Lord for His help in our time of need. Where would any of us be without the faithful prayers of people in our lives, especially the intercession of our Savior, Jesus Christ, who ever makes intercession for us before the Father?

Chapter Five
SOME THROUGH THE FIRE,
BUT ALL THROUGH THE BLOOD

W ITH A LEGACY of listening to the voice of God that transcends generations, the full story begs to be told. Sara and I are the third generation in our families redeemed by the blood of Christ. It started with our grandparents and then our parents, and now us; and by the grace of God, our children are all serving the Lord, for which we are tearfully grateful to God.

How our past, with its intricate leading, affects our present reminds us of God's delivering His people out of bondage from Egypt to their land of promise. Through many signs and wonders, God shows Himself mighty on behalf of those who put their full trust in Him. Like the children of Israel, many among them were filled with unbelief, and their weakness diminished God's opportunity to display His strength. However, when Israel of old repented, God took pity upon His people and delivered them with a mighty outstretched arm so that nations trembled in fear of the God of Israel.

This modern Exodus in the history of our ancestors is purposed in the heart of our God for the same reason, that the people of the earth will be without excuse, having seen the deliverance of Christ and His power made known through His own. *"But you are a chosen generation, a royal priesthood, a holy nation, His own special people, that you may proclaim the praises of Him who called you out of darkness into His marvelous light"* (1 Peter 2:9).

The Unchanging One Who inhabits eternity once again mapped out a journey of wanderings that would try the reins of the hearts of His followers. The final chapters would be written as He safely brought

His people to a land of plenty and then stirred up within their children a God-given desire to return to the lands their parents had once fled.

This last generation would take on a new giant in the land and prove to all the earth that the God of Abraham, Isaac and Jacob moves in the here and now and none can stop His plan no matter how powerful they think they are. Walk with our forefathers from the loamy soil of the Ukraine's whitened fields of grain to the snow-capped peaks of the Ural Mountains. Let us go with them into the hot, arid valleys of the Islamic republics, only to be catapulted by God across the Chinese borders. Traversing twenty-five years of sojourning in China, they finally exited to lands of God's leading. All the while, God has been establishing His mighty Church in the wake of their steps.

Come with us as we follow their steps where they settled into cities of the free world, scattered from South America to North America's west coast and from border to border in Canada. Let us follow them as the call of God intensely grasped the hearts of sons and daughters He had prepared by His Holy Spirit. With language and culture already in place in their lives, they journeyed from their comfortable homes to countries that had not heard of Jesus Christ.

Their journey is our journey. The trek through life, like ours, brought divine lessons in learning to hear and listening to the voice of God. Our collective obedience determines the measure of blessing or sorrows we will jointly endure. Sometimes our suffering plays a role in God's greater good, for the most profound sermon cannot be matched by the reality of innocents suffering injustice.

Like the cross of Jesus Christ where the Just suffer for the unjust, leaving the greatest historic testimony of God's infinite love, so also, Christ's servants are not above their Master. They too suffer injustice, scourging, mocking and ridicule and as we, the followers of Christ respond to our persecutors with selfless, Godly love. Our actions shout louder than any words heard from any pulpit. This inequity demands a resolution and so mankind condemns himself by demanding a final reckoning and judgment of the guilty. The Good News is that we have passed from guilt to forgiveness, through the completed work of

Calvary and the servants that declared this among the nations have brought the guilt of all mankind, liberating news, *CHRIST DIED FOR OUR SINS!*

It is estimated that over 40,000 people were swept into the Kingdom of Heaven from the 1920s to 1933, when missionary Ivan Voronaeff was mightily used of God. He was referred to as the Apostle of the South (The Former Soviet Union); and under his watch, over 700 churches were established and pastors raised up to disciple their new converts.

Brother Voronaeff had come from the foundation of a Baptist pastor in New York, only to be removed from his pulpit because of a new Pentecostal experience in his life. Having visited the Azusa Street Revival in Los Angeles, his heart was strangely warmed by the visitation of God and opened up to the things of the Spirit of God he had never tasted. After pastoring in the greater Los Angeles area for a short time, he took his wife and eight children into a missions venture in Turkey. This mission's beachhead operation in the Muslim nation lasted less than two years. Disappointed and discouraged, he made his way to the Ukraine on his return journey back to the United States.

Ivan Voronaeff's detour to the Crimea and the Southern Ukraine would alter the destiny of these nations. Here he found his place in God. As he preached the Word, prayed for the sick and saw the Lord deliver the demonic, God was present in great power to sweep children and the aged, and all in between, into a mighty outpouring of the Holy Spirit. Tens of thousands cried out to the Name of the Lord, and God heard their cry with saving grace.

The movement became so powerful that it took on the name of Christians of the Evangelical Faith. Satan and his servants could not tolerate the sons of God's Kingdom, and so the war began. Late one night in early 1933, a massive crackdown was conducted by the KGB. In one night, pastors and church leaders were awakened from deep slumber, traumatically arrested and taken from their homes to the nearest KGB holding cells. Many of them were forced out of their homes, wearing only their pajamas and no warm coats to protect them from the cold winter nights. They suffered severely from exposure in the icy Ukrainian winter.

From the KGB holding cells, the pastors and leaders were assembled and shipped by rail to the gulags of Siberia. These dark, foreboding regime prison camps had the notorious reputation for a ninety percentile death rate. Disease, weather and diet, accompanied by a heavy work regimen, all took their toll with 90 percent of anyone incarcerated for more than ten years never returning home alive.

Hundreds of thousands of unmarked graves in the frozen tundra of Siberia remain as a memorial to the valiant in their faith to Jesus Christ and to their uncompromising faith. Heaven alone knows the number of all the redeemed in the Lamb's Book of Life who won the ultimate reward: the martyr's crown. They had loved their Lord so intensely that they were counted worthy to suffer for the Name of Christ – in accordance with Christ's promise: *"...if we suffer, we shall also reign with him..."* (2 Tim.2:12a, KJV).

When missionary Ivan Voronaeff and his 700 leaders and followers were arrested, reports trickled from the gulags of torture, disease and execution. One of the elders relates a story to us many years after his ordeal.

Early in the 1970s, Sara and I had the privilege of meeting one of these patriarchs of Pentecost. It was a late sunny afternoon on a tram in the back streets of Odessa, Ukraine. As Sara sat on the double chair on the left-hand side of the tram, I sat on the wooden-slatted, single seat on the right-hand side of the wall across from her. The right single seats faced each other with a pole coming down between the seats to help stabilize the passengers as the trams jostled down the thoroughfares.

A Russian man, seemingly 85 or older, sat down in the seat across from me. With both of my hands holding the pole for stability, this Russian brother reached across to the pole, smothering my hands with his. His piercing eyes looked into mine and he began to prophesy in Russian. Now his hands held mine in a very firm grip as the profound prophetic words came flowing out of his mouth:

"You will see an hour where stadiums will be filled seeking the Lord Jesus Christ as Savior and Lord, where you will be preaching freely in opera houses and Palaces of Culture and even on the streets of the Soviet Union. The hour will come in God when the Scriptures will be printed on Soviet soil and churches will be filled to overflowing with people who have found the Lord and worship Christ in spirit and in truth. In this last day outpouring of His Holy Spirit, many cities will be taken and shaken for God and God will send teams from the Ukraine to bring in a harvest in Western Europe and nations of the free world. Your hands will touch, your feet will enter in and your eyes shall behold the glory of God as it falls upon His people. Many signs and wonders will be accomplished and Jesus Christ will be greatly glorified."

As Sara and I got off the next stop with our brother, he related the account of how he was one of brother Voronaeff's recruits and pastors. His story spoke of great devastation as the KGB ravished the church with the principal goal of destroying its leadership and then scattering the flock. In his own testimony, he was in a Gulag where 32 pastors were pulled out late into the evening and placed against a wall. The roar of machine gun fire caused his ears to ring and he fell over in fear, thinking he had been riddled by the hot lead.

Late in the night, revived from his fainting, our brother crawled out from under the corpses of his fellow pastors and Christian leaders. Over a span of six months, from one Christian home to another by a myriad of various transportation modes, he made his way back to his beloved Odessa. Having changed his name and grown a beard, it was a sufficient disguise for our brother to minister below the radar and behind the scenes in the Odessa church up to this particular hour.

However, this brother's vision was greater than the stifling demonic control affected then by the KGB in the early 1970s. He dreamed of a day where the hand of God would be made bare over this nation and justice for innocent blood shed upon the land would be finally realized. Having never seen this precious Christian brother again, I often see his face in my spirit after an altar call. Perhaps he was witnessing with me from the grandstand of Heaven the prophetic fulfillment of God's words spoken through him. Someday, I will introduce him to you in the courts of God where sower and reaper will rejoice together.

As teenagers, Michael and Nadejda were caught by the fire and fervor of this apostolic movement. Voronaeff's strategy was to send teams of teenagers and young couples in their twenties from village to village, declaring the full Gospel message with the power of the Holy Spirit. Thousands were healed and thousands of others broken loose from the bondage of generations of religiosity into a new vibrant relationship with Jesus, the Christ, the Savior of the world.

Michael and Nadejda shared the same longing for evenings to come, as this meant a two-fold blessing: a ceasing of their labors from the day and a renewed fellowship with God's people at night. Although from separate villages, these evening prayer meetings became the norm throughout the region.

Nadejda was from Krivorog in the north of Ukraine and Michael from Adamovka in the south near the Nikolaev area. The entire regions of Ukraine were being bathed in the heat of revival, and God would bring this couple together on Chinese soil a decade later.

As both of their families pursued the leading of the Lord through the prophetic word of the Holy Spirit, God had His divine appointment for their meeting and leading.

Chapter Six
ADAMOVKA, THE EARLY YEARS

In these revival meetings in the Ukraine, the arduous tasks of the day were behind them. This afforded them a time of rest and assembly in the Name of the Lord across the hundreds of villages of the Eastern Ukraine. These meetings were punctuated with the power and presence of the Holy Spirit in their midst. These services would often go on for hours and into the night. Fervent prayer interlaced with powerful songs and personal testimonies were the norm of the day.

Many from the villages were in attendance during these meetings. Who would miss these moments of divine communion, a time of meeting, a time of Heaven kissing earth? A few of the people that were affected by not missing these meetings were the drunks who were delivered, the thieves who restored their illicit goods, the liars who lined up to plead for forgiveness, and the gossips who wept in repentance for their slanderous ways.

And they went out and preached everywhere, the Lord working with them and confirming the word through the accompanying signs (Mark 16:20).

In the late 1920s and early 1930s, a heavy wind of change had charged the air. In the confused consolidation years initiated by Stalin, little was said or done to squelch God's move of the multitudes of people from Belarus to the Crimea, from Poland to the plateau of the Urals. It first came to the body of God's people as a warning: War would come, and many lives would be lost. Prior to the war, God warned of internal purges and of much persecution against God's precious people. Weeping with intense sincerity, prophets would traverse the land, repeating God's warning again and again. The Spirit spoke expressly to His people, but many did not heed or desire to hear His leading, having settled in their comfort zones. However, the lives of those who heard and obeyed were spared, being led by the precious Holy Spirit.

Hearing you will hear and shall not understand, and seeing you will see and not perceive. For the hearts of this people have grown dull, their ears are hard of hearing and their eyes they have closed, lest they should see with their eyes and hear with their ears, lest they should understand with their hearts and turn, so that I should heal them (Matthew 13:14-15).

One night, the first of many thunderings of God's declared and detailed instructions was heard: "Sell your lands, your houses and your farms. Leave your city, your village and your friends that will not heed My voice. If you hear and obey, you shall live, but if you hear and heed not my call, you shall perish with the people who harden their hearts and hinder God's doing in the earth."

Let us examine further the story of obedient and disobedient sons of dust. It is interesting to note that the village of Adamovka was named after the father of mankind, Adam. Adam's name means "son of dust" or, more accurately, "red dust." In Adamovka, all livelihoods revolved around cultivating and managing the soil, so the village was aptly named.

Adamovka, however, was uniquely different in several crucial ways. In order to make a success of farming the soil, the three prime ingredients were water, hard labor and patience. Adamovka was blessed to have two out of the three primary ingredients in abundance; the third, being patience, could only be a product harvested through the ordeal of testing and time.

In Adamovka three artesian wells brimmed over, providing all the irrigation for this loamy, sandy soil to produce a huge harvest. Orchards, melons, fruits, vegetables, potatoes and grain were the mainstay of the village's economy. The people as a rule worked the land with great passion, knowing that their labor was linked to their survival. Those that didn't work didn't eat. In those days, the only welfare program was what you could do for yourself and your family.

The Ilyins family lived in a close family cluster of farm houses down the main road of Adamovka. Residing just adjacent to one of Adamovka's most productive wells, and due to their hard work and unfeigned faith in God, the Ilyins fared better than most people in the community. Having escaped Poland some decades earlier, when there were waves of vicious religious persecution and anti-Semitic attacks, they settled in this Ukrainian village with deep appreciation for the tranquility it afforded them.

The bubble of peace was about to burst. On the one hand, there was the prophetic word of warning; on the other hand, there was the tyranny of man's injustice. Roving gangs, lazy and not desirous to work the fields, thought it much easier to pillage and destroy what others had earned through their hard labor. Because of the blessing of God upon His chosen people, the people of Jewish ethnicity were singled out by many of these roving marauders because of their high profile of success.

Little Michael Ilyin, a boy of almost eight years of age, grew up on one of these affluent farms. With a grandfather living on the one side and an uncle on the other, their large farmyard was by an orchard, large barn and a separate chicken coop. When these grounds were broken up after the war, their house and farmyard were divided up into six plots of land where six individual houses now stand.

Michael had little time for a traditional childhood. It seemed everybody from infancy on was involved in one level or another of crop harvesting, tending to the animals or doing chores of one sort or other. The weeks after the major harvest of grain and fruit were securely placed in the barn were the times that Michael best remembers; they were filled with visiting neighbors and friends and splashing in the local swimming pond.

The little country stream that flowed beside Adamovka was dammed up to create a small reservoir, the scene of much joy in the hot summer sun when the harvest was done. At the outlet end of the pond was the head gate of sorts where the high water cascaded over the top of another manmade barrier into a short but copious waterfall that allowed the stream to continue on its merry way through the countryside. Some fishing was done in the stream, but these moments were stolen out of busy seasons of intense labor, all focused on the family farm.

The Ilyins raised dairy cows for their milk, pigs for their meat, and chickens for eggs. The chickens had three good and faithful friends; three family dogs were assigned to protect the chickens from the constant threat of foxes in the area. These dogs adapted and adopted their task with personal relish. There were times Michael thought that perhaps the dogs considered the chickens as their own family. The devotion of these three dogs and their loyalty to protect the chickens was unsurpassed. It was this devotion and loyalty that drew Michael to these dogs and to all dogs throughout his lifetime.

We would be amiss not to mention Michael's great love for cats. Of course, on the farm, cats were necessary to minimize the field mouse problem. They also provided good company in Michael's childhood. Decades later, *Dedushka* (Grandpa) Michael picks up all the stray cats in his neighborhood to this day.

Metrofan was Michael's uncle, his father's younger brother. He seemingly was the most reverent among the several sons of the Ilyins. His Orthodox Jewish roots and passion for the Torah were the catalyst of his heart's search to find peace with God and fulfillment in serving the God of Abraham, Isaac and Jacob. In the process of his searching, he found his heart's desire in Jesus Christ. Truly the prophet Jeremiah foretold eternal truth when he declared, *"And you will seek Me and find Me, when you search for Me with all your heart"* (Jeremiah 29:13).

As the meetings of Voronaeff came into Metrofan's small community, it seemed like all his Old Testament studies had now come to a focus onto One Person: the One Who came to fulfill the law and to offer His own life as sacrifice for sin, Jesus Christ. He truly was and is the Lamb of God who takes away the sin of the world. The sacrifices of the old covenant could only cover sin for a year, but in Jesus Christ, our sins are removed, never to be remembered or held against us anymore.

Metrofan Ilyin was the first member of the family to accept Jesus Christ as his Messiah, Master, Lord and Savior. The life change that followed his experience in Christ was so dramatic that it drew others like a moth to a flame. Instead of destroying those that are drawn, the flame of the Lord only refines and burns up sin. Metrofan's brother, Jacob, was deeply affected by the transforming power he had witnessed in his brother. It wasn't just the words that were spoken, but it was the peace that was evident in his life and a joy upon Metrofan like he had never seen.

To complicate matters, however, Maria, Metrofan's wife, resisted grace and considered her husband's newfound faith something to be scorned; after all, the Ilyins were Orthodox Jews, tracing their lineage back to the very tribe of Benjamin. Had he forgotten his roots, or had he simply gone mad with this new movement that was igniting the southern Ukraine like a prairie fire driven by the wind? Maria had made Metrofan's life miserable, and her misery was not confined to the four walls of their house, but readily spilled over with fits of verbal abuse to Jacob, her husband's older brother.

Jacob was next in line to find Christ; and with that, in short order, many family and friends were swept into the Kingdom of God. The battle lines were drawn between the religious and the realities of their newfound faith in Christ. How would this conflict play out? Those questions were soon to be answered.

Metrofan and Maria finally came to know the peace of God in their home. Maria had found the Prince of Peace Who purchased peace by the blood of His Cross, the Lord Jesus Christ. She surrendered to the claim of Calvary in the drawing of the Spirit, embracing the grace of salvation. The family was whole again and in agreement with God's will and ways. They were some of the first to leave Adamovka, following the leading of God's prophetic word as they made their way by a horse-drawn wagon to the nearest railroad head. Later, they traveled by train to Tashkent, Uzbekistan, where Metrofan resided for over a year.

Chapter Seven
SATAN'S FURY EXPRESSED THROUGH STALIN

All the while, the Ukraine hung by a frail thread, caught between a rock and a hard place, with Stalin's fiery breathing down the necks of his oppressors. One summer morning, the thread finally broke as a plot was conceived in Stalin's twisted mind to take vengeance against his archrivals, the Ukrainian people. Joseph Stalin originated from the nearby Georgian Republic and had learned to despise his Ukrainian neighbors for reasons of jealousy and a futile rivalry that reached back centuries. This mad man's master plan would result in the starvation of millions in the Ukraine and other republics and a heavy siege of persecution against the Church of God.

In Adamovka, Christians continued to wait on God in prayer. There was reluctance on the part of many to leave their lands and their homes just before what was to be a record harvest of wheat that year. In this small community, the buzz around the wells, in conversation coming in from every quarter, was how bountiful this year's wheat harvest would be. It seemed everything had worked out perfectly. The soil had yielded its fruit in abundance. The weather had cooperated in maturing the grain, and no one ever recollected heavier heads of grain bowing with the weight of their bounty. It was just weeks away from the harvest in this sunny summer of 1929.

It was the lull before a hellish storm that would hit and consume the land. A collectivization of farms was forced upon the Ukraine by Stalin, who confiscated the entire harvest of grain. Should a farmer refuse to give up his harvest, his fields were razed to the ground.

History tells us that this institutionalized program knew its most severe years from 1932 through 1934. It is estimated that a quarter of the population of the Ukraine died during that time. Seven to nine million people lost their lives due to starvation and disease.

Stalin's ruthless decree had reduced the "bread basket" of Europe into a dust bowl of destruction. Many people resorted to cannibalism of the dead corpses that were the victims of these purges. This dark hour in history was suppressed in the Western press because of the West's preoccupation with the Great Depression and devastation in their own economy. This is the severe judgment that God warned His people to flee, and thousands who heard His voice were not subject to the screams of anguish and terror of friends and family left behind.

Right up to the final hour of the fields being burned to the ground by Stalin, there was another fire burning in the land: the continuous Holy Fire of God's revival. Nightly, hundreds were being saved from village to village, and the hundreds grew to thousands; and these would be visited by an outpouring of the Holy Spirit of God, with a profuse flow of the prophetic accompanying this move of Heaven.

There seemed to be a deeper urgency on the part of the prophets who declared the shortness of time and implored with the urging of the Spirit crying for the obedience of His sons. There was no time for vacillation. The time had come when either they believed the prophetic word of God and were spared by the Hand of God, or they disbelieved what God was saying and found themselves severely punished by the consequences of unbelief.

Jacob finally heard the voice of God resound with clarity. The Spirit of the Lord through the prophetic voice of Jacob's wife, Polageya, personally foretold that Jacob would see his younger brother, Metrofan, return from Tashkent, accompanied by another young brother in Christ. This prophetic utterance was confirmed by the prophetic voice of an elder from the church fellowship. Once again, Metrofan would return to Adamovka at the prophetic leading of the Lord. In their hearts they had a clear word to share with the Body of Christ, and that word would demand immediate obedience.

A few weeks later, after this prophetic word was given, down the rutted lane of Adamovka Main Street rolled a *brijka* (a long gated rail, horse-drawn wagon). Sitting behind the horses with the reigns in his hand was Metrofan and a young member from the Tashkent Fellowship who had accompanied Metrofan on this distant journey. The first phase of the prophetic word had come to pass in that Metrofan had returned from Tashkent as the Lord had foretold.

Phase two would be heard that night at a local prayer meeting. As the Christian fellowship assembled, eager to hear via testimony from the mouth of Metrofan what God was doing in Tashkent, they got more than they had bargained for. Metrofan, with tears in his eyes, began to share of the waves of grace that had followed them all the way back to Tashkent. When he had finished his testimony, tears of gratitude and thanksgiving had filled the eyes of the people, profusely flowing down the cheeks of all those who had assembled.

With this spirit of gratitude and thanksgiving welling up in their hearts, their praise and worship to the Lord was punctuated as the air was pierced by Metrofan's voice. No longer now speaking in soft, melodic tones of warm testimony, but in passion with power by the prophetic voice of God, Metrofan declared that this was Adamovka's last call.

Metrofan began this prophetic message by lifting both hands in the air as the voice of God cried through him:

"My people! My people! Heed and hear the voice of the Lord your God! I have called you many times, and many of you have doubted My leading. I will not call again. This is My final call. Sell what you can and move out quickly to the place that I will show you. I, the Lord Your God, will go before you and lead you by a mighty hand. I will be your rearguard and a wall of fire around you. None will harm you nor snatch you from the hollow of My hand, but you must believe and put your full trust in the Lord. If you disobey and doubt My voice, you will fall with the unbelieving and be part of the scourges and heavy bloodshed that will fall upon this land. Many thousands will fall by famine and by sword, but I, the Lord, desire to lead you out so that your name and your posterity will be preserved in the earth to the glory of My name."

Then, the Holy Spirit began to speak through another vessel of God, saying:

"I will make of you a testimony to generations to come that I, the Lord, do lead My people by a mighty hand and none can stop or stay My arm made bare. I will lead you to a land after many days that flows with milk and honey, and you shall eat the fruit of their labors and rejoice in the Lord your God as generations will be raised up in your dwelling. They will rise up as a mighty host of God's planting. Your fruit shall not fail, neither your limbs wither as you drink deeply from my waters of obedience, but your seed and your children shall return in a season of sowing. They shall harvest the cities that you had fled, and in your seed you will build up the broken-down places and establish My Church and My Kingdom among men. Great will be the glory that shall come to My Name. I only call to you to obey."

The hair on the back of little Michael's neck stood up. God had just made a "house call" in the form of a mighty visitation of His Spirit. Their obedience that night would change their lives and their destinies forever.

Chapter Eight
TASHKENT AND BEYOND

What friends and neighbors heard seemed like lunacy and was just too hard to comprehend. Their Christian neighbors were selling all that they could of prized possessions, livestock, dried fruit and grain, horses and wagons, and anything that could be turned into cash was being liquidated for pennies on the dollar—more accurately, *kopeiki* on the *ruble*.

At first, the unbelieving Russian Orthodox friends and neighbors thought this entire prophetic program was a joke, but then who could resist a good bargain? Hence, with abandonment the villagers began to buy into the scheme. It seemed only a few weeks, after Metrofan's message to the church fellowship, that all their wares that could be sold were sold.

The *brijkas*—narrow, wood-planked wagons with a front seat big enough for a driver and one passenger—were filled with the essentials of their upcoming journey. The caravan down the main street of Adamovka raised more than dust. It raised all of the surrounding neighbors from each quarter to gather in one large throng of jeering and mocking, as the Christians made their way out of town and out of these people's lives forever. Curse words flew as readily as sticks and stones through the air, branding these believers as *stunda*; this term comes from the German language and means "one hour." It had become a slanderous and derogatory term wielded by pagan unbelievers with their vicious agenda of persecution of the Redeemed. This term came into prominence as God's household of faith throughout Eastern Europe would spend a minimum of one hour in prayer daily. To the unbelieving mind, the term was synonymous with the scourge and the scum of the earth.

Metrofan, in the head wagon, pulled on the reigns hard to stop the horses abruptly. Standing up in his *brijka*, with a mighty anointing, the prophetic word filled his mouth. In the midst of the jeering and the raging throng, their voices were suddenly silenced as Metrofan's voice rang through the cool, morning air. The anointing of God was so powerful that the hair on the arms and neck of hundreds of onlookers stood on end. One of the scoffers who had been noted for his staunch stance for atheism became a believer as a result of this powerful message.

Here and there throughout the crowd, the Spirit of God was doing a sovereign work. Those that believed would join the exodus of God's faithful in the days, weeks and months to come.

The message resonated in the air. God spoke in a powerful prophetic word through Metrofan, saying, "There is a severe judgment coming; a famine and bloodshed will follow in the land. There will be tremendous persecution like you have not seen. I, the Lord your God, will gather My people from the ends of the land and deliver them to safety by a mighty outstretched hand. If you heed and obey My voice, I will spare you and your families, but if you disobey, you will pay heavy consequences." The message was not post-scripted by a final "Amen" but rather by the lurching of the horses as the reigns were applied.

Turning down the road and off into the horizon, the caravan left. As the last wagon disappeared over the distant hill, the villagers stood frozen in time, meditating on the message they had just heard. Standing in the ranks of the unbelieving were Michael's grandparents, Ivan Ivanovich and his wife. They had not bought into the emotionally charged scenario rehearsed by other family members concerning God's leading. Now, they stood there in unbelief, proudly and fully putting their trust in their Jewish religion rather than the *"rhema"* word that flowed so prolifically throughout the Christian community.

Some short 30 kilometers away from Adamovka was the railroad spur and station known as Radivka. When the Christians finally arrived in that village setting, it took some days to sell their horses and wagons. They took with them only what they could carry and purchased tickets for the two days' and two nights' journey that they would take to Tashkent, the capital of Uzbekistan.

Upon arriving in Tashkent, Michael was overwhelmed by the wonder of this huge city nestled among the foothills of the Himalayan Mountains. These peaks, covered with year-round snow, in some cases exceeded eighteen thousand feet. Little did he realize at that time that in a few short years, his young feet would trek along with his family and Christian fellowship through these ice-covered passes and on across the plateaus beyond and into China.

As the gap widened between the believing and the unbelieving community behind them, the consequences of their actions became more ominous in their spirits. Many of these villagers would die in a matter of months and years after this exodus. Letters and reports of horror and dread found their way into the hands of believers in Tashkent some time later, describing the once peaceful area of the Adamovka they knew, now as a killing field by famine and ravaging disease. Adamovka's nights were pierced with groans of pain as the population languished in wave after ravaging wave of devastations that plagued the small farm community.

Adamovka was one of the first areas to feel the heel of Stalin's tyranny. Stalin's thugs, backed up by the army, demanded the harvest of the entire crop of the surrounding village areas. If one was not cooperative with their demands, they would hang him from the nearest tree and pillage and burn his house and fields to intimidate other neighbors into compliancy. Starvation is a painful way to die. There were letters and personal words that had come into the hearing of the believers in the north that included accounts of family and friends who died with eyes protruding, with bellies swollen, and lips pleading for mercy that evaded them or rather that they had chosen beforehand to refuse.

A few late stragglers, ones who had heard the message spoken by the Holy Spirit publicly as this group was leaving Adamovka, were slow to respond; but, in the wake of the exodus of God's believing family, they began to process the truths that they had heard. They, too, began to rapidly sell their goods and joined their fellow believers as they had finally come to the saving knowledge of Christ. Their verbal reports were of a horrendously graphic nature and underscored the mighty deliverance that God had effected for His people.

Grandpa Ivan at long last found his way into the arms of His Messiah and Savior, Jesus Christ. The road of his resistance and unbelief was hard and heavy as marauding gangs organized by Stalin were given carte blanche permission to pillage and burn wherever they desired.

Some two years later after the Christians had left Adamovka, these thugs burst into Ivan's home and demanded all the money he had. When his wife was uncooperative, as she was not aware where her husband had hid the funds, she was dragged into a storage room and choked by a rope until she lay there limp and lifeless. Ivan walked in on the scene only to be brutalized by this gang of marauders. Being the cowards they were, they tied Ivan's hands and feet behind his back, slipping a pole between his feet and hands, and they carried him into the farmyard where on the ground, they began to brutally beat him with sticks. The thugs ripped most of Ivan's beautiful white beard away from his bleeding chin, smashing all of his front teeth with their blows and left him for dead.

When neighbors found Grandpa Ivan, miraculously he was breathing. When his lips could finally move, they were uttering a prayer. Thank God that Ivan and his wife had turned their lives over to Jesus Christ before this ordeal and he had the assurance that his beloved wife was in the presence of the Lord. It took several weeks to recover in a local clinic. All the while, the police would come and ask Ivan if he knew who committed these acts of violence and brutality against him and his wife. Ivan did know but was wisely silent in response to the police's constant questioning. Ivan's belief was that if he told the police, these thugs would be held for only a short time before their political bosses effected their release, and they would come back and finish their job by taking Ivan's life. When Ivan finally had totally recovered from the injuries of that horrific night, he, too, sold his goods and made his way into the arms of the fellowship of his Christian family and friends in Tashkent.

This, to me, is reminiscent of the book of Acts where it says:

And being let go, they went to their own companions and reported all that the chief priests and elders had said to them. So when they heard that, they raised their voice to God with one accord and said: "Lord, You are God, who made heaven and earth and the sea, and all that is in them, who by the mouth of Your servant David have said: 'Why did the nations rage, and the people plot vain things? The kings of the earth took their stand, and the rulers were gathered together against the Lord and against His Christ.' For truly against Your holy Servant Jesus, whom You anointed, both Herod and Pontius Pilate, with the Gentiles and the people of Israel, were gathered together to do whatever Your hand and Your purpose determined before to be done. Now, Lord, look on their threats, and grant to Your servants that with all boldness they may speak Your word, by stretching out Your hand to heal, and that signs and wonders may be done through the name of Your holy Servant Jesus" (Acts 4:23-30).

Tashkent, Uzbekistan, was an urban melting pot of over three and a half million people, a mixture of numerous ethnic groups, most of which adhered to the Muslim religion. Despite the opposition of the average residents, a church began to flourish as witness of Christ began to expand, sealed by the prophetic word of the Holy Spirit. Muslims, too, believe that Christ is a prophet, with a clear distinction from other prophets, in that Jesus Christ heals. This testimony of Christ is confirmed in the Muslim writings of the Koran. Healings became the drawing point for many confused Muslim hearts.

As the testimonies flooded of eyes being opened to see, deaf ears unstopped to hear, drunks and alcoholics delivered from their demonic bondage, there was no denying the weight of evidence. Christ was not only a prophet but a Prophet with resurrection power. This puts the Lord Jesus Christ in a unique category foretold hundreds of years before His birth, detailing every aspect of His life and demonstrating Christ's power over all the demonic of every age. Jesus Christ stands in the category all by Himself.

No other prophet declared of his life, *"No one takes it from Me, but I lay it down of Myself. I have power to lay it down and I have power to take it again"* (John 10:18). Only Jesus Christ offered Himself a ransom on the cross for the sins for all mankind. Death and the grave were not able to hold Jesus Christ in bondage. Satan, with all his hordes of hell, could not keep Him in the tomb. On the third day, Jesus Christ arose just like the prophecies concerning Him foretold and just like He, Himself had declared.

Good prophets do not lie. Isaiah declared Jesus Christ to be God in his prophetic passage where he called Him the Counselor, The Prince of Peace and Almighty God. Jesus Himself acknowledged that He is God. Only the blood of Jesus Christ would be powerful enough to appease the wrath of God and be the perfect sacrifice for all sins.

Nor is there salvation in any other, for there is no other name under heaven given among men by which we must be saved (Acts 4:12).

Muslim, Mormon, Hindu, Buddhist, Catholic, Protestant and even the non-religious atheists and agnostics have only one door to salvation: the living door, Christ Jesus our Lord and Savior and soon coming King.

The time in Tashkent, as it had been in Adamovka, was a season of hearing and learning the voice of God. In the gospel of John, Jesus declares, *"And when he brings out his own sheep, he goes before them; and the sheep follow him, for they know his voice. Yet they will by no means follow a stranger..."*

(John 10:4-5). To know the voice of the Good Shepherd personally and in this intimate fashion does not happen overnight. This is a process. To transition from being a goat—stubborn, self-willed, selfish and self-righteous—takes breaking by God's Spirit working in our lives. Oftentimes, the Lord allows adversity to be the teacher of the hearing process.

The book of Hebrews tells us that *Christ, as a son, learned obedience by the things He suffered* (Hebrews 5:8). The greater the suffering in the flesh, the more acute becomes the hearing in the spirit. All that remains is the compliance and surrender of our will. Only then does

God have vessels that bring honor to His Name. The longer and more intense the process, the greater seems God's glory at the point of our surrender.

Tashkent was their classroom on a daily basis of walking out the Word of God in shoe leather. They would become doers of the Word and not just hearers of it only. Neighbors, co-workers and even strangers on the street knew this band of believers because they were benchmarked by a special grace from God Himself. God had preserved their lives and brought them to this distant city to preserve life and declare life by their walk in the risen Lord. Their favor with God and with men greatly multiplied. Through an honest day's work, through moral integrity or just a kind deed of hospitality, word got out throughout the city of Tashkent that there were a very special people amongst them, the people of God.

After living in Tashkent for some time, the Word of the Lord came to these Russian believers again. The cloud of the glory of God had lifted and another trek of obedience was demanded of them one more time.

They had used every means of transportation available, but now they would be using rail and a ferry once again to cross over to the small community of Chardara, located on the Black Sea. The venture provided excitement in Michael's young heart. What new things would God have in store in this new location? What new testimonies would God generate in the community they were about to enter?

Chardara was a ready-made village for the vocations of the influx of Russian Christians from various parts of Ukraine and Russia. They had adapted quickly to the commerce at hand. Some families involved themselves by picking apples, others became vinedressers in the vineyard of the nearby hills and still others became experts in growing melons. In his youthful years Michael became quite a little "businessman" in the raising and selling of several types of melons that grew prolifically in this region.

Honeydew melons, cantaloupe and larger watermelons fared the best in this rich, sandy soil heated by long, hot summer days with temperatures rising to nearly 120 degrees. It seemed like Michael's melons continually needed water. By the time he carried the buckets via a yoke on his little shoulders and carefully poured at the base of his melon plants, it seemed only a matter of seconds before the earth soaked up the cool water like a massive brown sponge. His weeks of diligence paid off greatly. When harvest time finally came, Michael's little field produced wagon loads of melons for the local market.

In the meantime, Metrofan and Jacob were diligently working at the local power-generating plant. This afforded them a stable source of income, new technical skills and accompanied housing for their families; the electrical company provided a large work barracks near the plant of its operation. Things couldn't be going better. God was giving them favor at every front. Nightly, the Christians met in prayer. One evening, however, there was a distinct difference from all the other meetings.

Again, the voice of God broke through their conventional prayer time. The Lord spoke of a fire that would devastate the block-long housing barracks and that they were to ask for individual housing in this city. Armed with that declarative from Heaven, the very next day, Metrofan and Jacob began to talk to their supervisors, working their way up through the chain of command to the highest level in the power plant. Strangely enough, the request did not sound unreasonable as these diligent workers had proven themselves time and again to the plant officials.

After all, the Christians considered their employment was not just for the purpose of making a living, but they were employed of the Lord to be witnesses of His righteousness and mercy to the plant and its workers. Although the distance was very short, leaving their friends they had made in the barracks was hard. Settling into individual homes in the nearby village provided them individual housing. For the first time in such a long time, these precious believers had the luxury of their own privacy. With that privacy, they had an opportunity to wait on God day and night.

No longer were the groanings of their prayers to be restricted or muffled, nor the agony of their souls hidden, but they would intercede for hours on end for their city, their fellow workers and for their future. Surely this was not their final resting place. There was an un-rest in their spirits that drove them more frequently into their closets of prayer. When the answers were not clear, the protracted seasons of fasting and prayer finally gave way to a new directive declared by Heaven.

Weeks after the Christians left these barracks in Chardara, the news came of their former dwelling place, the barracks at the power plant: A strange fire had erupted on the second floor, fueled by the tar roof and paper-thin walls. In a matter of a few short hours, the entire barracks lay in ashes and ruin. Because of the intercession of God's servants, there was no loss of life that they were aware of except for one person.

Metrofan and Jacob, as well as other Christian families, had truly heard the voice of God and one more time had been spared the devastation that fell upon their fellow neighbors and friends.

Now if (all these things be true, then be sure) the Lord knows how to rescue the godly out of temptations and trials, and how to keep the ungodly under chastisement until the day of judgment and doom...(2 Peter 2:9, AMP).

Chapter Nine
'I SHALL SAY TO THE NORTH,
GIVE THEM UP...'

Just as the Lord had promised He would gather His people from the ends of the land, He overshadowed the fulfilling of His Word. While God was gathering the Ilyin family, along with their believing friends and neighbors, out of Adamovka and the Nikolaev region at the opposite end of the nation, He was speaking to other groups of Christians.

Nikolaev, the county seat, was near the mouth of the Dnieper River as it entered the Black Sea. Due north, several hundred miles at the headwaters of the Dnieper, lay a small industrial community called Krivorog. The same mighty manifestation of the Holy Spirit that captured the heart of the people of Adamovka was powerfully prevalent among the people of Krivorog as well. One of the families that would prove prominent in the forthcoming exodus would be the Vodopianoff family.

Here again, the prophetic voice of God began to stir the people in their newfound faith in Jesus Christ. Out of orthodoxy, out of lethargy and out of religion, they rose to a dawning of a new destiny and direction inspired by the Holy Spirit of God.

In the north of the Ukraine, villagers from all directions heard and were stirred by the stern warnings of the Lord. The Spirit was speaking expressly in their midst, saying, "Judgment, bloodshed, famine and war would be coming into this land and I, the Lord Thy God, want to deliver my people. My people must flee in the direction of the leading of Christ, or you will be part of this devastation and destruction in the land." Intense urgency to sell everything that they had also gripped their family's leadership and prophetic patriarchs.

Meanwhile, almost simultaneously, Maxim Vodopianoff, Nadejda's father in Krivorog, heard the Lord speak the same thing to him: "Sell your land immediately and leave this place, for there is coming great famine, war, bloodshed and starvation, and many of My people will suffer tremendous persecution."

Unknown to them at that hour, God was grooming little Nadejda to be Michael's bride in the decade to come. Maxim was hesitant to sell his land since he had many hectors of wheat that were ready to be reaped. He struggled with the urgency in his heart and that he couldn't wait to first reap the harvest, sell his tremendous wheat crop, make a profit and then leave.

The Holy Spirit kept speaking expressly, telling them to sell everything now; otherwise, it would be too late. Maxim, his wife Elizabeth and their children, Ekaterina, Nadejda, Grisha and Nikolai, prepared their little satchels with their most precious possessions before they left their birthplace and their friends and journeyed north.

The transaction for the land was made unusually fast, and a fair price was paid for the farm, the crops, furniture, cattle and other possessions. Within a short time, a caravan began to leave northern Ukraine, slowly making its way eastward towards the Ural Mountains.

Few realized that well over 1,500 families from various villages and cities in Ukraine were doing the same thing. Nearly 5,000 people had left their possessions to follow Christ. They were ridiculed by friends, family and neighbors, yet they still obeyed the voice of the Holy Spirit.

From over a dozen directions and by a myriad of modes of transportation, they came, supernaturally drawn by God to several points, one of them being the Urals. Those led by God were welcomed by people of the orchards and cave communities at the foothills of the Ural Mountains that divide Europe and Asia in the heart of what is today the former Soviet Union.

Uralsk, being the largest city in that region, was nestled in the leeward side of the modest Ural peaks. Here in the north, the Urals were not nearly as rugged with altitudes of only 4,000 to 5,000 feet. Their deep valleys, warmed by the compressed wind that crested the Urals, provided the ideal climate for the abundance of fruit orchards.

Here, God would shelter and shield their lives for a time and season of learning to hear His voice and to follow His leading. Lessons of listening for all believers are afforded us daily, but rarely do these lessons come with deadly consequences for disobedience.

Meanwhile in God's hidden place covered by His hand, some of the families were living in caves, which provided a natural shelter and shield of isolation with God's provision from every side. Provision by the Lord's hand was evident at their feet with fish from the rivers and fruit from wild orchards at their doorstep. The only thing lacking was bread.

Just weeks after lands were sold to friends and non-believing families, Stalin, in one of many mad moments, razed the fields of the Ukraine by fire. He declared, "I am tired of white bread. Give me rye instead!" Stalin sold the grain from the fields that he didn't burn to nations in Western Europe, thus forcing upon the people an artificial famine that slowly crept with its gripping pangs of death from one provincial area to another.

Rationing cards for the all-too-hard-to-find loaf of bread became the norm of the day. Coupons and rationing cards covered that need, as a few of the women would walk to town on market days and return with numerous loaves of fresh bread. However, one particular day would be different.

The KGB (undercover secret police) was on the trail of thousands that were rumored to have escaped Stalin's purges in the Ukraine. Those who remained behind were all too ready to betray their Christian neighbors who had escaped. They gave up names in exchange for merely a crust of bread.

Standing in line was commonplace under communism. As a matter of practice, it was planned so you would not plot against the government. By emphasizing long lines, your corporate dependence on the government for all your needs from a head of lettuce to a bag of rice or flour was assured. One could not eat if he or she were an enemy of the state under Stalin, and you could be designated an enemy of the regime merely by professing faith and being a believer in the Lord Jesus Christ. At the fall of communism in the late 1980s, it was noted that an average 70-year-old under communism had stood in line for 10 years, thus giving little time to revolt and no incentive to do so if he or she desired to eat.

Early one morning, three believing sisters had the task of going with their rationing cards to the distant village market, in hopes of receiving bread, while the rest of the believers were hiding in the caves. This day, as they stood in line, would be uniquely different from all other days. Normally, just showing their ration cards was adequate, but today they were asked for their names. To the astonishment of these three sisters, none of them could respond! They stood there absent minded, not knowing what to do. Looking at each other, not one of them could remember their names nor assist in remembering the names of each other.

Now the communist leader, a plain-clothed officer, raged with rhetoric they had never before heard, swearing at them in satanic sarcasm: "So, you women are so smart that you can't even remember your own names? If you're that stupid, you don't deserve to eat! Get out of line, and get out of my sight!"

Bewildered, the three Christian sisters walked away in confusion and apprehension. Because they could not remember their own names, they had to return with no bread for the body of saints waiting for them.

Rounding the bend back to the caves, soon they would know the reason for their strange dilemma. Despondent because of their failure to provide for their family and children, their hearts ached at the thought of what had just transpired.

One of the brothers (just off his knees in prayer) had heard from Heaven and ran to warn our three precious sisters in Christ. Upon meeting them, he jubilantly exclaimed how the KGB had a list of names and stood to the side, waiting to hear names from their list given at the rationing food line. As the sisters heard this, they rejoiced together for in their temporary blockage of memory, God had spared their lives and the lives of many believers.

These truly were God's chosen people who had given all in obedience and were living by faith. Some from Jewish heritage, others from Gentile roots—all had come into relationship with God and each other through the precious blood of Jesus Christ, their Savior.

Sometimes, even when we apparently fail, we win in Christ. The failure of our flesh and limitations of our perspective often bring opportunities to learn from the Holy Spirit. God was daily honing the hearing ear of His house. They *had* to hear His voice. It was imperative, or they would perish! Our time of trial in the free world is yet coming. Our preparation for times of persecution does not come in peace. It's time now to hear and heed in lesser trials.

In this you greatly rejoice, though now for a little while, if need be, you have been grieved by various trials that the genuineness of your faith, being much more precious than gold that perishes though it is tested by fire, may be found to praise, honor and glory at the revelation of Jesus Christ, whom having not seen, you love (1 Peter 1:6-7).

If you have run with the footmen and they have wearied you, then how can you contend with horses? And if in the land of peace in which you trusted, they wearied you, then how will you do in the floodplain of the Jordan? (Jeremiah 12:5)

The multiple groups that were led by the Lord had several factors that they shared in common. The first factor being that they all had been led divinely by the Holy Spirit through an unusual clarity and gifting of the prophetic. Secondly, a large majority of the more prominent groups shared the common exit point from the former Soviet Union in the garrison city of Jarkent, which would later serve as a bridge point crossing the frontier into China.

Most major groups settled for decades in Kuldja, China, where they built churches, raised their families and were prepared of the Lord for the last leg of their journey from bondage into freedom. There are many dynamic stories to tell of God's divine intervention and leading during their time in Kuldja before some of the groups exited China via Harbin, Urumqi, Shanghai and Hong Kong.

Chapter Ten
JARKENT, THE LAST FRONTIER

In a vicious war that re-carved the borders between China and Russia scores of times over, Jarkent had become a pawn in this border skirmish. Presently on the Russian side of the border, this once tranquil community had been leveled by artillery fire from the nearby Chinese border. All civil population had moved from its city limits, and the entire city was presently occupied by Russian military platoons. Buildings lay in ruins seemingly at the turn of every corner. To secure the city, the military had encompassed the entire town with guard towers and barbed-wire parameters.

In the confusion of the early years of communism there was afforded many opportunities for numerous aggressive elements to become little dictators. These tyrants desired to have total dominion over their departments or geographic jurisdiction. Jarkent fared no better in this sea of confusion and at this tempest-tossed time in history.

About two years later, covered under the wing of God with His nurturing and nestling of His people in the Ural Mountains, the orders from Heaven commanded the believers' migration again. The Lord spoke prophetically of a city that nobody knew of its exact whereabouts, nor was the location of the community on local maps.

Jarkent would be their next port of call. The prompting of the Holy Spirit caused God's people to once again gather their meager belongings and start out toward the Chinese border community of Jarkent, just barely inside the Soviet zone.

From surrounding cities they would come, moving in D.S.T. (Divine Standard Time), each having heard from God, each obeying

His Word to that particular family and group of believers. This new haven was the scene of numerous border battles and tossed to and fro by rival parties of Chinese and Soviet communists. Satan's house was indeed divided against itself as it is this day; therefore, his house will not stand. Yet, in God's wisdom, it provided a new place of supernatural safety.

Leveled by heavy artillery shelling from a Chinese civil war, Jarkent awaited bricklayers that were due to come from Moscow to rebuild this military outpost and garrison community. Jarkent lies just a few kilometers within the Russian-controlled military zone, centered in the heart of Kazakhstan.

Commanding officers of Jarkent had wired Moscow asking for assistance to rebuild this broken and demolished city. As is often the case, the wheels of bureaucracy grind exceedingly slow, especially in a chaotic, communist nation. It is not a matter of knowing what the right hand or the left hand is doing, but rather a matter of the nation being clueless and without direction as to what needs to be done.

Over the hill like beleaguered sheep they came, pots banging and children crying from exhaustion from walking and traveling many kilometers over numerous days. Their feet were aching, and many of them were famished.

Could this be the long-awaited crew of carpenters, bricklayers and artisans Moscow had assured via telegram were coming to Jarkent? The guard towers all buzzed at sighting a large caravan coming in a single column straight for their gated garrison. Troops scrambled behind the tall stone walls in preparation for meeting this entourage. Were they friend or foe? Who was to know?

The grand iron gates of the fort creaked and the guards confronted the approaching company. One officer, backed by scores of trained rifles, came out through the gate and commanded the column to halt. He demanded documents; and on behalf of the entire group, Maxim Vodopianoff, Nadejda's father, said, "We have been sent here to help rebuild your city, for we are bricklayers, and I carry the work permit."

Maxim's permit was one of the few pieces of official documents that had survived the ravages of fire from his distant pass in the Ukraine. These multiple companies of Christians had no passports, no visas and no birth certificates on their person or in their baggage. Inquiring for such certification would have alerted the officials at their home-fronts of their desire to escape.

The officer confronting them was relieved of the tension in realizing these were friends and not foes. Upon receiving and reading the work permit, waved with his hand for the entire company to pass, assuming they were all sent by the high authorities in Moscow. (Little did he realize that the Highest Authority, our Supreme God, Savior and King, had truly orchestrated this event for His people moving to Jarkent, providing them with work and protection.)

What a sense of humor God had as the entire company of believers now had the task of rebuilding this military garrison! This would be their home for several years until God could refine His people and bring others to Himself. Through the vehicle of evangelism, some of the local communists and unbelievers would be saved. In conjunction with this move of salvation, other Spirit-led believers would arrive to join them from the uttermost reaches of Russia and Ukraine.

Jarkent was a staging area, a mere gathering point where they camped until God led them into the neighboring country.

Maxim and his leadership were the first-fruits of God's leading into this new terrain. While chronicling the accounts of such obvious divine intervention, the question begs to be asked: In a present day of uncertain sounds and confused voices in the prophetic, why and how did these Russians and Ukrainians hear the voice of God so clearly and so profoundly?

Upon contemplating this theme, two thoughts came by revelation to my heart: one being of the depth and dynamic of Godly conviction doing a deep work of grace and salvation in the lives of these Pentecostal patriarchs. The other thought is that this was a "*kauris* moment" because of the momentum of the Spirit for this historic hour.

The point is best illustrated in the salvation testimony of Maxim's own conversion. It seemed but a few short years ago in Ukraine that Maxim was living an immoral life, catering to placating the lust of the flesh, womanizing, and in rage against people of true faith. His first wife was a victim, dying of a plaque that ravaged the poverty-stricken villages in the Ukraine. It seemed that sickness and disease often are the traveling companions of poverty and famine. Maxim's first wife had given him a beautiful daughter named Ekaterina, affectionately called Katya.

She was the love of her daddy's life. To say that her beauty was striking would be to understate the case. Katya's beautiful blond hair, her porcelain clear complexion and her ever-ready smile turned heads wherever she went. A few villagers with cameras were constantly asking permission to use her as a photography subject. With her bouncing, thick blonde braids of glistening hair, she would often plop herself on her father's knee, snuggling her daddy with warm affection. Katya truly was a consolation after the death of Maxim's wife.

One day, another beautiful creature sent by God caught Maxim's eye. After a short time of courtship, he married Elizabeth. Added to his family was a second daughter, Nadejda, affectionately referenced as Nadia. She filled her father's heart with overwhelming joy. Elizabeth also gave him two sons, Grisha, known as George and Nikolai.

Maxim's new wife was a staunch Jewish believer. Her devotion to the God of Abraham, Isaac and Jacob and to His Word, the Torah, was unwavering. Elizabeth's line and lineage could be traced back through the generations to the tribe of Ephraim. Her gracious manner endeared her to friends and family; however, being religious and of good disposition is not enough for entry into the Kingdom of God.

One day, a young evangelist, a son in the faith of the great apostle Ivan Voronaeff, preached in her village; and for the first time in Elizabeth's life, all the types and shadows of Judaism became clear in their fulfillment by the very personage of Jesus Christ, from Moses' prophecies of God raising up a Prophet that the people would hear, to Abraham offering up his only son, Isaac. The Old Testament came alive with New Testament reality. When Isaac as a young lad inquired, "Where is the sacrifice?" Abraham prophetically responded by declaring, *"God Himself will prepare a sacrifice."* God stayed the hand of Abraham from slaying his son, and the ram caught in the thicket was a prototype of the sacrifice on Calvary. The thorns that held the ram fast were symbolic of the crown of thorns pressed into the brow of the spotless Lamb of God. God's perfect Sacrifice for sin crucified on the cross gave Himself freely as our Savior. Jesus rose again the third day, completing the plan of God as death and the tomb could not hold our Risen King and Conqueror, Jesus Christ.

So many prophetic truths came rushing and gushing into Elizabeth's soul. As she heard this young preacher declare Christ, she couldn't restrain her voice or the emotions of her heart a moment longer. She cried out in anguish of her sin, "My Lord and My God, Jesus Christ, forgive me!" In the deep agony of her heart, she knew that she had grieved her Heavenly Father. At that moment she realized all her religious self-righteousness was like filthy rags before the unfathomable depths of God's holiness. She needed a Savior and was mindfully aware through God's revelation that there is only one Mediator capable of becoming her Messiah and Master.

Elizabeth's 180-degree turn from religion to reality and a relationship with Jesus on a personal level left Maxim isolated, dumbfounded and angry. He forbade Elizabeth to attend any of the church functions, even a prayer meeting. Elizabeth, however, had to obey her newfound Savior and Lord. She would often slip away from the farm home, finding herself at the nearest prayer meeting or Bible study where she offered continuous prayers accompanied by tears for her unsaved husband.

Joining with Elizabeth in covenant agreement were saints whose newfound faith and fervor linked with hers through fasting and prayer until one by one they saw their families drawn into Christ and His saving grace.

Maxim resisted as long and as strong as he could, but one night after falling into a deep sleep, Maxim was given a vision by God of a lake of fire. As he saw his beloved Elizabeth rising into the presence of the Lord, being clothed by beautiful white raiment, he felt himself falling headlong into the burning fires of hell. He cried aloud as he felt the fury of the flames, smelled the sulfur and heard the screams that emanated from the caverns of the dam which was so terrifying that he awakened himself by his own screaming.

Perspiring in a cold sweat as the reality of his separation from God sunk into his spirit, he heard himself saying, "Elizabeth! Elizabeth, don't leave me! Take me with you!" Imploringly he said, "Don't let me go to hell, for the flames and fire torment me!" God had used this vision as a means of bringing salvation into Maxim's life as he was led that night into salvation by his wife.

The very next day, Maxim made his way to the House of Prayer where he confessed his faith in Jesus Christ publicly, but still the tears would not cease. Maxim's brokenness over violating the laws and the love of his Savior caused him to weep uncontrollably, trembling in the presence of Almighty God for days on end. The depth and dynamic of our personal surrender at the point of repentance determine how much revelation and reality we receive of God in our early stages of Christian growth.

It is such a tragedy that we live today in an hour of easy "believism" where our pulpits tell us that all you have to do is "believe," but the Word of God declares that even Satan believes and trembles. Believing is not enough. In the Laodocean church today, pulpiteers tell us to close our eyes with no one looking around so as not to cause embarrassment to ourselves at the point of our conversion.

I have heard one evangelist say, "If you are with me in this sinner's prayer, with every eye closed and every head bowed, move your eyebrows up and down." Somehow the jargon of the day does not align itself well with the eternal Word of God. God says, *"If we confess Jesus Christ before men, He will confess us before the Father and angels that are in Heaven, but if we deny Him, He will deny us before the Father and angels of Heaven."* So-called "seeker friendly" churches, having a form of Godliness but denying its power, find themselves powerless and ineffective.

This was not the case of generations that have gone before us. Godly sorrow had effected deep repentance in our forefathers. They did not ride the rollercoaster of up one day and down the next in their steadfast pursuit of being disciples of the Living Christ. Their unwavering, uncompromising decisions were brought forth with the birth pangs of the spirit. The result was that their hearts and minds were purged of sin, leaving a vessel that God could fill with pure gifts, so when they declared, "Thus says the Lord," it rang with all the resounding power of Heaven behind the prophetic.

Cities and nations were swept up by the wind of the Spirit. A generation was led by the prophetic voice of God from the ends of the earth. Oh, how we need that clarity again, and the only way to receive it is with a deep purging of every gray area of our hearts and lives to purity by the power of God that consumes us until we hear clearly the voice of the Lord.

God not only raised up Maxim, but scores of leaders who were divinely cut out of the fabric of time and had the hand of God pen *Eternity* on their hearts. Their Godly steadfastness preserved their families, spared their cities and was the means of leading thousands of God's people out of bondage into true holiness and wholeness through the blood of Jesus Christ.

"Therefore the Lord will wait, that He may be gracious to you; and therefore He will be exalted, that He may have mercy on you. For the Lord is a God of justice; blessed are all those who wait for Him...He will be very gracious to you at the sound of your cry; when He hears it, He will answer you. And though the Lord gives you the bread of adversity and the water of affliction, yet your teachers will not be moved into a corner anymore, but your eyes shall see your teachers. Your ears shall hear a word behind you, saying, 'This is the way, walk in it,' whenever you turn to the right hand or whenever you turn to the left" (Isaiah 30:18, 19b, 20-21).

Chapter Eleven
FORTIFICATIONS AND FOUNDATIONS LAID

Honing the hearing of God's servants often is most effective in the furnace of affliction. When there is no systematic pressure or persecution by Satan or his surrogates, self-inflicted pressure must be applied for spiritual growth. Fasting and prayer is often the vehicle of God's choosing, not that we earn favor with God, but rather we become sensitized to what God is saying and wanting to say to us.

The din of life often becomes a barrier or dam holding back the clarity of God's voice. It is in times of isolation and sole dependence on God and His Word that our solutions become apparent and our obedience to the Lord's prompting becomes our deliverance.

Jarkent, being primarily a military community, had the first work brigades of Christians, by and large focusing on military offices and barracks. Once these structures were completed, other civil buildings became the focus. The buildings of personal homes were the least important on the priority list. At least so it seemed by the commands of the government. Finally, due to the diligence of the Christian community, the city was totally rebuilt.

Younger elements of the Christian families that were not suited to the difficult tasks of removing ruble, such as carrying blocks or bricks, were assigned plots of ground outside of Jarkent's wall. The farming duties overwhelmed these large Christian families as due dates for harvest drew near. Work days would often begin before sunrise and continue well after the sun had set. Sore muscles, aching joints and blistered hands and feet were common among young and old alike. Despite the hard labor, there was joy in their hearts often expressed in song.

This evident joy was something the military garrison had never witnessed. Many of the city officials and residents were drawn in to this effervescent spring of rejoicing. Their joy and life showed a strength that was beyond the natural. All their labors were done as unto the Lord. Excellence and perfection were the benchmark of all they put their hands to. This open, grateful lifestyle shouted a sermon so loud that even the deaf could hear.

"You are the light of the world. A city that is set on a hill cannot be hidden. Nor do they light a lamp and put it under a basket, but on a lampstand, and it gives light to all who are in the house. Let your light so shine before men, that they may see your good works and glorify your Father in heaven" (Matthew 5:14-16).

As mentioned previously, Maxim Vodopianoff and his family were some of the first-fruits visiting Jarkent. Paul the Apostle tells us, *"If the first-fruits be holy, then the whole lump is also holy"* (Romans 11:16). In other words, if the first part is consecrated to God, then all the rest is blessed. The Vodopianoff family played a key role in preparing a place for God's people, both in the natural and in the supernatural. Because they arrived in Jarkent early, they were also blessed to be one of the first groups that left Jarkent for China.

By this time, the growing Christian population diligently laboring in God had rebuilt and polished the city into a gleaming gem in the midst of a sea of hostility. There were so many Christians in Jarkent, and so much work being done both inside the city and without, that one family or two would not be missed. The influx of Christians coming from various parts of the country, led by the Holy Spirit were an acute contrast to the military leadership keeping busy trying to manage multiple projects at once. This bee-hive of activity gave the Vodopianoff family the covering they needed to slip out in the dark, making their trek toward China.

The distance from the outskirts of Jarkent to the Chinese border was approximately 30 kilometers, or 20 miles. The dark night provided many alarming sounds to the children as they walked, so they held the hands of their parents tightly. At the first rays of the rising sun, their weary feet had finally arrived at the Chinese frontier. All that they had worked for and all their life investments over the last few months had been left behind. Only a few precious items that they could hand carry were at their side.

Kneeling to pray, they asked God for guidance and wisdom as to how to approach the five Chinese guards that blocked their entry into China at the bridge over a small creek. The entrance before them was an obstacle of seemingly insurmountable difficulty. As they prayed, the voice of the prophetic came from among their own ranks, telling Maxim that he should show his work permit to the Chinese guards stationed at the opening of the bridge.

The word of the Lord declared that God would confuse their mind and put His own words on this Russian, well worn, work permit that Maxim carried. This document once again allowed all of God's faithful little ones, which encompassed several families, to cross in safety. After a season of prayer, which ended with a time of thanksgiving, Maxim got off his knees and made his way down into the valley, walking straight toward the five Chinese guards.

Being multilingual, the guards tried Girgizi and then Russian to request to see their paperwork. By now, Maxim had been joined by his wife, Elizabeth, their children and several other families that had heard from Heaven and stood there waiting on the Lord, believing God for a miracle.

One guard read the Russian work permit to himself with his lips moving. His response was, "I can't believe what this document is saying." Without further elaboration, he handed the work permit to his fellow soldier and upon his reading the document, he exclaimed with a similar expression, "I can't believe it." To that, the final three guards in unison read the paperwork and to the amazement of the Russian believers, they were waived on into China.

Upon crossing the bridge, the Christians found themselves touching the Chinese soil for the first time. Well out of the hearing and sight of the Chinese guards, they said to one another, "I wonder what the document said? I wonder what God turned those words into when He said He would confuse their minds and blind their eyes?" God had used an insignificant little bricklayer's work permit as the means of entry for all these little ones in His care. They had walked far enough from the border and were well beyond the horizon, still visible to the Chinese border guards.

They took this occasion again to drop to their knees, but this time, hot, salty tears flowed down their faces as they verbalized their thanksgiving to the God Who could open the eyes of the blind and blind the eyes of the hard hearted.

Meanwhile in the city of Batum in the south, the stirrings of Heaven were awakening Metrofan and Jacob out of an unsettled and fitful sleep. They had been promoted in a matter of months from mere entry workers to manager and assistant manager of the entire electrical works of Batum. This was an expression of God's hand of favor that rested heavily upon the people of His following, especially those who diligently sought His face.

Favor from friends, neighbors and co-workers made their soon-coming departure bittersweet in their eyes. The protocol and procedure were once again followed, selling all nonessential, personal items and only carrying in small cases or satchels of what they deemed most valuable.

A short ferry ride brought them from Batum to Kootejnika, which was the local railroad head for that area. From there, tickets were purchased, and the long journey to Jarkent began. Some family groups arrived to Jarkent by rail, others by truck and still others by horse and wagon, the Christian population in Jarkent continually swelling.

When Jacob and his family arrived, it wasn't difficult to find housing, as there had been a constant ebb and flow of Christians arriving into Jarkent and Christians escaping across the poorest borders into China. Little Michael and his family adapted quickly to the regimen of hard work and then the praise and worship that finalized each night.

Stories had come from China of freedom and opportunities to worship God according to the dictates of one's heart, as this Russian zone felt the heel of Stalin's famine. Food became more and more scarce. Many families slipped away in the night, fleeing to a land where they could raise their families in the fear of the Lord. This was a land where food was plentiful and hard work was rewarded with the fruit of success. This northern part of China had not tasted the lunacy of Mao's social experiment called communism. The bitter taste of that cup would be drunk decades later.

As a concerned father, Jacob decided one night that the risk of raising his family under Soviet-style communism with its bent towards atheism was more than his family could bear. Certainly the rumors from China had come from Godly sources and could be trusted.

Jacob had made up his mind that he would no longer subject his children to the propaganda that prevailed over Jarkent through loud speakers for hours on end. Before the pure innocence of the minds of his children could be defiled, they would slip across the border into the nearby freedom that China afforded.

At last, the night came when their plan was to be implemented. The cover of darkness provided the opportunity that Jacob needed to make his escape. Gathering his family and a few faithful Christian neighbors, he made his way with them under an overcast sky into the night toward the borders of China.

As morning light drew near, the Christian families found themselves huddled in the cattails and rice paddies that terraced the border area. Weary from their night's journey, their awkward escape had left them ill prepared with no provisions or food to strengthen them on the way. Jacob's wife, Polageya, and another Christian sister named Marusia decided to enter a semi-deserted Muslim village that lay between Jacob's hiding place and the Chinese border. Here they could use several items they had to barter in exchange for local bread. Jacob, however, was very unsettled with this new plan.

When our heart is unsettled, the best approach is to consult the counsel of the Prince of Peace, Jesus Christ. As the little group prayed, God once again faithfully clarified His heart and direction through a prophetic word given by Polageya, saying, "Go straight into China. Do not stop or hesitate either going to the right or to the left. If you go for bread, while the bread is yet in your mouth, your family will be arrested and returned to Jarkent."

Despite the clarity of the Lord's voice, Marusia insisted on slipping away for just a few moments to buy the bread that she and her Christian family needed. She encouraged Polageya to join her in her detour of disobedience. Because their stomachs rumbled with hunger, they listened to the flesh rather than to the directive of the Holy Spirit.

Upon the return of the two sisters, they handed out freshly baked rolls of white flat bread (*lipeshki*); and as they broke and gave it to the families, Jacob's youngest son, Vasya began to cry. These two-year-old little hands couldn't wait to grasp the food that had been offered to others. Before his mother could break a piece of food off to silence Vasya's whimpering and crying, a garrison of Russian patrol guards heard the crying child in the tall grass near the edge of the *kamishi* (like bamboo sticks).

As Marusia saw that their hiding place had been discovered, she directed the Russian guards to where young little Vasya was crying. In the confusion of people running in all directions, grabbing for their children and their belongings, Marusia slipped out of this snare and slipped across the border into China.

Jacob and his family along with others were arrested, and he was separated from his wife and children. The men were rounded up and forced to march with the military at their heels, being escorted to a barrack and prison close to Jarkent. This was an overwhelming ordeal for Michael, a ten-year-old little lad, to see his father so helpless and distraught over the separation from his wife and children.

The men were stripped of all outer garments while the guards foraged through their pockets and clothing for any valuables or documents. With only their underwear, they were imprisoned with no bread or water for three days.

Michael, in a separate compound with his family, found a small hole at the back of one of the cells. It was just barely big enough for a skinny little boy like him to squeeze through. As he looked through the hole to see that all was clear, he saw the local dogs being fed scraps of bread and bones thrown on the ground at their feet. When the guards left their dogs snarling over their meager meal, Michael hashed a plan. He made his way through the hole in the wall and after finding several rocks, chased the dogs away, took a few crusts of bread and threw them through the barred window to his father and friends.

As the dogs bolted from the barrage of flying rocks being hurled by Michael, they ran past the guards that had fed them. The guards, turning on their heels, ran back to see what the source of agitation was for these mangy prison dogs; and as they rounded the corner of the prison barracks, they were shocked to see that a skinny little ten-year-old boy in his ragged clothing was the cause of such a stirring that morning. Although Michael was ten, due to malnutrition, his little body looked more like a seven-year-old. The guards in turn had picked up sticks and stones and hurled them at the young lad, with a barrage of harsh words, chasing him away from the prison compound.

As the Lord would have it, just as little Michael exited the parameters of the prison yard, not being seen as a threat by the two sleepy guards at the gate, he ran back to the compound where his mother, brothers and sisters were. The other Christian sisters who had been separated from their husbands were also in this smelly, repulsive facility. This was no five star accommodations as it had no toilets or running water or other hygiene features. This group was forced to join this large cell with other Christians placed there by Russian soldiers.

Without breaking stride, he ran straight into his mother's arms and found the hugs of his mother, sisters and brothers to be a sweet reunion of rejoicing and relief. There they were, all excited to greet Michael. In a circle encompassing him there were Maria, Lena, Vanya and baby Vasya. How the tears of joy flowed!

Michael's precious father was imprisoned with fifty other men that had been rounded up from various borders trying to make their escape out of Russia and into China. Michael, his mother, brothers and sisters were held for three days in the makeshift prison camp near the border.

Finally being released, they began their forced march back to Jarkent. Upon walking some distance with his mother and family, Michael, being the oldest boy, persistently asked his mother whether he could run on ahead, stopping at some of the cooperative farms in the nearby village to ask for any food they may have to feed his destitute family.

At first, his mother's answer was an emphatic "No." However, his childlike enthusiasm and persistence won her over. The soldiers that followed them from the prison compound had dropped off and returned back to their barracks, satisfied that these wives and children would continue walking, making their long journey back to Jarkent. The men of the group, however, were driven on by a brigade of communist officers on horseback, leaving their wives and children behind them, walking at their own pace.

Michael was a little man on a mission. His wiry little legs raced across the fields; and with his sincere, pleading voice, he implored farmers for help and soon was rewarded. He had already accumulated a loaf of bread, a few potatoes and even some boiled eggs. He was so intent on his task that time slipped away from him. Hiding the bounty that Michael had received from local farmers and farm hens under his torn shirt, he tucked his shirt deeply into his trousers to secure his treasures.

Where had the day gone? It was already approaching twilight. Michael decided his best approach was to return to the main road where he had left his family some time before. He estimated that he was about a half hour ahead of them, considering the pace that he had run from farm to farm.

When he stood at the road's edge, only seeing trucks with goods, wagons and other vehicles pass by, his heart began to sink with disappointment. A myriad of questions filled his little mind. Had the soldiers come back and taken his mother and family to the prison compound, or had their pace been so slow that he should wait for them? *Where is my father and the men who had been driven by the horsemen?* He thought to himself that maybe he had not estimated the right place and time and his family had already gone ahead of him. As tears of loneliness coursed down his cheeks, fear and uncertainties filled his heart.

Michael began to wave down any traveling vehicle. Finally, a truck stopped, and its generous driver made room for him on the front of his loaded goods. This driver was carrying wool, winter linings for boots and other woolen wares. He sat Michael in a comfortable seat next to him in the cab. "Little son," he said, "where is your family and where are you going?" Michael couldn't stop crying. Finally as he got his composure together, he told him what had happened. The driver said, "Don't worry, sonny, I'll get you reunited with your family. I'll get you fed and make sure you are safe."

Before Jarkent, the truck came to a sudden stop, and the truck driver helped Michael to the ground. Stopping at a roadside café, Michael had his first warm meal in many days with this kind stranger. Across the table from Michael, the trucker kept on asking, "Where are you going to go?" As Michael blurted out of his innocent heart the events of the last few days, a look of disappointment covered the driver's face. He, the driver, was not going into Jarkent, but a few kilometers short of that city; there was a Y in the road, and the right fork would take him down into the community.

The truck driver and Michael agreed that that would be a good place for him to wait for his father, mother, brothers and sisters. Certainly the ride in the truck had put Michael well ahead of the pace of his mother and family walking up the sandy, dusty road that wound its way into Jarkent.

At the junction of the road, the kind truck driver stopped along the edge of the main trucking road, and he let Michael off. A very appreciative and thankful young man said his farewells while, the grinding of the gears and the backfiring of exhaust, echoed in his ears, the truck slowly disappeared. At this Y in the highway, there was a deserted Muslim community noted for its particular type of clay huts, known as *yurtas*.

The war zone of this area had left many communities derelict and deserted in the fury of redrawing multiple battle lines. Michael had his choice from many deserted little huts. He chose one that seemed to be the driest with the largest capacity to receive his mother, brothers and sisters. Evening was beginning to set in, so Michael scurried to find dry straw for bedding, wood and coal for a small fire, utensils, and water so that when his family arrived, they could cook a small meal from the food that was still tucked under his shirt.

The glass in the windows had been broken, so Michael found rags that he hung as curtains and filled the openings to reduce the flow of air. With all his preparations in place, his eager eyes watched through the makeshift curtains he had fashioned. He frequently ran outside to see if there was any trace of his family in sight, with his little heart pounding, wondering if he would ever be reunited with his family again. The gripping fear of not seeing any sight of them was almost beyond the capacity of his aching little heart. It seemed like an eternity. Michael began to cry out to the Lord, asking Him to settle his little spirit and to take away the fear and loneliness. He began to beg the Lord to somehow reunite him with his family. After a time of crying out before the Lord, he got off his little bony knees and felt an assurance from God that his mighty Savior was doing a work of deliverance in his life and family.

When Michael felt a peace come over him, he realized that Jesus Christ was not just a religion, but he felt His presence and reality in his heart and life. Running outside, feeling an assurance and confidence in his heart, he believed God for a miracle of being reunited. At the last rays of the setting sun, far in the distance, he saw a plume of dust arising on the darkening horizon. Michael rubbed his eyes for a better look. It seemed like an eternity before he made out the figures of his father and approximately 50 other men being herded along the road on horseback by Russian soldiers. No wonder the cloud of dust had filled the horizon, as about fifty men were pushed to keep up with horses on their forced march back to Jarkent.

There were only a few yards of distance where Michael stood at the side of the road, from where this procession was allowed a short rest stop. Michael and his father hugged firmly, both shedding profuse tears of gratitude and euphoria. In the prison where all the men's clothing had been seized and searched, Jacob slipped his son Michael in the confusion of that moment, twenty rubles which Michael quickly hid in the sole of his shoe. He knew the separation of that sole where the shoe had worn out would come in handy some day. Now it had provided just the perfect hiding spot for a twenty ruble note. This was the total sum of wealth the Ilyin family had left. The other twenty rubles that Jacob had secured deep in the pockets of his ragged shirt had been confiscated by the communist guards that had been their captors at the border.

This group of prisoners was allowed to sit at the roadside café to rest their weary feet and allowed refreshments and food if they had funds to pay for it. All the prisoners' belongings had been carefully scoured and ransacked. So Michael pulled the twenty rubles out of his shoe and offered it to his father who, in turn, bought food and *chai* (tea) for himself and offered it to his son and fellow prisoners around him. Michael said to his dad, "No, thank you. I have already eaten and have had tea to drink." He then began to spill out of his heart the story of the benevolent truck driver that God had used as an instrument of mercy.

The one-hour rest was interrupted abruptly by the communist officers mounting their horses and driving their fifty prisoners back onto the road toward the city of Jarkent and the prison barracks that awaited them there. With the departure of his father's image fading over the horizon, Michael's heart sank to its lowest ebb.

Sitting there for a while at the restaurant table, the voice of God began to fill his heart. The mothers and the children were left to fend for themselves without a military escort. Their thought was that there was nowhere for them to go except back to their point of origin, Jarkent, where they could solicit the help from their family and friends.

What seemed like hours was in reality but a short while as a second cloud of dust appeared. This time, the distant party he saw coming was that of his mother, brothers and sisters, accompanied by other wives and family members. Michael couldn't wait for this slow procession to pass. His heart pounding wildly with the anticipation of finally being reunited with his family, he ran as hard as he could to meet them.

He told them of the food and provision that God had given just a few meters away. Michael could not contain his joy, bubbling up, sometimes almost incoherently, with all the details of what that day had brought his way, including the reunion with "papa" Jacob and the meal they shared together at the roadside. They all cried and rejoiced for God's deliverance and protection over little Michael and their family.

That night before falling asleep, a long thankful moment was shared, reflecting as they lay on their warm straw bed on how deeply their Heavenly Father had cared, even when mistakes were made in their lives. The family had ended their weary journey that evening on their knees in prayer with thanksgiving, and now at last their bones and their bodies would rest in sleep in the presence of the Lord. With their tummies satisfied and their hearts full of gratitude, they fell into a deep sleep, snuggling one another for warmth.

Chapter Twelve
LED BY THE SPIRIT

In the Apostle Paul's first letter to the Corinthians, he says in chapter 15, verse 46, *"However, the spiritual is not first, but the natural, and afterward the spiritual."* One often perceives what is happening in the spiritual realm by carefully evaluating what happens in the physical realm. The physical dimension is merely a reflection of the spiritual dimension in many cases. These principles proved true in the lives of Jacob and his family.

Their first attempt to escape from Russia was based on opinion, good intentions and an urgency to provide for their family. Disobedience, the same as obedience, comes with specific consequences and rewards. Jacob was released after a month of incarceration within Jarkent. As he rejoined his beloved family within the safety of the walls of Jarkent, tears of gratitude flowed to God for His mercy and tears of thanksgiving for the joy of uniting together complete in Christ.

Their family, during that turbulent month of Jacob's imprisonment, had gone from friend to friend, from neighbor to neighbor, looking for some sense of stability and a place to settle. The Ilyins' previous housing had been ransacked and destroyed. They were at the mercy of their Christian friends for a night or two here and a weekend there until the day of Jacob's release.

Upon Jacob's release, the family decided to go north of Jarkent, 15 kilometers to where various housing had been available in the past. Empty huts were available as people had fled for freedom, leaving their clay huts behind. Their trip to the north acquainted them with another strong church fellowship whose leaders had been marked for ministry by a heavy anointing of the Lord.

Alexander Shevchenko, a young man in his twenties, was a gentle giant of strength and spiritual wisdom. He, along with other Russian Christian leaders, would become a prominent influence in their exodus out of the Soviet Union through China and into the West. Alexander, with his gentle heart would later fall in love and marry the darling of Vodopianoff family, Ekaterina.

The next days and weeks found Jacob and his family applying their new freedom with extra diligence to their duties. They all were assigned a task that added to the care and comfort of the whole. Each family member participated in the key role he or she played. Jacob returned to his first love—the tending of orchard and fruit as well as working in rice fields. Polageya returned to caring for her family and utilizing her homemaking skills to provide a nurturing and caring environment for her sons and daughters. Orchards and nearby fields were yielding the bounty of their harvest, so there was plenty to preoccupy their time from the least to the greatest.

All of their daily routine, however, focused in the evening hours upon their assembling together to pray, seek the face of God and to hear from His Word. Some nights, these meetings were simply the gathering of the Christian neighbors in a single-family residence. Other nights, the gatherings included the entire corporate body of Christ in the city when a building would be available. On many occasions in the evenings, they obtained the use of a barn as a place of assembly. After all, if the King of kings and Lord of lords could make His entry from eternity into time by way of a manger, His servants were not above kneeling in the straw and calling on His Name. Sometimes, the more humble the setting, the closer Heaven seems to appear. Perhaps it's not so much the setting as the attitude of our hearts that open the portals of glory.

During one such prayer meeting when twenty-five to thirty of God's prayer warriors did Heavenly battle through their intercession, Polageya, prophetically declared that the unbelieving in their midst who wouldn't listen to the leading of the Holy Spirit would fall in their unbelief and doubting. The prophetic word had no sooner escaped her lips when suddenly she fell forward from her knees upon her face. Her breath had been taken away from her instantly and the mourning saints picked her up and placed her lifeless body onto a bed in the room where they had all been praying.

Through deep cries and powerful groaning, the anguish and agony of her loss assailed the Heavens. After a season of deep soul-searching, intercessory prayer and strong groanings, God prevailed. Unexpectedly, Polageya leaped from her bed and back to her knees to join the prayer meeting, bringing it to an awesome climactic crescendo of praise. The God that they served was even able to raise the dead, but Jesus Christ our Lord preferred to work with the willing hearts of the living. This illustrated message shook the body of Christ deeply into realizing the severity and the goodness of the Lord.

Jacob's testimony, rehearsing what the Lord had done for his wife, not only encouraged the saints but emboldened his children. In the days that followed, Lena, the seven-year-old daughter of Jacob, was overheard declaring to her communist neighbors about the power of Christ in their lives. As she got the details of her mom being raised up by the Lord across to the jaw-ajar audience, she finished her presentation with a unique, climactic closure. "If you don't believe, we have sticks and we will beat the 'hell' out of you!" To a seven-year-old heart and mind, there is no gray area. The battle lines are clear—believe or do not believe. Unfortunately, the solution for a seven-year-old mind concerning unbelief is not as clear as beating the 'hell' out of the unsaved. God in His mercy gives each mortal His choice of free will.

While Jacob was working in the rice fields and nearby orchards, his friend Mihail Danchenko, whom he assisted as a mechanical engineer in the electrical company in Batum, came to Jacob. The communist government had offered Mihail to start a new electrical station in this nearby community of Jarkent. Since Mihail Danchenko and Jacob worked so well together in Batum, Mihail asked Jacob to become his assistant again in this newly established electrical power station that they had to set up.

Jacob was delighted, as this provided him a stable job in the midst of famine and starvation. The opportunity also provided better housing for him and his family. The new housing facility had all their bedding in place, kitchen utensils, plates and tables waiting their embrace. What a change from a little mud hut where there was little warmth, just a tiny little brick cooking stove. Jacob was overwhelmed and thankful for the provision of the Lord. God truly takes care of His children in a marvelous way.

Almost two years later, in one particular meeting the voice of God began to speak again. Lessons had been learned in hearing and heeding God's voice alone. At the close of one long, ordinary workday, a new urgency of God's leading was effected in the hearts of many of His people. Some of God's servants had received previews of the Lord's leading by word of knowledge or prophetic revelation during the day's working hours. They came to the House of the Lord in Jarkent with great anticipation of further leading and clarity. Groups of families from all quarters assembled in the Jarkent main Evangelical Church.

When the body of Christ came together in one stream of unity, a prophetic voice thundered in their midst. The individual prayer that had been offered throughout the day now culminated in a powerful prophetic declaration. The time had come for all that had heard the voice of the Lord to rise up and be delivered by the outstretched arm of their God.

Masha, the wife of Ivan Verhovod, who was the leader of the overall collection of churches and families, prophetically echoed the timing of Heaven to the waiting ears and hearts of God's servants on earth. The Holy Spirit spoke through Ivan, saying, "When you hear the clock strike one, arise with your children and your families and exit the House of God and go out singing and praising My Name, for I, the Lord of Shabuoth, will go before you and effect a mighty deliverance and deliver you with my outstretched arm. I will scatter your enemies with a blast from My nostrils, and you shall go out in power praising My Name."

As the message matriculated into the minds of God's servants, the illogical demands began to frustrate the carnally minded. It would be one thing to slip out under the cover of darkness holding their hands over the mouths of their children. This would stifle any whimpering or crying and minimize the noise of their exit. The logical approach would be to tip-toe over the cobblestone main road, hoping no- one would awaken their sleeping neighbors. There was also a secondary issue of how would they exit a city that was walled and guarded by tall guard towers, machine guns and specially trained guard dogs? All these natural barriers and obstacles flooded the minds of these people, causing their hearts to waiver in fear.

What if the prophetic message that they just heard were merely conjured up in the mind of the messenger and not from the heart of their Master, Jesus Christ? They wanted to believe, but their unbelief seemed to be an insurmountable mountain and barrier before them. Their thoughts and misgivings were now shattered by the song of the Lord that Masha began to sing: "Arise, My people, and go out in boldness. Trust Me, and leave now."

As children were awakened from their slumber and pots and pans began to clang upon their arising, the procession had begun. Ivan Verhovod led the way and behind him was his wife, Masha. Upon the first note of her song, an unusual sound accompanied her chorus. Suddenly, outside the sanctuary, a strange, warming wind began to blow. There was no time for rationalizing, only time to realize that God had begun His move.

As the second sister in the middle of the ranks began to sing, she was soon joined by a third sister in the Lord, Vera, Alexander Shevchenko's sister, who was toward the back of the column. This procession stretched out over a city block in length. A peculiar phenomenon had enveloped the people of God as they began their march toward the outskirts of the city and its main gates of Jarkent. The wind howled in its fury, stirring dust and debris in all directions. In an unusual fashion, these Christians were in a tunnel unaffected by one speck of sand or one whisper of the blowing wind.

Down the cobblestone Main Street they came. Trees on either side were violently bent with the blast of the prevailing storm. However, where they walked was a supernatural calm that defied logic. The song of the Lord in three-part harmony through these sisters rang through the night, echoing the same words, melody and music. Its origin was not from terra firma, but rather from the courts of Heaven.

In the Russian language, the Christians could only hear the prophetic message sung in their ear: "Be bold and be unafraid, for the Lord vanquishes all His foes. He will go before you, and He shall also be your rearguard. He shall place around you a wall of fire, and none shall touch the apple of His eye. You are a chosen people set apart to show forth God's praise on the earth. I, the Lord Your God, will be your victory and your Victor. I will be your provision and your supply. I will lead you, and I will guide you by My Spirit, says the Lord."

Again and again the chorus rang out in the night. Its message was not for the masses and multitudes of the city, but for the comfort and encouragement of the redeemed of God.

Sleeping neighbors did not hear a sound other than the howling wind. Government patrols ran for cover from the burning blast of the sand in their eyes. The wind was so severe that the trained police dogs fled for shelter. The gates of the city, which should have been a barrier and an obstacle, opened before them of their own accord. This group of Christians walked out of Jarkent, hundreds of them leaving this chapter behind them in the dust.

Upon walking some distance from the city, a choice had to be made. They had passed the airport, and the road split in two directions. Would they take the hard surface and cobblestone route of the main highway or would they take a less-traveled cart trail that cut to the left?

The prophetic voice of God directed them to go off the beaten path. Masha's voice rang out with clarity that they were to go to the left and their God would go before them, delivering His people. The wind had died down as suddenly as it had appeared. Whisperings and murmurings could be heard in the ranks of the redeemed.

Other sisters and brothers in Christ exclaimed that God had spoken through some of them in times past, and certainly the Lord would not require them to take the small trail with its bushes and briers through the dry desert sand. It would certainly be the Lord's leading to walk on a road upright and unashamed, as the Lord had led them out by His mighty hand.

Once again the prevailing voice of God through the Holy Spirit admonished His children to take the lesser beaten path. However, the voice of the murmurers prevailed, and the entire company walked down the main road, including Jacob and his family. As they rounded the bend of the road, leaping out of the dark, a shepherd with his shepherds crook stood in front of the procession. He demanded money and took the best of the outer garments of one of the young leaders, Alexander Shevchenko.

Alexander was a strong young man and could have easily overpowered this lone shepherd, but when people walk out of the will of God, their strength is diminished and they become a prey to their foes. God had used this light lesson to once again teach His people a principle: The Kingdom of God is not run by the decisions of a committee, but rather by directives from Heaven. God's Kingdom is a benevolent dictatorship, and the Lord does not allow any descending voice.

This concept puts grave responsibilities on those who speak in the Name of the Lord and a greater responsibility on those that hear the voice of the Lord to weigh its veracity. Paul writes in Corinthians, *"Let two or three prophets speak and let the others judge"* (1 Cor. 13:29). Prophecy is not above scrutiny, but rather the Lord encourages us to examine the prophetic against the benchmark of God's Word. Peter writes in his epistle that there is a more sure word of prophecy, that being the written *logos* and cannon of Scripture.

Just like the mercy of the Lord's heart that pities His flock, the Good Shepherd of Heaven spoke again to His wandering sheep: "Return back to the trail" where the Lord had shown them and He would guide them and guard them, covering them with the hollow of His hand.

They had no sooner gotten off the broad road and onto the narrow path with the coverings of shrubs and bushes behind them, when a noise to their rear startled the group. Entire families dropped on the ground, creating as low a profile as possible. At that moment, a motorized column of military personnel searched with their torches for any people that had escaped in the night. Although they were only a little ways from the road, God had blinded these communist guards' eyes, and none of the Lord's children were seen or heard, not even the whimper of a child. A miracle had happened, as these trained soldiers searched diligently, but to no avail. They continued to proceed down the road.

Long after the patrol had passed, the Lord admonished His people to travel at night and rest in the shade of the day. This wisdom would best suit them in the dry upper desert that they would soon encounter as well as protect them from roaming patrols that crisscrossed the border region.

Three nights into their journey, they found themselves deep into China, facing a vast expanse of rolling sand dunes with very little vegetation. What should have taken three days wound up taking eleven days due to the murmuring of the people and their disobedience to the Holy Spirit. They were pragmatically fulfilling the last verse of the book of Judges, which declares, *"Everyone did what was right in his own eyes."*

Some of the Christians would say, "Let's go to the left as we see lights in the distance which could be a village or some type of civilization." The Holy Spirit, however, urged them, through the prophetic, to go to the right. God had promised through prophecy to be their compass, guide and guard if they would diligently heed His voice.

Again, the majority overruled the minority who sought the Lord at every turn. The group wandered into the desert, veering off to the left. God would put obstacles before them, coaxing their obedience to return to His ways, but many would stumble over the barriers of grace and forge on regardless of God's leading.

Not too many kilometers from the border, packs of wild dogs were used to secure the long expanses of unpatrolled frontier. As the Christian column crested the hill, they were encircled by vicious dogs that stealthily surrounded them, snarling and glaring with eyes full of fury. To the wild beasts, these Christians represented fresh meat, which they had not eaten for days.

To the understanding Christian, this encounter with evil was allowed by God to redirect their lives and forge repentance in their hearts. The Christians dropped to their knees with no physical defense. No sticks or stones were present in that location to fend off these ravaging rogue animals. As God's children cried out to the Lord, their cry came into the hearing of Father God Who hears and cares for His own.

Just as suddenly as the dogs had appeared, for no explainable reason, the dogs began to back off, opening a large corridor in their circle through which the believers walked, eyes brimming with tears and lips filled with praise and adoration to the Almighty God.

The Christians, however, continued on their path toward the left until their hope of a distant settlement and the illusion of distant lights had gone. There had been no city. There was no sign of civilization in the direction where they were going. The moonlight dancing off the distant hills had given them the illusion of light.

What an overwhelming feeling to know that you are lost—lost in a land without a compass, without a map, without a living soul to ask directions of and, perhaps the most frightening of all, in a land where you did not know the culture or the language. Communication is a gift from the Lord, but in this wilderness, intercepting any nomadic tribe and not being able to communicate their intentions as being friend or foe, provided its own terror.

Their wilderness wanderings seemed to be aimless over the unending sand dunes and mountains. Their water supplies had vanished. They no longer traveled at night alone, but in their desperation, their trek took them into the hot oven of the noonday sun. They pressed on hopelessly, but with a sense of urgency, desperately trying to find water, food and lodging.

Some openly voiced their complaints before God and their fellow believers saying, "It would have been better for us to have remained in Jarkent than to die here in this God forsaken, hot desert."

Through cracked, parched lips, the children responded first by dropping to their knees in the sand and lifting their little weary hands and voices to God in broken repentance. Michael, the young lad nearly twelve, and Vanya, his younger brother, led the way before some of their siblings crying out to God: "Lord forgive us for turning in our own direction where we turned to the left, whereas you asked us to turn to the right. We have wandered now for many days, and we cannot go an inch further. Our weary limbs and blistered feet can't endure one more step. Please, please! Jesus, give us water or we will die in this desert!"

As parents saw their children repenting, weeping with their little hands lifted up before the Lord, the weight of conviction pressed them to their knees beside their sons and daughters. The whole valley was filled with the groans and crying of God's repentant people.

The voice of the Lord came one more time in the midst of His children, promising mercy for their obedience and grace for their repentant heart. The Lord spoke: "Just go a few yards to the right and there dig in the sand, and I will supply you with My water, water not from the desert, but water from the provisions of My mercy and grace; for you are a called people that I have set apart to show forth My mercy in the earth and My power to generations to come."

Children were again the first to respond to the directive voice of the Lord. With their bare hands and a few sticks that they found, they began to claw the sand beneath them. Going a few yards to the right from where they had walked, the children converged on their knees into a frenzy of flying sand mixed with tears of desperation.

One of the brothers, recognizing their expression of faith, joined them in their frantic effort. They had dug perhaps two feet into the crust of the surface when the sand became cooler. Was it possible that it was even moist to the touch? That little bit of encouragement caused the digging frenzy to increase. Now there was no mistaking, the sand had become moist, very moist to the touch of their parched lips.

Handkerchiefs and cloths taken by the parents scooped up the moist sand and wrung its few droplets into the parched mouths of the children. The children now joined their parents as the prospect of water became a reality. The murmuring of doubters decreased as more and more moist sand was uncovered. One young son echoed the sentiments of all when he said, "Thank you, God, for these few drops, but we need much more to satisfy our thirst."

No sooner had the words passed his parched lips, than all of a sudden a fount of cold, fresh water erupted from the earth. The tears from moments before had turned into glee and gregarious laughter. There was laughter of joy that filled the mouths and hearts of the company of God as they drank until their bodies and souls were content. They filled all their water vessels. Some even washed their clothes and sponge-bathed in the excess of water that bubbled from the earth.

As suddenly as the waters had come, after their need was totally satisfied, it disappeared again—as if it had never happened. The only testimony that assured them of this miracle was their satisfied thirst and their vessels with water full to the brim by the provision of the Lord.

They gathered stones and set up a memorial in that place, scratching into the stone a testimony in the Russian language: "God had provided water for us out of the desert, and He was truly a God Who forgave His repentant children."

Before their journey in the desert was complete, they had set up seven memorials in different locations where God had repeated the process to make provision of water for His people.

Beside the need for water, there became an acute need for milk for the younger children and meat and protein for everyone else. Again God's people young and old knelt in the desert sand and called upon the Name of Christ, Who had provided for them water day after day. While they were yet calling to Heaven, with their eyes tightly closed in reverence, somebody opened their eyes to notice that a flock of wild goats had crested the nearby hill and were making their way straight to the believers.

At first, the believers thought these goats were being driven by some nomadic goat herders. When no one appeared behind the flock, the realization dawned on them that the Shepherd of Heaven had answered their cries and prayer.

Wild goats do not approach people, but these goats, on cue from Heaven, made their way right into the camp of kneeling believers. God's people jumped up from their knees. The female goats were restrained and milked, providing needed protein for children. Some of the male goats were taken and slaughtered, providing meat that the people of God roasted over an open fire with great celebration.

As the families lay on their blankets that night, watching the panorama of the stars above, thoughts began to fill their hearts and minds. Were the events of the last few days a mirage or a miracle? Their stomachs were filled, their water vessels overflowed and now their hearts finally began to understand that what God had done to Israel of old in their Sinai experience, He was doing again, showing His care for those who put their full trust in Jesus Christ.

"And He said, 'My Presence will go with you, and I will give you rest.' Then he [Moses] said to Him, 'If Your Presence does not go with us, do not bring us up from here. For how then will it be known that Your people and I have found grace in Your sight, except You go with us? So we shall be separate, Your people and I, from all the people who are upon the face of the earth'" (Exodus 33:14-16).

Chapter Fifteen
ORPHANED, BUT NOT FORSAKEN

"When my father and my mother forsake me, then the Lord will take care of me (Psalm 27:10). A father of the fatherless, a defender of widows, is God in His holy habitation". (Psalm 68:5)

Their steps became slower as their weary feet finally found a change in terrain. The blistering heat of the desert and their disobedience to God's voice had left a mark on young and old alike. In their desperation to find water and food, they had forsaken the pattern of traveling only at night, and for the last several days traveled in the daytime, and on occasion into the night. The blazing sun had left every appendage exposed to its burning rays, resulting in badly blistered faces, arms and feet—red and swollen from the intensity of the sun's fiery blast.

The lambs of God's flock in going to the right at last had found pastures that were green. The gritty sand of the desert over the last nine days was finally behind them. Stretching before them to the horizon were rice paddies and occasional patches of bamboo islands in the sea of green rice shoots. In the Russian language, these patches of bamboo are called *kamishi*.

The *kamishi* provided cover for the people of God to hide in when any activity or stirring in the surrounding areas caused them to fear. As they moved farther to the right, at last they found themselves on the outer fringe of a small border village inside of China called Sujdun.

As the majority of the group hid in a large patch of bamboo, it was suggested that they send out three Christian sisters to the neighboring community to barter with goods they knew to have value in exchange for bread and food for the rest of the group. The sisters were chosen because they presented no threat to the local farmers or merchants and would raise less questions from the local villagers.

The three sisters began their task, walking with excitement down the road that led them into the small farming community. As they came around a bend, they noticed a large rock to the side and discussed among themselves the strategy that they would take. They decided to break up and go separate ways among the farms of that region, maximizing their efforts to forage for food. They agreed that upon completion of their task, they would all return to this notable rock and wait for one another and then collectively return to the group.

This seemed like a good plan, with the bartering for food taking on a three-dimensional approach. It meant that they would probably receive better results in a shorter period of time. Before breaking up to go their separate ways, they stopped for prayer, asking the Lord's blessing upon their efforts, knowing that their success or failure determined whether the children, mothers and fathers would eat that night.

The trek began during the heat of the day, so in their light summer dresses gently rustling in the breeze, they broke up after prayer and applied themselves diligently to finding food for their families. Polageya was one of the three sisters on this assignment.

The afternoon quickly slipped into the evening hours with dusk rapidly approaching and Polageya returned to the rock. The rendezvous place that they had selected had absorbed the warm rays of sunshine that beat on the rock surface in the heat of the day. It provided a comfortable and warm resting place when she returned to it with the heavy load of bread and food that she had successfully collected. Polageya waited for the other two sisters to arrive. At first she thought it would be only a short while before her fellow sisters would join her, but the moments turned into hours, and the sun dropped behind the horizon.

What Polageya did not know was that the two sisters in Christ had quickly met their quota of food provision and had returned to the rock before Polageya had arrived. They waited briefly and decided among themselves that Polageya probably had come before them and, in their anxiety to feed their young children, went on to return to the group.

When the two sisters had arrived at the bamboo hiding place where the group had been waiting, Michael, his sisters and younger brother immediately asked where their mother was. They told the group that they had assumed that Polageya had gone on ahead of them to the group. Fear instantly gripped Michael's little heart as well as his family's. It was now getting dark, and the mother was nowhere to be seen.

Several of the men, after having eaten, urged the rest of the group to travel on in the dark because of their proximity close to the Chinese border but within the Russian frontier. Jacob, Polageya's husband, protested vehemently. He used the Bible illustration in John 10 where Jesus, the Good Shepherd, left the 99 sheep safe in the fold and went out to search for the one lost little lamb. Surely, they weren't going to move on and leave Polageya behind!

Jacob suggested sending a search party, but his appeals and pleadings fell on deaf ears and, seemingly to him, insensitive hearts. A commotion in the dark off in the distance, sounding like that of horses on the hard surface of a little country trail, finalized their response. The fear factor had kicked in and the group gathered their meager belongings and trudged on into the night. Poor Jacob, his broken heart wrenched with weeping over having to leave his wife behind, pulled his children by the hand into his arms. Their tears mingled together in sorrow at the loss of their mother, wife and good friend.

At the urging of the rest of the group and the help of a few friends, Jacob's weeping family was carried off into the darkness with the rest of the group. A myriad of questions had come from the Ilyins children's mouths. Why did they have to depart so urgently that night? Where was their mother? Would they see her again? Where would they meet up again? A myriad of questions flooded their hearts, and no one had an answer.

As the group continued on their night's journey, Jacob's mourning had turned into convulsing and uncontrollable shaking. It was more than just the loss of his wife. The one month in prison in Jarkent with its meager diet and forced labor was now taking its toll. What complicated the matter even more was that the sun had set, the temperature plummeted and the waters that would have been refreshing during the heat of the day became a chilling source of hypothermia.

Jacob and his family struggled farther and farther behind the group until they called out for help. Alexander Shevchenko and Lejrva Dumanovsky each supported Jacob on their shoulders as he wrapped his arms around their necks.

Others of the Christian families took the little Ilyin children, and slowly the procession began to move again.

Jacob had been weakened by his recent ordeal, being shackled to the wall in prison. Now, trudging through the heavy mud of the rice paddies was more than he could bear. Jacob and his helpers, Alexander and Lejrva, got farther and farther behind the group. In the darkness, they lost sight of the families that were in front of them. Jacob began to shiver and shake uncontrollably as a severe case of hypothermia had set in. There was no getting out of the waters of the rice paddies, which covered the Chinese Frontier and now his body refused to take another step.

Jacob's body became as a lead weight on the necks of his two young Christian brothers. Alexander and Lejrva picked him up and carried Jacob as far as they could; however, with the added weight of Jacob, their feet sank deeper into the mud of the rice paddies. Hours later, Jacob's shivering stopped, and Lejrva and Alexander realized that Jacob had gone "home" to his reward.

When Alexander and Lejrva came to a group of bamboo shoots on a little knoll, they found a place to bury their brother in the Lord. Their trek through the deep mud of the rice paddies had also left the two brothers in the Lord exhausted, but now the first rays of the sun were shining. To their shock, a local Chinese landowner came upon their hiding place. Alexander and Lejrva implored the landowner to allow them to bury their friend here at the edge of the rice paddies.

This gracious Muslim farmer told Alexander and Lejrva that they could bury their friend in his farmland. He supplied them with a pick and shovel and a blanket to wrap Jacob for burial. Before they dug the grave, the well-to-do landowner asked Alexander if they were alone. Alexander, reaching into his spirit, felt that it was okay to tell this man who had been so kind to them that they were part of a large group of families hiding somewhere in that vicinity.

Armed with that information, the farmer and his two Russian friends found the group several hundred meters away hiding in a stand of bamboo as they heard some of the children crying. The farmer welcomed the entire group into his large Chinese home and farm complex. He got his wife and servants to warm up loaves of pita bread called *lipeshki* to feed the entire group until their hunger was satisfied. Fresh straw was placed on the floor of the house, which was their bedding for the night.

Alexander and Lejrva reflected in their hearts the miracle of God's provision that had just transpired. Not only had this Muslim provided hospitality for these Russian Christians, but he also helped them in the burial of their fellow brother, Jacob. It's amazing that this Muslim farmer also had a good command of the Russian language. All these details fell into a divine pattern of God's consolation in the midst of sorrow.

Who would tell these little lambs that the shepherd of their fold had been smitten? Young Alexander, strong as a bull, was too broken with tears, so he deferred the task to his mother (*babushka*) Anuyta. With a lump in her throat and tears coursing down her cheeks, she huddled together the group of little Ilyin children. When they heard the bad news, there was a shriek of denial. "No, no, it can't be true!" But with a tender hand caressing their cheeks, babushka Anuyta dried their tears and assured them that their father had gone home to his Heavenly reward.

The house radiated with the recently fired ovens that had baked bread and satisfied their hunger. The Ilyin children huddled together, clinging to each other with whimpers and trembling lips. What had happened to their mother was still not known to them. What their future held was even more terrifying to their little hearts. Losing a mother that night was bad enough, but how could it be that their father was taken in the same night?

The Ilyin children's mourning wore their little bodies down into a fitful, deep sleep. Tomorrow would be a new day, and the Lord would comfort them through His people and by His Holy Spirit. The Lord Jesus Christ would answer many questions of their inquiring little hearts. After all, our God is a Father to the fatherless.

With morning light, the Muslim couple that owned the farm approached the group and told them that they were unable to have any children. They wanted to adopt little Michael; after all, Michael's suntanned skin was dark as their own. Michael would easily fit into this Muslim family. "This little boy even looks like us," the farmer said and went on to plead his case by saying that he was very well to do and would cherish and love little Michael, giving him nothing but the best in bringing him up and giving him a good education. He went on to say that Michael would be very well off as their son. Something in this Muslim's heart and the heart of his wife had been tenderly drawn to little Michael as they sensed his sincerity and his love for their family.

Babushka Anyuta interrupted the dialogue with an emphatic "Nyet" (No). She said, "These little ones have suffered enough. With the loss of their father and not knowing the whereabouts of their mother, who has been separated on the Russian side of the border, to leave him or any one of these children behind would break their little hearts." "He is our son, and we will take Michael and the rest of these children with us; and as long as the Lord gives us strength, we will raise them up in the admonition of Christ."

"It would be unconscionable to harm this little boy's heart in this manner, so Michael is going with us."

After two days of rest, refreshed and fed by the hospitality of this unassuming farming nobleman, the group was given directions to go on to the nearest community, Sujdun, which would play an important role in their lives in years to come.

Chapter Fourteen
KULDJA, THE REHOBOTH OF THE LORD

In Genesis 26: 22, it says, *"And he moved from there and dug another well, and they did not quarrel over it. So he called its name Rehoboth, because he said, 'For now the Lord has made room for us, and we shall be fruitful in the land.'"*

The word "Rehoboth" from Genesis 26:22 appears for the first time, as Isaac named the third well he dug with a prophetic title: *"For now the Lord has made room for us, and we shall be fruitful in the land."* This modern exodus of God's redeemed was fulfilling their personal prophetic destiny: called by God out of their culture, out of their language, out of their nation. They were pioneering a beachhead in missions that would prove in generations to come to be one of the most productive corners of harvest in northern China.

Pioneers go beyond borders and barriers that have never been broken. They paved a way for others to follow, and in the wake of their obedience to the Holy Spirit, others come, walking on the highway of God's calling. The generations to come will run faster, do more and accomplish greater things in Christ. These sons of righteousness, through walking out the Gospel, reshape Spiritual geography with the ultimate goal in mind: *"The kingdoms of this world shall become the kingdom of our Lord and His Christ"*, and Jesus Christ shall reign upon the earth over all nations.

Polageya believed this truth with her whole heart, but in her lonely hour of being left behind by the rock, she questioned deep down in her heart whether God really cared or was He too busy to attend to a small little family walking out their salvation through the nations? The cold and darkness had taken its toll. With the sun dropping, the temperatures in the upper desert dropped like a stone. Her thin clothing left her shaking and shivering with hypothermia.

How welcomed the first rays of the sun were to once again light up the earth and share their warmth with mankind. How wonderful it was to be alive. Even with all the questions of her heart, there was still the song of the Lord in Polageya's heart. It seemed that this was Polageya's gift. Every morning, the Lord had given her a fresh song, an anthem of praise. Sometimes it was hymns and choruses she knew; other times it was the overflow of her heart in adoration of her God Who had redeemed her soul and saved her family. If you know Christ, you have no other need in life. Christ makes us complete.

There was another urgent task at hand: to catch up to the group and be again united with her family. The sisters she had waited for had obviously gone on before or been apprehended. Regardless, as a mother and as a wife, Polageya, as much as she loved her precious sisters in the Lord, had a family for which to be concerned. With that maternal instinct driving her actions, Polageya reluctantly left the rock and began her long journey from the Russian frontier, deep into the heart of China.

One of the first barriers that confronted her was that of a Russian river with the spring run-off from recent snow on the mountains. The waters of the river were cold, and its banks overflowed with the swelling. There were no bridges in sight, and if there were, they would probably be guarded. At the risk of her own personal peril, Polageya forged the river, taking all her personal belongings in a satchel on her head. Slowly and steadily she stepped across the slippery stones, chilled at first by the cold night she had endured and now chilled to the bone by the freezing waters.

She made her way further to the far bank of the River Karhoz. The river was a lot deeper than she had anticipated, and now it was up to her neck. With every step, there was the threat of being washed away by its current. She prayed and said, "Lord, if the river gets any deeper, it will be over my head, and I don't know how to swim. I don't want to perish in these waters. I want to see my family, Lord. Please help me through this turbulent crossing."

Polageya knew her strength came from her Lord and Savior, Jesus Christ, and although every step was strenuous and threatening to her life, she forged ahead through the powerful current and biting chill of the water. By the grace of God, the worst was behind her as she now walked into shallower waters on the other side within the Frontier of China. When her feet at last touched the far bank on Chinese soil, she collapsed with the exhaustion of the ordeal.

There, violently shaking on the shore of the river, unable to catch her breath because of the spasms of chills that racked her body, Polageya cried out a prayer of thanksgiving to the Lord. She had finally made it across the river and into China. Her mind lapsed from consciousness to unconsciousness, and in a few moments' time, she blacked out on the clay bank of the river.

It just so happened that a Chinese family found her there some hours later. They wrapped her in blankets, carefully put her into their wagon and brought her to their humble home. These Chinese "angels" had been used divinely by God for the sparing of her life. On a straw mat near the fire, Polageya recovered after three weeks of being nursed back to health. It was fortunate that this border area had been drawn and redrawn many times over history and that most families living near the border were bilingual.

Polageya shared her faith with her Chinese friends in Russian, their common language. This gracious couple had made sacrifices in their poverty to welcome this stranger into their midst. As Polageya's recovery seemed to improve, the last sacrifice this precious little couple made was scraping together the funds they had received from bartering the items Polageya had made with their merchants. While Polageya was recovering, she knitted socks, shawls, mittens and hats out of wool that this couple supplied her from their herd that they raised on their *kolkhoz* (cooperative farm).

The time finally came when this family hired a horse-drawn covered wagon to take Polageya to the major city of Kuldja. Rumors had it that there was already a Russian Christian community assembled in Kuldja.

Polageya had no idea whether or not her family had already arrived in Kuldja. Although she knew Kuldja was the destination their group had hoped to reach, she also knew there were many obstacles in getting there.

Metrofan had heard among fishermen that there was a band of Russian Christians temporarily residing in the small city of Sujdun. Metrofan, a man of influence and means due to the favor of God, purchased several wagons and hired drivers and horses to begin a search for his lost family and fellow Christians in the neighboring community. Metrofan, like Maxim Vodopianoff had been led earlier to these Chinese communities to pave the way for massive Russian, Christian immigrants to follow in their footsteps. After traveling a distance of about 40 kilometers (a little less than 30 miles) of steep, rugged terrain, these weary pioneers collapsed from exhaustion.

When Metrofan found his family in Sujdun, he embraced the children, aunts and uncles with a whirlwind of emotions. Whispers among his immediate family and relatives made Metrofan suspect that something was awry.

No one dared share what could possibly have gone wrong. Seeing the hesitant looks on family members' faces, he inquired, "Where is my brother Jacob?" Someone from the crowd blurted out, "Jacob died in his grieving from Polageya being left behind and was buried some distance back towards the border."

Crushed by the impact of what Metrofan had just heard, he dropped to his knees, sobbing and weeping, "My brother! My brother!" His brother had at last walked his final mile. The children had tried to console their uncle, but to no avail. The tears would not cease; the grieving process had to take its natural course. At first, his mind stepped into denial, but when asked for more detail of his brother's parting, reality came back into focus. Eventually, the bitter cup of acceptance was embraced.

Thank God for the comfort of the Holy Spirit in our hours of grief! It is natural to grieve. It is supernatural for the Holy Spirit to pour His oil and wine deep into the cracks of our souls and heal and mollify what man cannot touch. No counseling, no kind or understanding words can take that hurt and pain away, but the Spirit of the living God, Who is our Comforter, comes alongside of us, caring and sustaining us when we can no longer walk in our own strength. Where would any of us be without God's tender-loving care?

After several days of brokenness, Metrofan got a hold of himself and the purpose for which he had come. They loaded up all their most precious possessions in the wagons, and only the children had a place to sit as the caravan moved out of Sujdun. All the adults walked, as even with numerous wagons in the caravan, there was no room for all to ride. The 40-kilometer journey seemed an eternity, for it was laced with grief and sorrow, occasionally punctuated by open sobbing and the groanings of inner agony.

Why did these believers have to walk through such a deep valley of sorrows? Was it perhaps that the great God of all the ages had a more eternal goal in mind than just the comfort and solace of the flesh? God cannot entrust anyone with great callings and anointing until He has tried and tested their character. Gifting should never be our focus, but the image of God's character should constantly be our goal. Our fiery trials refine us as gold and then only do we reflect a clear image to the world of our Maker and our Creator.

The wagons finally crested the hills, and in the valley before them lay Kuldja, a city of close to a million people with seventeen districts of distinct nationalities making up its populace. Each section had a gated entryway often displaying the wares and products for which that nationality was noted. For example, tinsmiths would display samples of their product on the wall by their gate. All the types of kettles, funnels and other utensils that the artisan would make were openly shown. Another gate and wall would be known for its wrought iron and blacksmith works. Shoe manufacturing was famously known throughout this entire region of China.

These communities rarely came together, maintaining their cultural and linguistic distinctions until market day. Then all barriers came down, and sales and profits drove all cross-cultural interaction. Each community converged in an open market to sell and trade its wares to merchants that transited the city. Others would bring in their products from surrounding communities. Market days were the highlight of Kuldja's bustling commerce. The atmosphere was filled with the sounds of bartering and bargaining and the air was charged with the fragrance of roasted lamb dishes. Music came from every direction, and the normally quiet city of Kuldja resembled an ant hill of activity with thousands of people coming and going.

Metrofan's little hut on the outskirts of town was a beehive with additional small mouths to feed and the orphans that he had adopted from his brother Jacob. Marusia, the oldest Ilyin daughter, was almost 14 years of age; Michael, twelve; Lena, seven; and Vanya, five. During this time, Marusia became a nanny to a Muslim household in Kuldja and was able to live with them, doing very hard chores day and night.

Three weeks later, Polageya, with her health semi-restored, made her way into Kuldja. It took her several days to trace down her family, and when she found Metrofan and Maria covering her forlorn children for her, she embraced them with tears of gratitude. She then spent special time hugging each of her children. She, who was lost now was found, and her little lambs celebrated with exceeding great joy.

The crowded condition of the little house, with the addition of Polageya was more than the four walls could bear. Polageya would have days when her health relapsed, fever often racking her body until nearly a month of continuous lapses of pneumonia took their toll. Between Polageya's grieving and continued illness, it was more than her little frame could handle. She clung to life as long as she could for the children's sake and also with the hope of being reunited with her beloved husband, Jacob.

Metrofan said to the Christians visiting his little home not to mention to Polageya that her husband had passed away, as he knew her heart would not be able to bear the sad news of Jacob. However, a sister walked into the house, unaware of the previous warning given to those in the hut, and blurted out, "Polageya, did you know that your husband died in the rice paddies coming to China?" When she found out that her beloved Jacob would not be joining her in Kuldja because he had joined the host of Heaven at the throne of God; the contractions of pain and sorrow, compounded by the fever were so severe that Polageya died several days later.

At times like this, we ask the question, "Why?" The Word tells us that our days are numbered by the Lord and none of us have a guarantee of tomorrow. That's why it is so imperative to live each day to its fullest with eternity in mind, loving each family member, cherishing and appreciating each friend, for we never know when we will have to walk the final mile.

The hut had too many sorrowful memories to contain the sobbing of the Ilyin children. Little Michael ran down the streets, eyes blinded by hot, salty tears. It seemed he ran for miles, finding some comfort in the wind blowing in his face and the excursion of his little legs running across the cobblestones. Eventually, he returned back to the house. Metrofan and the local church made preparations for the funeral. After Polageya's passing, the house they lived in no longer was a sanctuary of peace, but a place of turmoil.

Metrofan and Maria took their little battle-worn nephew, Vanya, leaving the other Ilyin children in Christian families dispersed throughout Kuldja. Little Michael did not see his younger brother Vanya or sister Lena after the dispersion for many years.

After the funeral of Polageya, remaining in Kuldja was more sorrow than Metrofan and Maria could endure. So they took their adopted nephew, Vanya and moved to Aksu. The distance of 300 kilometers over the rugged terrain from Kuldja to Aksu seemed like a lifetime journey. This impoverished, mountainous village did not lend itself well to Russian strangers; however, Metrofan fit in as he provided a needed service to the community in the form of being a master shoe maker, electrical engineer and builder. He taught Vanya as an apprentice in shoe making in Aksu, a vocation which would serve him all his life.

PHOTO GALLERY

Front, from the left: Babushka Maria, Metrofan Ilyin, Jacob Ilyin (Michael's father). Back, from the left: Maria, Michael and Vanya (John)

Maxim Vodopianoff
(Nadejda's Father)

Nadejda (Sara's mom) with her brothers, Nikolay and Grisha Vodopianoff

Michael Ilyin and Nadejda Vodopianoff, before marriage

Michael and Nadejda Ilyin
in Kuldja, China,
on their wedding day, 1942

Maria (Michael's older sister) and Joseph Lockteff on their
wedding day in Kuldja, China

Br. Ionko Sr., one of the many prophetic voices God used to direct His church in China

Michael (far right) and his sister Maria (far left), China

Church choir in Kuldja, China with Michael (back middle)
and Nadejda (with a scarf)

Top left, Nadejda, with the Christian sisters from the church
in Kuldja

Shanghai, China, the Ilyin family
Front row center: Fred, Sara (bow in hair), Natasha;
Middle row right-center: Dad, Michael Ilyin (holding Natasha),
Victor and Walter behind Dad;
Back row center: Walter (in light jacket); Victor (between Mom and Dad)

1959, Ilyin family in Shanghai,
before leaving for Hong-Kong and
Australia

Mom and the Ilyin children's immigration picture in Hong-Kong, China.
Top left, Sara, Victor; front left: Walter, Fred and Natasha

From left: Pastor Alexander
Shevchenko, Mom
(Nadejda), Katya (Mom's
sister) and (Dad) Michael
Ilyin

Left, back: Pastor Shevchenko, Michael, Mrs. Lee (affectionately called by us, "Auntie May"). She helped hundreds of Russian families with documents emigrating from Hong-Kong

Grandpa Vodopianoff remained in Australia until his home-going at the age of eighty-six

Ilyin's first house in Australia

Victor, Walter, Sara, Fred and Natasha (front).
Mr Lipen (one of the helping sponsors), Michael and
Nadejda (back), new immigrants to Adelaide, Australia

Home of our first sponsor Ivan Sidorchuk in Australia

Sponsor, Ivan Sidorchuk, with Maria

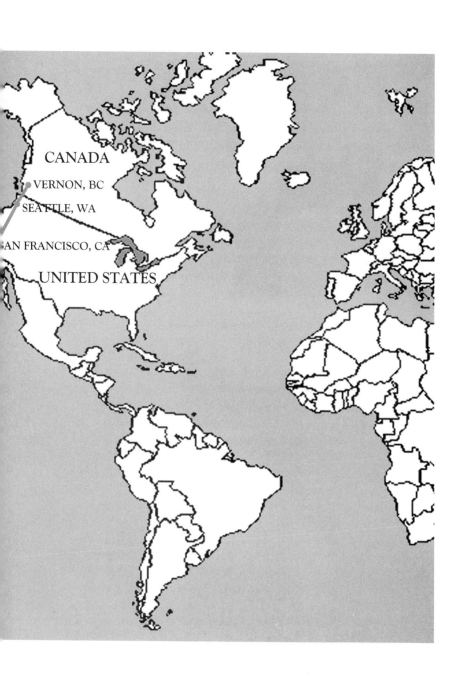

CANADA

VERNON, BC

SEATTLE, WA

AN FRANCISCO, CA

UNITED STATES

1962, Ilyin's children with Paul Ionko, a Sunday school teacher, Australia

1963, just before immigrating to America. Mom expecting her third daughter, Ruth

1963, en route to America, with stop in Honolulu, Hawaii,

1968, our home in Seattle, Washington.
Ruth and Liz on dad's lap, Natasha (front), Fred and Sara (in back)

Ilyin family in Seattle

Richard and Sara's wedding, August 28th, 1971, Seattle, Washington

Mom and Dad Ilyin on Sara's wedding day

Papa (Roman Michalski) and Papa (Michael Ilyin)

Mom and Dad Ilyin on their 50th wedding anniversary in Vernon, B.C

Michael and Nadejda with their children at their 50th anniversary

Extended Ilyin family at their 50th anniversary,

*Sara's graduation from Inglemoor High
School, Bothell, Washington 1970*

*Richard & Sara with
their children*

*Right: Richard
holding Jonathan*

*Center: Sara holding
Jason*

*Top: Jeremy, with
Leah to his right*

Michalski family - Richard, holding Jason, Jeremy, Sara
Front: Jonathan & Leah

Richard & Sara's 25th Wedding anniversary celebration with family

Michalski Family at Michael and Nadejda's
65th Anniversary in Canada, 2006

Michalski Family: Top: from left: Nicole (Jeremy's wife);
Heather holding our granddaughter Grace Elizabeth; Richard
& Sara; Rachael (Jason's wife); Leah, our only daughter.
Bottom: From left: Jeremy, Jonathan & Jason (our sons)

Chapter Fifteen
A HAVEN OF REST

It is traditional in a Russian culture, children with proper upbringing never would refer to an older person by his or her first name. They would always preface the name with Auntie, Uncle, Grandma, or Grandpa. So it was in Michael's life. His parents had trained him to love the Lord and respect other people. Calling an older woman *"babushka"* (grandmother) did not necessarily refer to a blood relative. In like manner, *"dedushka"* (grandfather) was not always necessarily referring to one's actual grandparent.

Babushka Anyuta was revered and respected by her church community as a wise, warm, and loving mother in "Israel," and her motherly heart could not be resisted. Although the Shevchenko family had enough mouths to feed, there was always room for one more stray little lamb. Michael was joined to the Shevchenko flock and was warmly welcomed by their tender solace. Being so young, Michael could not be left on his own, so he had to go with Babushka Anyuta during the day hours to her place of employment.

Babushka Anyuta's job—besides making meals for a growing, robust family, keeping her house in Godly order and maintaining a warm environment of Christian nurturing—involved working at the local military hospital. Here, she served in several capacities as cook and cleaner. Her contagious joy had filled the kitchen and the corridors of the hospital wherever she went.

With a strong Russian military presence in Kuldja in this province of China, there had been civil war on several fronts. Her hospital duties of cooking and cleaning often overwhelmed Babushka Anyuta. Due to her heavy work schedule, she was unable to give personal care to Michael in the weeks after his mother's home-going. She tried her best, but there was just so much of herself she could share and just so many hours in the day.

The young, wounded-hearted little orphan found himself cowering in a corner at the end of the long entry hall off the kitchen. With so many wounded transiting through the hospital and such tight quarters, sicknesses were spread quite readily. There was very little disinfectant; even the basics of hot soap and water were scarce in making this hospital a germ-free environment.

In Michael's grieving state, his body's resistance had broken down, and he was vulnerable to this disease-ridden environment. One day, Michael was seen shivering and shaking in his corner of the corridor; it was not due to the lack of heating, but rather obviously to a fever that he had contracted.

When hospital workers found Michael scrunched down in a corner, trying to make himself as inconspicuous as possible, they noted that he was obviously sick, but their obligation was first and only to the military. Nobody had the place or time for a little orphan boy, especially one who had a raging fever. Several of the hospital attendants shooed Michael out of the hospital, scolding him for using the hospital quarters as his place of rest. These workers were not aware that Babushka Anyuta had brought this little one in under her wing.

Evicted from the hospital with nowhere to go, Michael found himself under a bridge not far from the hospital's entrance. Like a little mouse, he hoped the covering of the bridge would hide him from any further hurt or abuse by strangers. With Metrofan, his uncle, having departed to Aksu, there was nowhere else for him to go. So for two weeks, the little "mouse" would come out of hiding, find what scraps of bread or rice he could find and scurry back under the bridge for cover, shaking and shivering throughout the cold night watches.

This outside environment took its toll, and little Michael contracted a severe case of pneumonia. But by the grace of God, one day Babushka Anyuta was crossing the bridge and heard the deep-chested cough and the little voice of a boy she recognized. Her compassion in Christ caused her to look under the bridge, where she found the frightened eyes of Michael looking back at her from the dark. She coaxed Michael away from his hiding place and escorted him back to the hospital quarters where she gave clear and explicit instructions for all the attendants to keep an eye on her little "foster" son.

In her heart, she hoped that some doctor would take compassion on little Michael and tend to his fever and progressing pneumonia. Her plea for help fell on deaf ears; dirty little street kids had no priority in the world of the military, especially in time of war.

Several times a day, Michael's high fevers were accompanied by seizures as his pneumonia grew worse. Then one day, the commander and general of all Russian troops in China who lived in Kuldja came to the hospital to encourage the wounded under his command. Michael's low profile huddled in the corner on a little bit of straw couldn't have been readily seen in the darkened corridor; however, the coughing could be heard some distance away. General Uglin stopped abruptly with his entourage beside him and began to inquire from staff: "Who does this little boy belong to?" The response of hospital personnel was, "He really doesn't belong to anybody. His mother and father have recently died, and he is alone in the world."

God can melt the heart of stone or soften the heart of a Russian general. Upon further questioning, Babushka Anyuta admitted that she had temporary charge of Michael. Upon hearing this, General Uglin gave command to the doctors to spare no expenses in treating this little sick child. Michael was bathed in warm, soapy water and given a fresh set of clothes. He was cared for intensively because the general had commanded it.

General Uglin seemed to make excuses to find himself at the hospital more frequently than normal. This was because God was tenderly wooing this man to fulfill a destiny for one of God's sons. Day by day, the general would make meeting Michael a part of his visiting routine and by the end of a week was starting to bring special gifts, showing his endearment to Michael. If candy could heal, Michael would have been the healthiest person on earth.

This general, who had never had children, suddenly redeemed years of frustration using Michael as a surrogate son. Nurturing Michael brought a personal satisfaction and fulfillment in his life that was void of offspring. He brought bags of candy on a regular basis. Was it the candy or the caring of the physicians, or was it truly the covering of the Lord that caused Michael's health to be restored within several weeks? God had healed this little lamb to take his next steps in fulfillment of his destiny.

General Uglin, at the end of two weeks, spoke with Babushka Anyuta. He wanted to adopt Michael as his own son, train him, and give him only the best that a Russian commander and general could offer. So it was that Michael now had a second father and mother who loved him sincerely and who poured affirmations and affections upon him continually.

In just two weeks' time, Michael had gone from a street child hiding under a bridge, to a palace of royalty in the commander's compound. Commander and General Uglin had the best tailors come and outfit Michael with numerous changes of clothes, including school uniforms and casual wear. General Uglin commanded his servants to take Michael for a special haircut by a barber. Michael had never felt so important in his life as during this process of being pampered and treated as royalty. He was even taken to a special *banya* (sauna, bath-house).

At the command of General Uglin, Michael was escorted to a private school in a military caisson; that is today's equivalent of arriving at school with a military escort in a stretch limousine. How gracious our Heavenly Father is in caring for His children!

Each evening, the military detachment would attentively stand waiting for Michael's dismissal from school at 3:00 in the afternoon to transport him to the general's home. The servants would be waiting for Michael's arrival to change him from his school uniform to his casual wear. This palace compound was enormous, and General Uglin had many servants living in their own quarters on the premises. Michael was given his own humongous room where he would often sit and think about his family and how they could have all lived in his room, yet he knew that was not possible.

Michael's favorite part of the day was waiting for the general's arrival at the palace. That could vary from evening to evening, anywhere from 4 to 6 o'clock. Michael watched anxiously out of his manor window, anticipating the arrival of his surrogate father. These evening hours were precious to Michael and provided a great source of comfort and healing to his wounded heart.

Michael was not treated as a servant, but truly as a son. His surrogate mother would use every occasion to hold Michael in her arms and offer him fresh bread, butter, and jam with the greatest *"chai'* (tea) Michael had ever had. The routine was repetitious, but never grew old. Michael had become the focus of this family's affection and fulfillment of their joy.

When the general would come home, he would first take off his military jacket, loosening dozens of his gold, shiny buttons. Michael would carefully take his father's coat, hang it in the entry closet, and take the general's gun and holster and attach it to the same hanger with the coat. Then Michael would take slippers he had warmed by the fire and slip them on the general's feet after Michael had removed the military boots and propped them up smartly at the base of the closet.

With this procedure behind them, the general would pick up Michael, tickling him until the laughter filled the whole house or set him on his knee and inquire of how Michael's day had gone in school. There was always the occasional treat slipped into Michael's hand or pocket after these times of developing their father-and-son relationship. Michael would not cease to talk about his God, but General Uglin would tell Michael that this God that Michael believed in was nothing but propaganda.

Inevitably, God would give Michael words about the reality of Christ and His existence that would quiet down the general. Michael would never eat any meal without standing up, giving thanks to God, and asking for God's blessing on the meal. In this perfect environment, there was only one ingredient missing, and that was satisfying the yearning and longing in Michael's heart for a deeper relationship with his Heavenly Father.

Michael missed the fellowship of his friends, the church, and the fraternity of Christian family. If there is no compatibility on a spiritual plane, every facet of life is affected. Through much pleading, Michael finally managed to get General Uglin to relent and allow Michael to return back to his local Pentecostal Church. The servants of the general would deliver Michael in the military wagon and return for him at the close of each meeting. After some time, however, the general refused to allow Michael to continue to go to church, as he claimed that Michael was being brainwashed with religion.

Since the entire palace and military compound was guarded by soldiers, there was no way to escape out of the house without being seen. Michael prayed to the Lord to make a way for him to be able to have fellowship with his friends and believers in Christ. How he had missed the songs of the Lord, the praise of God's people, and most of all the preaching and teaching of God's Word!

Michael was growing by leaps and bounds, both in the natural and in the supernatural. The fervor of the Word that had come from anointed servants inflamed Michael's heart again. With every service as an installment, Michael would return home to bubble over in the overflow of his heart charged with faith. These trips to the House of Prayer gave Michael ammunition and boldness to share his personal relationship with Jesus Christ to a Soviet general who had been trained in the most militant, atheistic schools of his day.

The general would speak of logic and science, and Michael would counter with experience and a relationship with God through prayer and through the Word of God. The general loved Michael so much that he tolerated what he considered being a "flaw" in Michael's character. The Soviets were taught that believing in God was a sign of mental weakness and that true intellectuals did not need the crutch of religion in their newly formulating empire.

Communism had taught General Uglin well as he had believed the lies of Marx, Engle, and Lenin—who were his Trinity. General Uglin could not put his trust in a God he could not quantify by the scientific mode or method. In order to keep peace in the home, both Michael and General Uglin backed off in their polarized position. It was obvious that Michael would never deny his faith in Christ, and it was obvious that General Uglin needed more evidence in order to have faith.

General Uglin's statement to Michael was "If you continue believing in God, all you will amount to is a herder of oxen"(a despised vocation of the day)—to which Michael responded, "I would rather be a herder of oxen and have a redeemed relationship in my Lord and Savior, Jesus Christ, than to go to hell and be tormented and lost forever."

Months passed quickly and blurred into years. General Uglin had a special plan for Michael's life. Moscow had given the general the release to choose four of the brightest and best out of his provincial area to receive special pioneer training in Moscow to become devout communist leaders. This full scholarship was a prestigious appointment. Being a son of a general automatically would elevate him in the ranks of the Communist Party and a bright future as a leader of men.

Michael suspected that something special was coming when tailors came to outfit him. As a young teenager, he was never outfitted for such an unusual uniform. That was the first warning. Michael's friends at school one day on the playground shared a secret with him that they had heard that he would be leaving them that day. The terror of separation from his family and most of all the separation from God caused Michael to run frantically off the school grounds and down the streets of Kuldja.

Finally, Michael chose one of the fatherly grandpas of his House of Faith who lived about two kilometers away from the school. Surely this Godly Christian man could be trusted to hide him. Grandpa Kornienko was asked by Michael not to divulge his whereabouts to the general or the platoon that was searching for him in the city. After three days, knowing the three of the four hand-picked students had already begun their journey to Moscow, Michael came out of hiding.

With fear and trepidation, he made his way back to Babushka Anyuta's house late at night.

Michael was unaware that the house was under surveillance by soldiers trying to find the general's son. Soldiers had been sent to search for Michael throughout the city of Kuldja. The city was like a beehive of soldiers everywhere. Apprehended before he could even enter the door of Shevchenko's home, Michael was whisked off by a military escort back to General Uglin's manor.

General Uglin waited for his son's arrival. When the soldiers finally brought Michael past the gates and into the palace to the general, he hugged and kissed Michael as if nothing had happened. "Michael, my dear son," he said, "where have you been these three days?" Michael responded, "I've been with a grandfather who has a little donkey on this little farm not too far from the school." The general responded, "If you stay in China, you won't get professional training or have a good career. All you'll wind up doing is 'pulling the tail and herding donkeys.'" Michael replied, "I would rather pull the 'tail of the donkeys' than to deny my Lord and Savior and be brainwashed by being trained in Moscow into becoming a communist and a heathen."

In response, General Uglin told Michael that he would even be willing to take his little sister, Lena, and send them both to Moscow to receive a higher education. Michael refused this offer and kept telling the general that neither he nor his sister would go back to Russia, no matter how much they tried to influence him.

The intense confrontation that followed left Michael and his surrogate father further polarized them. General Uglin, enforcing his positioning, declared to Michael in strong and harsh terms that this was to be only for Michael's good. Moscow would train him up as a leader amongst leaders, as a young man to be proud of. The general reinforced that he had only Michael's best interests at heart.

When the general saw that Michael had no desire to pursue a military career, in frustration he asked, "Then where do your interests lie?" Michael mused on this thought for a precious moment. He had always loved working with his hands. There was such a sense of fulfillment with doing things right and building something that not only was beautiful, but practical. As the thoughts rolled through Michael's mind, out of his mouth burst the words, "Carpentry. That's where my interests lie."

The general said, "Sonny, tell me once and for all, do you truly believe in God and that there is a devil?" Michael responded, "You became my dear father when I lost my own father and my mother. You and your wife have taken me in and treated me well, for which I am grateful to my God. Yes, I believe and always will believe that there is a God who loved the world so much that He sent His only begotten Son, Jesus Christ, to die on the cross for my sins and yours so that we could accept Him as our Lord and Savior, repent from our sins, and surrender our lives to Jesus Christ. He will forgive you of all your sins and give you eternal life. Yes, there is a devil that came to steal, kill, and destroy your life and soul. However, Jesus has come to give life and that more abundantly."

With a reluctant release of Michael from the general's military ambitions, Michael began an apprenticeship as a finishing carpenter. These skills would serve him all his life. (It appears to this day that "Grandpa Michael" is never quite satisfied until he's building something or has built something for someone else to enjoy.)

Chapter Sixteen
DESTINIES MEET

The years like the sands of time in an hourglass quickly sifted away. Michael's apprenticeship as a carpenter had taken him to many varied jobs and building assignments. He found himself heavily occupied with working at the new airport construction which was presently underway. The days' work would fly by as an eagle pursuing her prey.

One aspect of Michael's life had deepened and grown more ardent day by day, and that was his all-consuming desire to love and worship the Lord his God with all his heart. No matter how arduous the hours or how heavy the task, every time the church assembled, there was always one thing for certain: Michael would be there.

No longer just a student sitting in a class, now he was wholeheartedly involved with singing in the choir. This brought Michael great fulfillment and many friends. Friendships mean so much when one is an orphan, and so Michael not only had a close camaraderie with the fellow singers in his tenor section of the choir, but also found many friends in the youth group of that precious church body.

It was the custom after services and choir practices for many of the youth to gather at the riverside when the seasons permitted or to gather in one another's small homes for chai and fellowship. Here their relationships deepened toward one another as well as toward the Lord.

One day rumbling across the bridge came a wagon that would change Michael's life. Coming in from Aksu after a ten-day journey, due to the rugged terrain, came Metrofan and some of his fellow brethren. Their trek was not due to the market that was open, but rather he had come to hire four woodworkers and carpenters for the finish work in the government's provincial summer palace in Aksu. As they crossed the bridge, Uglin's command of soldiers stopped their procession, not allowing them to advance or retreat at the narrow bridge entrance.

After much persuasion, Metrofan convinced Uglin's officers that his intentions were harmless and that he was merely looking for laborers to work with him in Aksu. Detained in Kuldja for some time, Metrofan went to the local church, knowing from their ranks he would find the talents and dedication he was looking for. His dilemma was voiced abroad throughout the church body, and when Michael found out that Metrofan was not allowed to return to Aksu where his family and several other Christian groups had settled, he made his appeal to General Uglin.

Coming to General Uglin, Michael, with hat in hand, greeted his surrogate father. Uglin was stricken with the overwhelming awareness that his little Michael standing before him had grown up into an eighteen-year-old young man. "Where have the years gone?" Uglin asked. From when this little young man had sat on his lap and had brought his slippers and greeted him at the door every evening, time had indeed slipped away fast. The general's reminiscent thoughts were broken up by Michael's words. "You and your wife have done nothing but good for me," Michael passionately appealed to his father "You gave me unconditional love when nobody seemed to care, and now I am asking you to release Metrofan and his company to return to their family in Aksu. Metrofan has asked me to be one of the carpenters who are going with him to work." General Uglin mused over the decision by rubbing his chin with his strong right hand.

He said to Michael, "Why would you want to go to Aksu? There is really nothing for you there. There is no good school of higher learning, and so your opportunities are limited. You would be better off remaining in Kuldja and inviting Metrofan's family to return back to live in this city." But Michael's passionate request prevailed, and he was told to return to the general's manor the next morning where all the proper paperwork and documentation would be ready.

In preparation for the trip, Michael took the money he had squirreled away from his earnings as a carpenter at the airport and made the major purchase of three horses.

When Michael returned back to General Uglin's estate, the completed paperwork awaited them. The farewells were said, and Michael's departure accompanied with General Uglin's love, exemplified by a wagon loaded with gifts and sweets in the form of cakes. Uglin and his wife said farewell to their son, embracing him and kissing him fervently. The treacherous journey had at least the security of Uglin's personal blessing; paperwork and documentation that would serve them well. When confronted or stopped by lesser military units these documents would serve him well.

How different the years had been when God had used a bricklayer's permit to confuse border guards in letting His people go through. Now in their possession were sealed releases from the highest authority in the land, assuring their safe passage and expediting God's journey of destiny.

When Michael arrived in Aksu, he never imagined the project would be as large and extensive as he soon found it to be. This provincial governor was not only Russian in ethnicity, but also came from Jewish stock, which immediately warmed his employers to Michael and his fellow workers. While working there for nearly a year, the friendship grew until the project was complete.

Many fond memories of the soil of Aksu's gentle hills remained with Michael. He was baptized in the waters of the local river in Aksu with the entire church fellowship and his dear friends attending. He had found deep and lasting friends; and now, once again, he was not left alone but found himself living with Metrofan and Maria. He gave them all his earnings from his carpentry work.

This arrangement would soon change as the winds of war began to blow across the land. The orders for evacuation from Aksu came suddenly without warning. Battle lines were drawn on the frontiers, and varied factions were fighting again. The units that came to Aksu gave the order to evacuate only the Russian families back to Kuldja.

The Muslim families living in Aksu had not retreated; hence, they purchased many of the Christians' furnishings and their wares prior to their leaving Aksu. They were to gather their personal belongings and assemble them into the wagons as the military escort led them on a meandering two month journey. A straight trek was impossible because the battle lines would pin them down for a few days or weeks in the "Dungani War."

Due to the fluidness of the battle lines, their trek to Kuldja was barred and they had to retreat to safe zones. Instead of going directly south to Kuldja, they went north to Urumchi, avoiding the heat of the battle.

The military escort would stop in various villages to find accommodations for all these Russian families. The group would sleep most of the time in barracks that were empty after previous military operations. In Urumchi, the accommodations that were found were a series of motels, which meant the Russians could bathe and eat warm food while there. They were told that the caravan would remain only in Urumchi three days before departing for Kuldja.

In Urumchi, Michael was in for several pleasant surprises. Michael pled with Babushka Maria, for a small portion of the wages that she had kept for him, but she was not willing to sacrifice even one kopeiki (equivalent to a cent). Michael then made his appeal to an elder in the fellowship, Mr. Shevchuk, who went to Maria and asked her, "How can you be so cold and unfeeling, seeing Michael wants the funds to redeem his sister, Lena, out of boarding school. Michael just wants to see his sister whom he hasn't seen for many years."

Maria finally relented and gave Michael a small amount of funds that would help with his transport across town to the small community where Lena was boarded. Upon entering the school, Michael came to the offices and asked permission to see his beloved sister. He was informed by the office that this was their morning recess and that Lena was playing with her friends.

When Michael approached his sister that he had not seen for many years, he kissed her on her cheek to which she retorted, "Who are you and what are you doing here?" Michael then explained that she was his younger sister, and he went on to assure her that she still had brothers and sisters that she had not seen for numerous years. It took all of Michael's coaxing to persuade Lena that his story was true. Once convinced, Michael hailed a taxi that whisked them across town to the point of the departure of the Russian caravan.

Their two-month journey of wanderings had come to an abrupt end with one telegram from General Uglin. The roads were now open, and the first two trucks had already left Urumchi, making their departure over the treacherous windy roads that would take them back to their original homes in Kuldja.

Michael's taxi with Lena came to a screeching halt just as the last Russian, caravan truck was about to pull out. Through much pleading and persuasion, Michael convinced the driver to stay just a few moments. The reunion of Lena, her older sister Marusia, her younger brother Vanya, and her uncle and aunt, Metrofan and Maria, was bittersweet. Lena had given up on believing that her family was still alive. She had even given up on God, Who had preserved her life to this moment. Hugs and kisses were abbreviated by the honking of the horn on the military truck. With tear-stained cheeks, Lena went back to the taxi that would return her to her boarding school. Lena waved from the taxi window, tears streaming down her cheeks. As the last truck vanished and Lena's family was on the horizon, her heart was overwhelmed both with excitement and sorrow.

That night, Lena wondered if the surprise visit of the day was a dream or a mirage. For the first time in a long time, she breathed a prayer of gratefulness to God and asked Him to someday let her family be reunited again. The atheistic training of her school years was broken by one encounter of grace. Perhaps the detour and the battle lines being redrawn were only for the redemption of one little orphan soul, Lena Ilyin. *"When my father and my mother forsake me, then the Lord will take care of me"* (Psalm 27:10). God would answer Lena's prayer three years later when she graduated from school. She was finally free to go to Kuldja to join her beloved family.

Chapter Seventeen
WEDDING BELLS RING IN KULDJA

Maxim Vodopianoff and his family lived on the outskirts of Tekes. This community was about 350 kilometers away from Kuldja. Nadejda, their second oldest daughter, was working for a very wealthy millionaire family of Russian Jews. Maxim would call his daughter "Nadia" for short, a form of endearment. When the family moved to Tekes, Nadia was asked to work for Gregory and Sara Guteev.

The Guteev family, due to their wealth and prominence, had a summer home in Tekes and wintered in their palace in Kuldja. Tekes was predominantly a Muslim community, yet there were many Russians living there. It was along the river with beautiful orchards, gardens, and farming. The Guteevs had between 200-300 cows, horses, and over 40 servants and workers. The workers lived in *yurti* (skin covered tents), and this is where Nadia would stay throughout the week.

Nadia's family lived in Tekes, 15 kilometers away from her work at the Guteevs. She was allowed to go to her family during the weekend after work. Nadia had a white horse that was her pet. She would saddle the horse in the early morning, and by evening she would arrive at the home of her dear family.

One day as she was returning from her home to Guteev's, she came to a little creek she had to cross. During the day, it had rained so much that the waters in the creek had risen. Just before crossing the creek, Nadia's horse stopped abruptly. Nadia kept coaxing her dear horse to continue, but it refused to go. Suddenly thunder and lightning struck a tree just on the other side of the creek, splitting the tree in half as well as knocking the horse and Nadia to the ground. Nadia's horse got up and stood by her, rubbing his head against her arms. Nadia began to thank the Lord for sparing their lives. Mounting her beautiful white horse, she was finally brought safely to Guteev's home.

Sara Grigoryevna Guteev and her workers loved Nadia. Whenever Nadia would milk the cows, she would always give the leftover skimmed milk that the family did not want to the Girgizi workers. Nadia lived with four other women workers in the *yurti*, but was constantly interrupted to come cook and clean as the Guteev's were frequently having guests from various parts of the country. These duties took her into the kitchen throughout the night seasons on numerous occasions—churning butter, peeling potatoes, and other general food preparation and cleaning. There were many nights without any sleep, yet the daily chores had to be done whether Nadia got sleep or not.

One day, Gregory Ivanovich Guteev decided he needed some carpentry work done and had mentioned this to his friend, General Uglin in Kuldja. Michael was referenced as a well-skilled carpenter; hence, he began a project for the Guteev family. Although the family had many servants, there was one light brunette, hazel-eyed maid that struck Michael's immediate attention. As Michael labored day by day, installing doors and windows, Sara Grigoryevna Guteev noted the chemistry between Michael and Nadia.

To play "Cupid" and advance the relationship, the governess told Nadia at teatime to give Michael extra tarts and rolls, extra sugar in his tea, and to care for him in a special way. Michael was falling in love with Nadia while knowing that there were two other young men from the church that were interested in her. One of the young Christian men was very educated and knowledgeable in the Word. Nadia loved to discuss subjects from the Bible, and only the leaders had Bibles. The Word of God was very rare amongst the believers. Meanwhile, Michael's job was completed all too soon, and he knew he wasn't going to see Nadia that often anymore.

It wasn't long after this project that Nadia became a seamstress apprentice in Kuldja. Here again, she was able to work for her precious Jewish family with whom she had fallen in love. Her seamstress skills were so good that Sara Guteev hired her for many of her sewing jobs at their winter mansion in Kuldja. Nadia had rented a small home that was on the Guteev's gigantic compound in Kuldja where Maxim and his family moved to for a short while.

What a delight it was for Michael to see Nadia more frequently at the church functions and youth gatherings. He went to Babushka Anyuta in Kuldja and told her his dilemma. She comforted Michael by saying, "God can change Nadia's heart as you and I pray together in agreement for God's will to be done." She went on to say, "We love the Ilyin family, partly because Marusia found a Godly spouse in one of the young choir directors named Joseph Lockteff." Her own son, Alexander Shevchenko, had married Katya Vodopianoff, Nadia's older sister. Babushka Anyuta thought that Michael's future marriage would strengthen the link in a family she had adopted in her heart.

Was there something in the water in Kuldja, or was it just that love was in the spring air? Two weddings in less than three months! It certainly seemed that God was busy uniting hearts and destinies.

Shortly after Michael's presenting his petition to Babushka Anyuta, his opportunity came. One Saturday evening after the church service, the young people were walking to a home fellowship. As Michael saw Nadia walking with several ladies and two young gentlemen, he tried to get enough courage to interrupt them so that he could speak with Nadia privately. One of the gentlemen who liked Nadia was a doctor and very interested in pursuing a relationship with her. He was a tall, dark-haired, handsome Christian man.

Michael, quietly under his breath, asked the Lord for boldness and strength to talk with Nadia. He thought to himself, *How can I ask her to pursue the relationship, and how can I tell her how I feel?* Then came boldness upon Michael which he knew was from the Lord. He quickly accelerated his pace to catch up with the group. Now he found himself standing before the group, his heart pounding. It had been more than just the race to intercept the gathering. Excusing himself before the group, Michael asked to speak to Nadia privately.

Michael began: "Nadia, I saw a dream where I took your hand in church and we went out together. We got into a vehicle and drove off. Nadia, you will be my wife?" Hearing this shocked Nadia; and in her state of being overwhelmed, she said, "There is no way, as you are much shorter than I am." Michael replied, "No way! I am not shorter than you! Do you want me to measure us? Your shoes just make me look like I'm shorter, but in reality, we're the same height."

Nadia had interests in the doctor who had been previously walking alongside of her. There was much she wanted to know from the Word, and it seemed his knowledge in the Bible attracted her to the doctor; whereas Michael, on the other hand, seemed to Nadia not as educated or knowledgeable in the Bible as this other young suitor. However, she expected that Michael's meeker spirit would not allow himself to be self-promoting nor would his principles allow him to belittle others.

That evening when Nadia got home, she told her mother, Elizabeth, what had transpired and how Michael had asked her to pursue a relationship with him. Elizabeth said without hesitation, "Nadia, Michael will be the perfect person from God for you. He is an orphan with a tender spirit and who loves the Lord with all his heart, soul, and being. If you marry him, you will be blessed." "But mother," Nadia said, "he is so much shorter than I am." Elizabeth then told her daughter not to look at his height, but to pray for God's perfect will.

Meanwhile, Michael went to Babushka Anyuta, sharing his broken heart with her about Nadia not being interested in him. Babushka Anyuta had decided to not only agree in prayer with Michael, but she went and talked with Nadia privately. Babushka Anyuta said to Nadia, "Don't kick your heels at this God-fearing, wonderful young man. He will be the best husband you could have. He loves the Lord and is a very good Christian young man."

Nadia wanted a confirmation from the Lord regarding her agreement and life with Michael, so she went to pray with an elderly sister who knew nothing about her situation. During prayer, the Holy Spirit spoke prophetically through this little babushka, saying, "Daughter, the man I have chosen for you whom you are resisting, yield to and agree. I am blessing your union with him. Therefore, don't be reluctant or doubtful in My leading, for you have a destiny with him, and your seed will come back to these regions and do a mighty work for My Kingdom." Nadia realized that only a few people and God knew her reluctance to marry Michael; hence, she surrendered to God's will. Within a short time, Nadia agreed to marry Michael after having received the blessing from the Lord as well as from her father, Maxim, and her mother, Elizabeth.

The day had at long last arrived. Nadia had sewn her own wedding dress as well as a wedding suit for Michael. The time had come where Michael and Nadia were united in marriage. Pastor Ivan Gavrilovich had a lengthy ceremony, admonishing and giving a powerful message from the Word for this wonderful couple. The celebration continued with songs and ended with prayer. The celebration went on with a wonderful meal for everyone. They had set up a tent outside of the church where the festivities continued for many hours. There was much singing, poetry, personal testimonies, and enjoying one another's fellowship in Christ.

Michael had been working at the airport for several years as a carpenter, receiving good wages. He had hired a special Muslim chef who cooked a tremendously delicious meal. They had barbequed lamb, stir fry, *plav*, and all sorts of deserts. This was in April of 1942, just before Easter. This was a day when God blessed their union in a mighty way.

The next day, Michael and Nadia went to register at the Registry Hall of Kuldja, dressed in their wedding attire where they were registered and photographed, legally confirming their marriage.

A little orphan boy had found the love of his life; and not only had he found true family, but in short order, God blessed them in establishing their own family. No longer would Michael be lonely. The ache in his heart was filled with so much gratitude to God for his answered prayers, the sparing of his life time and again, and bringing

Nadia into his life. The DNA of destiny was set in place for God to use them and their offspring to bless generations to come. Truly, the steps of the righteous are ordered of the Lord.

Chapter Eighteen
CANNONS ROAR IN KULDJA'S CIVIL WAR

The Apostle Paul states in Romans 8:28, *"...all things work together for good to those who love God, to those who are the called according to His purpose."*

Michael sat one day looking at the starry sky above Kuldja and mused in his mind how well God had brought all the loose ends together. His family had been scattered to the four winds. Marusia, the oldest, had married the choir director and young composer of the church, Joseph Lockteff. Lena, orphaned at first, was later given to be adopted by a Russian family who put her into a corner of their home and treated her worse than an animal until her brother had found her. Through Michael's apprenticeship's master, he got Lena proper treatment and an education that took her to Urumchi. For the next ten years, Lena was trained in the best boarding school of the region, only to lose her way and her moorings of faith in God.

Leaving the moorings and faith of his uncle, Metrofan, Vanya wondered as a prodigal for a short time in Kuldja. At the time of his wonderings, Vanya was ensnared by a Godless family who pretended to be Believers in order to adopt the youngest Ilyin boy. What they really wanted was cheap labor to run their little store. When Michael found Vanya some years later, he found him selling cigarettes and vodka. When Michael found him in this condition, he was heartbroken. He asked his younger brother, "Vanya, what were you thinking, living this worldly lifestyle?" Vanya's foster father insisted that Vanya belonged to him and that Michael had no rights to discourage or deter his brother from his chosen career. Michael retorted, "I would rather see you as a herder of donkeys, knowing peace with God and serving Christ, than to find you serving this pagan, Vanya."

When Michael realized that there was no persuading Vanya's foster father, he devised a plan to kidnap his younger brother and place him into a Christian family in Tekes. At night, Michael snuck in quietly to Vanya's bedroom and aroused him gently without awaking a soul in the house. By morning light, Vanya was well on his way to a Christian home, to be raised in the admonition of the Lord.

All these plans had been woven together by the hand of God with His blessing. With Michael now married to Nadia, he reflected upon how faithful and good God had been to him. God had not only cared for his brothers and sisters, but even heard the little cry of the orphan Michael and established him in a family.

As wonderful as this hour seemed on the surface, there was an undercurrent of war below the horizon. In humanity's history, there are very short periods of time with the absence of war. War is primarily due to the warfare that lies within our hearts. Our greediness, desiring to gain at the cost of another, is the very underpinnings of war among friends, family, and nations.

Thousands of miles away, Europe was being ravaged by a mad man in the form of Adolf Hitler. His war machine, with its blitz-Krieg (lightening war) had devoured Poland, the Czech Republic and was now knocking on the door of Moscow itself. The Ukraine in a desperate attempt to throw off the yoke of Stalin had sided with Hitler's appetite for conquest, thinking that they would have a better life under the German rule, rather than the heel of Communism. Their calculations were desperately wrong. Not only did the Nazi's mistrust the Ukrainian Allies but through the scorched, earth policy, were responsible for killing tens of thousands of Ukrainians and burning their fields to the ground. This proved only to be a prelude to Stalin's vindictive anger that would be singularly focused on the Ukraine.

It seemed that the beast of war could not be satisfied with his insatiable thirst for innocent blood. In the midst of all this slaughter, God had delivered His children by a mighty hand. The small skirmishes in China could not be compared with the devastation that paralyzed the heart of Europe during World War II. So isolated were the people of God in the heart of China that many of them were not aware until years later of the upheaval of World War II that devastated Western Europe and their homeland in Eastern Europe.

The civil war in the Kuldja region had been a simmering pot for many years that eventually boiled over into massive attacks dividing cities and provinces, families and loved ones. Within Kuldja, the urgency in the Spirit had not been heard in some time. Although many prophetic words had been declared, there had not been the trumpet call of the Holy Spirit with the clear message of graveness and resounding warning. God began commanding His people to heed and hear His voice carefully one more time. Their obedience to the voice of the Lord would determine whether they would live or die. The fellowship on the north side of the river was resonating with the prophetic voice of Heaven. God was urging them to pack up their valuables and belongings and to flee the city.

The fellowship on the southern part of the river was hearing an urging from God to stand fast, to refine their hearts, and to remain in their homes. The confusion came as brethren began to compare the two different messages from within the same city. Both groups felt they had heard from the Lord, but God was giving the opposite directive to each separate group. God is not the author of confusion, but man's lack of understanding often tries to second guess God.

The group from the north fled the city with their belongings while the groups from the south stood their ground, immovable in God. As the heat of the battle drew near, it wasn't till weeks afterward that the Christians perceived how clearly the directive of the Holy Spirit from the Lord had been. Artillery and cannon fire had been lobbed over the southern part of the city to devastate its population on the north banks.

When the shells and shrapnel finally ceased and the smoke cleared, truly the wisdom of the Lord had been applied. No Christians that heeded the voice of the Lord found any harm to their persons, but many of their homes were destroyed. In the south, no shell dropped in the city parameters, and the Christians standing their ground were spared their lives and their families protected.

Alexander Efremovich Shevchenko, a leader by now of prominence in one of the fellowships in the north, had led a group of believers up through the ravines and through the nearby Mountains of Kuldja. The "Kalmaki," a violent, nomadic Muslim group of herders, took advantage of the confusion of war to carry out their vendetta against the Russian people. Some Russians had wronged them in the past, and they were going to take revenge on the blood of all Russians in the present.

These masters of horsemanship, who had ruled a region within northern China through their many raids and ravaging of the countryside, praised Allah for delivering these "lambs" into their hands. Right before them was a large group of ragtag Russians carrying all their pots and pans and wares, climbing up the mountain valley. This would be a great slaughter for these Kalmaki to avenge a generation of senseless hatred.

"...because the Philistines dealt vengefully and took vengeance with a spiteful heart, to destroy because of the old hatred... "(Ezra 25:15).

One of the Kalmaki's top captains mounted on an Arabian stallion and yelled to the Christians in the valley, "Are you armed?" His voice roared through the chambers of rocks and echoed in the hearing of the Russians. Masha, with an instant powerful surge of the Holy Spirit through her being, prophesied back to the warrior captain in his own dialect: "We are all heavily armed!"

With that response, one of the Christian brothers felt an overwhelming urge to hold up over his head the largest butcher knife he had from his kitchen. As the knife caught the fleeting sunrays of the evening, it glistened in the twilight, looking more like a sword. The captain of the Kalmaki would not be deterred. After all, these were just a group of old men and women, with exception of a few younger men and children among them. This was an action this warrior thought he could handle on his own. With his lance lowered, he dug his spurs into the sides of his horse, invoking it to charge this group of wanderers. He would take out Alexander Efremovich, who was at the head of the group, and the rest of the gathering would scatter like frightened sheep. That was his plan.

God's ways are higher than our ways. As high as the heavens above the earth, so much loftier are the ways of God above our own understanding. Hearing the thundering of hoofs on the rocks of the charging horse and rider, many of the children ran for cover. Alexander waited until the last second. Just before the warrior lunged with his lance attempting to impale him, Alexander quickly stepped aside and used the man's own momentum in lunging forward to grab his lance and pull him off his mount.

Christians nearby settled the horse while the Kalmaki captain lay stunned and dazed on the ground. Alexander came over to the horse, and with the strength of the Lord, got underneath the horse, straddling the horse's front and back legs over his shoulders. With a prayer under his breath, he began to straighten his legs up to where the horse was in the air, beating the wind with both front and back legs, not touching the ground.

Alexander returned the horse back to its stance; and having disarmed the warrior, he put the man on his mount and returned him up the valley to his fellow soldiers. When these Kalmaki people saw this, a great fear fell upon them. The soldiers retreated to the top of the valley, hiding behind their *yurti*.

Slowly and steadily, the Russian Christians made their way into the heart of these Kalmaki people. The only ones to receive them were the women and children because their men were hiding in fear and trembling. Again, the word of the Lord came in the native dialect of the Kalmaki through one of the Russian Christians, telling them that the Russian Christians had come in peace, and declared to them under a heavy anointing of the Holy Spirit the power of the blood of Jesus Christ to save.

What seemed like only moments, in reality had been a while. The Gospel had been made clear to them in their own native tongue, to which some of the people responded with bended knees and contrite hearts of repentance. There were some within this village who had come to Christ. With the Russians remaining there for several weeks while war raged in the valley, a new Christian fellowship had been birthed and discipled among these Kalmaki people. Their years of rage and hatred had been washed away by one encounter with the blood of Jesus Christ Who forgives all of our past, cleanses our present, and promises us a future in His presence.

With the war raging in the valley, peace had come to the hearts of these people because Jesus Christ made peace by the blood of His cross.

"For it pleased the Father that in Him all the fullness should dwell, and by Him to reconcile all things to Himself; by Him, whether things on earth or things in heaven, having made peace through the blood of His cross. And you, who once were alienated and enemies in your mind by wicked works, yet now He has reconciled" (Colossians 1: 19-21).

Alexander Shevchenko and his band of believers returned to Kuldja when the roar of cannons ceased. Upon their return trek, they sang the songs of God's deliverance, praising God for what they had seen and what He had allowed them to do. These Kalmaki people would no longer dump Russians into the river; they had truly become their brothers and sisters in Christ. The animosity of years was quenched by God's love, and a relationship in Christ had begun.

As the group came to the edge of town, they realized how great the wisdom of God had been as they saw nothing but death and devastation where they had formerly lived. The Russian Christians dropped on their knees, thanking God for sparing their lives. That night, as they crossed the bridge to go to the southern part of the city, they met their brethren from the south. How sweet their reunion was in the House of Prayer! Tears of rejoicing, songs of gladness, and prayers of thanksgiving filled the air. Both had heard from Heaven, and both had their lives preserved by the mighty hand of God. *"For as many as are led by the Spirit of God, these are sons of God"* (Romans 8:14).

Chapter Nineteen
THE BUGLES OF BATTLE SOUND AGAIN

Do you remember your first days of marital bliss?—when it seemed at every turning things were accentuated in their intensity: colors of flowers seemed deeper, grass seemed greener, and the blue of heaven was punctuated now and again by a fleeting puffy cloud. Michael and Nadia had found a plot of land and a rental house on the outskirts of Kuldja. It wasn't much to look at from the outside because the outer walls were made out of mud and straw; however, inside their dwelling, the tender loving care could be seen at every turn.

This little two-bedroom house through love had been made a home. The house had a unique heating system with a kiln-fired brick furnace that warmed the inner brick linings of the outer walls of the house. This meant that the Ilyin house was toasty and warm in the winter and provided an ideal setting for this rapidly growing family.

The cellar provided storage for all of Nadia's canned fruits, vegetables, meats, and other foods. She would bake many loaves of bread in the brick Dutch oven and place them in storage on the shelves in the cellar since they did not bake daily. Michael had been working at the airport, applying all his carpentry skills with diligence, to support his young bride and children.

The home of the Ilyins would soon be rattled once again by the sound of war. This time different factions played their key role. The Russians and the Muslims joined in a unified front against the Chinese tribal groups of that region. Although no one dared verbalize it, these Russian -Muslims were merely surrogates for Stalin's Soviet brand of communism. Their Muslim identity was superficial in hopes of rallying a stronger support base for their cause.

The Soviet command was directed by General Uglin. The same General Uglin who had been Michael's foster father had an elite troop of 80 soldiers under his command in the immediate vicinity of Kuldja. Unbeknownst to him, his foster son, Michael, was drafted into the heat of the battle within that command.

Leaving his family and children, Victor and Walter, was the most difficult thing Michael had ever done; however, the alternative was unthinkable. If he didn't go to war, his only option would be severe punishment by the authorities, which was unconscionable, or they could have sent him back to Russia. Many Russian Christian brothers in the local church fellowship were also forcibly conscripted into battle units.

Nadia couldn't stand the possibility of losing her beloved "Misha" (Michael), so she got one of the sisters from the church to look after Victor and Walter and made her way to General Uglin's military compound. When she at last received an audience with the general, she made an impassioned plea to have her Michael released from military service. Her petition was instrumental in saving Michael's life. General Uglin was shocked to realize his "Misha" was part of his command. Already the battle group of 80 men had been reduced in three months' time to 8 survivors. The orders to release Michael from duty were issued immediately by General Uglin.

The reunion of Michael and Nadia was filled with tears of thanksgiving, worship, and adoration on their knees before the God Who had spared their lives and allowed them to unite again. What an awesome and faithful God we serve!

General Uglin found himself embroiled in an ever-deepening controversy.

Moscow was never confident in loyalty. They definitely feared people in power. Their mistrust and paranoia were the keys for ordering General Uglin's return back to Moscow. Before General Uglin departed, he sensed a great mistrust even in his own household. He asked for Michael to come and change all his locks. He used a foreign lock system, perhaps one that was even made in America, that would slow down those spying on him.

General Uglin's sudden departure left a huge vacuum in the power structure in the region, so Gregory Ivanovich Guteev took Uglin's place. As you recall, Gregory Guteev was the employer of Nadejda Vodopianoff some years before. He had been the governor of a region, but now he had become the commander of the province. All civil and military authority was placed in his charge, and Guteev's advancement would be crucial in the releasing of the Russian Christians in the years to come. God often puts saints in "Caesar's household" in critical times in history to influence the hearts and minds of kings and authorities.

"The king's heart is in the hand of the Lord, like the rivers of water; He turns it wherever He wishes"(Proverbs 21:1). "He removes kings and he raises up kings" (Daniel 2:21b).

He alone, the God of all ages, rules in the Kingdom that is from everlasting to everlasting. All flesh is like dust before our living God of eternity. The grass of the field one day springs up, its nobility like flowers blooming for a season; but when they are removed by the hand of God, there is no trace of where they had once been or the place they once stood.

Sadly General Uglin was never heard of again by the Christian community in Kuldja. Alexander Shevchenko and many other Christian men returned from the battle lines of war, and God blessed their families as they raised up many sons and daughters in the Kingdom of God. Alexander and Katya Shevchenko were blessed with Alexander Jr., Benjamin, Luba and Raya—all born to them in China. There were other children born to them in South America: Nikolay and Nadia.

Down the streets of Kuldja, another family was beginning to grow rapidly: Michael and Nadia's household, now blessed with Victor and Walter. The church was growing by leaps and bounds. If nowhere else, it was definitely seen in the cradle roll. How beautiful it is to see families graced of Heaven and filling up their quivers with God's gift of children!

The time finally came for God's sojourners to move on. The Holy Spirit once more began to speak prophetically, both through Michael and Nadia, saying that the time had come for them to go to Tekes, as God had a ministry work for them to do in that community. God said that He would establish them in reaching their own people for Christ. Although Michael had a good job in Kuldja, and the family seemed to be settled in well, they knew they had to be obedient to the voice of the Holy Spirit and go where the Lord was calling them to go.

On one hand, Nadia was excited to go, as her family Maxim and Elizabeth Vodopianoff and her two brothers lived in Tekes. Yet, on the other hand, she had grown so close in relationship with the church fellowship there in Kuldja, she dreaded to leave their comfort zone. However, she knew that it was better to obey the voice of God and His leading than to pay the price in the currency of personal sacrifice.

It did not take long for the Ilyin family to be able to sell all their commodities and move to Tekes, where they would live for only a little over two years. Michael was blessed by God to have found a little home right next to Maxim's family; this was a tremendous blessing to Nadia to have her beloved mother next door to help take care of her little grandchildren, Victor and Walter.

Life in Tekes was very good. Michael loved growing melons, tending the orchards, and establishing a small farm on the side. At the same time, Nadia's parents and her brothers, Nikolay and Gregory, who lived nearby, made life so much more enjoyable for her, and Nadia could help Michael with his job. But this euphoric season, like all things on earth, was temporary.

Maxim Timofeevich Vodopianoff, along with another pastor, had their pastoral duties. Maxim was very zealous in sharing his faith in Christ with other Russian nonbelievers in that community as well as discipling his flock. In Tekes, there were many Russian families who had come to know Jesus Christ as their Savior and who had joined the Pentecostal fellowship. Some of them are friends of the Ilyins and even neighbors in the same city where they dwell to this day: Vasily Minchenko, Dimitry Chirkoff, Golins and Tarasenkos, to mention a few, some of whom would play a role in the lives of the Ilyins in the years to come.

Out of their lineage and roots would arise pastors, choir directors, and sons and daughters that would intermarry with some of the Ilyins, and who would cause the prophetic word of the Lord that came to the Russians so many years before, declaring, "Your seed shall return to the land that you had once fled from and shall establish many churches in the Urals and throughout the straits of Siberia." Michael and Nadia clearly realized the sovereignty of God in bringing them to Tekes.

While life was good for the Russian Christians in Tekes, little did the Ilyin family realize that God was leading some of their family and relatives who had remained in Kuldja to Urumchi and out of China into the Western world. It would be many years before they would see their loved ones again. In Kuldja, God began to lead Alexander Shevchenko and his family and some other families such as the Dumanovsky, Lockteff, Metrofan and Maria Ilyin with Vanya and Lena, and many other Christians back to Urumchi.

There was already a large group of Russian believers in Urumchi with a thriving Pentecostal fellowship. Urumchi, having an international airport, became the point of exits for many of these Christian groups. Some of them flew from Urumchi to Manila in the Philippines and from there made their way to Paraguay and other South American countries. There were some families, including the Lockteffs', who were even able to fly to the United States of America. This was a miracle of miracles, as China was not often willing to release people to America during those years. The influence of many of these Russian Christians in South America is felt to this day, with churches and Christian fellowships being established by many Slavic people in the nations of Paraguay, Uruguay, Argentina, and Brazil.

After a prescribed waiting period, this first group received visas to come to United States and to settle in the San Francisco Bay area. Currently in Los Angeles and in San Mateo, California, there are several Slavic fellowships that hold bilingual services in either Russian or Spanish or Ukrainian and Spanish. In addition, some Slavic people intermarried with some precious South American Christians and have produced families who serve God in music ministry and in the Word with the greatest sincerity.

Lena Ilyin married Anatoly Kozachuk from South America, and God gave them three sons, Anatoly, John, and Peter. God in turn has given their spouses lovely wives and families from South America. Last but not least, John Kozachuk married Nadia Shevchenko many years later and were blessed to have lovely children of their own.

Marusia married Joseph Lockteff, who became the music director for the Full Gospel Russian Church in San Francisco under the leadership of Pastor Alexander Efremovich Shevchenko. God blessed Joseph and Marusia with three sons and three daughters: Nadia, Peter, Ruben, Helen, Lydia, and Jacob.

Vanya married Sophia Necuik from South America, and God graced their family with three sons and three daughters: Vera, Peter, Lily, John, Paul, and Rita.

Some of these children are in the ministry, with a strong testimony for the Lord. What else could they do with such a great legacy of God's great faithfulness in their lives and in the lives of their parents and grandparents?

Meanwhile, back in Tekes, God was stirring Michael and Nadia as well as Maxim to return their family to Kuldja. Once again, they had to make preparations to sell their cattle along with farming and household commodities that they couldn't take in the wagons. Maxim with his two sons joined the Ilyin family to Kuldja.

Their trek to Kuldja seemed to have taken much longer than usual. Oftentimes when we become unsettled in our spirit, moving from one place to another, it is God's way of fine tuning our spiritual hearing. The Ilyins continually moved from city to city and on some occasions retraced their steps, returning to the city they once fled from. In looking over their shoulder, they realized in hindsight that God had spared their family and fellowship from the ravages of war.

Civil war and major conflicts with the swift movements and seizure of lands and properties would not catch them off guard. They had a Guide Who knew tomorrow and Who holds His own securely in the hollow of His hand, and none can snatch them from His care.

As Michael and Nadia settled again in Kuldja, they were able to find a home quickly. Maxim and his family were blessed to be living nearby as well. Elizabeth was enjoying her grandchildren, and there were two other children born to Michael and Nadia: Vasya and Katya. Little Vasya, at two years of age, died as a result of an accident and went to be with Jesus. Shortly after the child's death, Katya died of crib death. Nadia began to ask God to give her some daughters that would help her with household chores and be a blessing in their lives. Michael and Nadia had committed their children to the Lord. God graced their home with Sara, which means princess with God, and Theodore, affectionately called Fred.

Elizabeth became very ill and told her family that she was ready to be eternally with her Lord and Savior, Jesus Christ. She knew her time had come to receive her eternal reward. Nadia was very heartbroken over this situation and began to fast and pray and plead with God to heal her beloved mother.

Within a short time, God had miraculously healed Elizabeth, and she was back to tending to her grandchildren, teaching them Godly principles, sharing about the power of Christ and to believe and live for Him. How merciful the Lord was in allowing Nadia to spend precious quality time with her family and especially her mother, Elizabeth.

During this time, Gregory—or, as the family would call him, Grisha—had been drafted into one of the civil wars. Nadia prayed for God to extend her mother's life from the deadly illness until Grisha could come home. She asked God to intervene miraculously and bring her brother home, no matter where he was. God heard her prayer. A few years went by when suddenly they were all surprised by Grisha's return from his military service. It wasn't long after Grisha's arrival that his mother, Elizabeth, got very ill again. This time she said to her daughter Nadia, "Don't pray for my life to be extended, as the Lord has already prepared a place for me in glory, and this is my time for my home-going."

Nadia had forgotten her petition before the Lord about bringing Grisha home before her mother passed away. Nadia would not leave her mother's side, but cared and prayed for her night and day. However, deep in her spirit, she knew that she would have to say farewell to her precious, dear mother. It was only by the mercy and grace of God, and due to the prayers and unwavering faith in God, that Grisha had been released from his duties in the military and was united with his family at home.

Elizabeth passed away and went home to be with the Lord. Maxim and his family grieved for Elizabeth, yet the Holy Spirit comforted them in these times of sorrow. They knew that their faith and hope was not in vain but had the assurance that through Christ, they would be united with their loved ones in glory. Elizabeth Vodopianoff was buried next to her two grandchildren, Vasya and Katya, in Kuldja.

Life continued with the Ilyin family as their children seemed to be growing quickly. Nadia would sew clothes for her children and enjoyed dressing her little daughter, Sara, with frills and cute hats. Sara enjoyed her little brother, Fred, and would often tease him. However, he would love to pinch and get back at Sara. Some of Sara's close friends, with whom she enjoyed playing, were the Golin girls, Lucy and Nina; Vinaev girls, one of them called Nida, with whom Sara would share her little "girly secrets." There were many other young children in the Kuldja Russian Pentecostal Fellowship. They provided a back-drop of Christian inter-action, fostering character growth.

What better place to find friends and grow in grace than the House-hold of Faith. We wish this blessing on you and your family and like the Psalmist David says, "...surely goodness and mercy will follow all the days of my life; that I may dwell in the House of the Lord forever." Psalms 23:6

Chapter Twenty
LET MY PEOPLE GO

One morning after prayer, the Spirit of the Lord spoke prophetically to Nadia and another sister simultaneously for them to go to the Russian consulate and appeal for the release of the Russian Christians. Nadia suppressed this message until it was confirmed by this other visiting sister to their home. They decided to get on their knees for prayer without telling one another what the Holy Spirit had spoken to them individually.

During their time of prayer, God in His sovereignty began to echo, confirming word for word what the Holy Spirit had spoken to each one of them. Armed with the witness from the Holy Spirit, Nadia and her friend made their way across town to the Russian compound and consulate.

Numerous attempts on the part of the remaining Russian Christians had been denied by local officials for immigration out of China.

When they made their appeal to the guard at the gate for them to see the consulate general, they were abruptly dismissed as silly women with no chance of seeing the man in charge. The anger and fury of the guards, with their raised voices and shouting, alarmed the consulate general who was passing at that moment. He stopped the guards as they were forcibly removing the two women from the gated area.

"What do these women want?" The guards responded by saying, "They want to talk to the consulate general about a matter amongst the Russian community." To the guards' surprise, as the general stepped back into his office, he said, "Send them to me." He had not seen the women due to the massive pillars and gate blocking his view.

As one at a time the women stood before the consulate general, they made a passionate appeal to let God's people go. The consulate officer, an ardent atheist, mocked their faith and told the women that if he saw their face again, he would send not only them, but their other Russian families as well, back to Russia where they belonged. Both sisters were desponded and disappointed. The last words they heard the consulate general gruffly say to their faces were "If you insist on this action, I will make personally certain that you will be returned back to Russia."

The two sisters talked on their way home. They had questioned whether they truly had heard from the Lord and why should not God have used one of the brethren from their fellowship? After all, men were more respected than women in China. Certainly a man making an appeal for his family and friends would have held more weight.

I have often said facetiously, "I have figured God out!" God takes the most unlikely place, the most unlikely kind, and the most unlikely personnel to get His work done so that the glory is not of man, but rather all glory goes to God. So it was with this experience of obedience.

Six months later, Nadia and her friend were invited to the consulate general's office. They said their farewells to their family and friends, made certain their "house was in order," thinking they might be going to their execution, but instead, received permission for the exodus of God's people out of northwestern China. One can never tell what a single step of obedience in a moment of surrender will bring about in the hand of a mighty and merciful God.

Many Russian Christians began to leave Kuldja into one of the larger cities where people were allowed to immigrate from China and into the West. Maxim Vodopianoff and his sons were some of the early ones who left for Shanghai with a group of other believers.

Across the Il-ya River in Kuldja, the sunny banks caught the warming sunset longer, therefore making an ideal growing area for truck farming. Each individual plot of ground would be featured with a little garden shack that would serve as a tool shed and a place to sleep when work carried on into the late summer evenings. Nadia would tend to the chickens and her vegetable garden while Michael loved growing melons. Victor and Walter would accompany their father into town with their ripe, sweet melons, selling them to different vendors.

They had a German shepherd dog, Pirjat (Pirate), who loved the family and especially the children. Pirjat would chase off the crows that loved to feed on the sweet, ripened melons. Pirjat somehow adopted the chickens in Nadia's care and protected them while playing his dual role of protector and living scarecrow.

While Michael was tilling his little plot of garden with the horse and plow, preparing it for the next season's crop, the boys decided to play near the Iliya River. They were told not to go swimming on their own because the river was very deep, and the depth along the shores was very deceptive. The weather that day was hot, and the boys wanted to take a quick dip at the edge of this river.

One of their Russian friends, Paul Lizogubov, noticed the boys going swimming. Minutes later, Paul saw Victor sink out of sight, pulled under by a whirlpool. He ran to Michael screaming out the alarm that Victor had been towed under by a whirlpool. With panic filling his heart, Michael left the horse and plow, ran to the rivers bank, and dove in fully clothed where Walter had seen Victor last. Michael couldn't find his son; and as the current was swift, Michael began to pray, asking the Lord to direct him to his son's body.

Michael submerged a second time into the murky waters. He prayed to find Victor in the river's swirling depths. Knowing that this would be his last dive before the current would sweep him away, God suddenly answered Michael's prayer as he felt Victor's limp hand. Retrieving the body of his son, almost out of breath himself, Michael whispered a prayer in his heart, imploring God for his life and the life of his son. Pulling Victor to the bank, Michael started to resuscitate him. Victor's lifeless body seemed as though it had slipped away. As Michael cried out in anguish to the Lord, and at the same time tried to resuscitate Victor, he began to cough up water and then began to breathe in response to his father's prayer and his resuscitation.

Quickly, Michael put Victor onto the wagon and rushed him across the bridge to the nearest hospital in Kuldja. Nadia held Victor tightly, praying for God to continue His miracle within their son. Meanwhile, the rest of the Ilyin children were being cared for by one of the Russian babushkas. The doctors treated Victor the best they could, but due to their lack of medical equipment and medicine, Victor had a major hearing impairment. However, the doctors were amazed that Victor had survived.

Nadia and Michael were told to take Victor to saunas as much as possible after this accident; so whenever they could, they did this for their son. Victor began to recover quickly and was back to his happy self. The only unfortunate thing was that Victor had lost a large percentage of his hearing due to the drowning accident. Nadia spent special time training Victor in how to read and write in spite of his handicap.

Michael had a side job where he and some of his friends, Dimitry and Sergey Chirkoff, had horses and wagons, pooled their energies together, and went to the nearby mines by Kuldja. They were able to earn extra money by hauling this needed cut coal, selling it a factory in Kuldja. As Michael earned enough funds, he and Nadia, at the urging of the Holy Spirit, prepared to go to Sujdun in preparation for leaving for Shanghai.

Michael asked his friend Sergey Chirkoff to accompany him on this trip to Sujdun and on to Shanghai. Michael was unable to persuade Sergey to go. Without the use of the horse and wagon, Michael used the family bicycle to peddle his way the 40 kilometers (approximately 28 miles) to Sujdun, the first city they had entered on their trek into China. This was a truck-and-bus distribution center for travel throughout this region.

Indeed there was a narrow window that the Holy Spirit had spoken of. Upon Michael's arrival to Sujdun on Monday evening, he was informed by a Muslim friend, who had worked with Michael in Kuldja. He now lived in Sujdun and was aware of the quota for

Russian passengers and their quota allotment had been filled. This friend gave Michael this critical information. That night, as Michael slept on the fresh hay in his friend's barn, inspiration came to his heart. Borrowing his Muslim friends' *halat* (robe), boots and hat, Michael made his way early in the morning before the trucking office opened to ask for passage, paying full fare for six full tickets. He did not mention that four of the passengers would be his children because the truck was taking predominantly adults. Being able to speak Girgizi and the local Chinese dialect meant Michael could bypass the quota limitations set for Russians only.

With Michael's Jewish olive skin, suntanned by the many hours of working outside and speaking a local Muslim dialect, Michael succeeded in purchasing the six tickets he needed. Indeed, the Lord's promise was true that this trip would be blessed of the Lord. Michael had no idea how much more blessing was coming his way.

As he made his way from the ticket office, he stopped to visit a Russian Christian brother living in the city. This brother shared with him a dilemma that he had: the going back for his daughter and belongings in Kuldja. This brother's ticket for departure had been purchased and scheduled some time earlier. To persuade Michael, he offered his horse and *britchka* (wagon) to be sent back to Kuldja to collect their daughter. Upon the purchase of the tickets, Michael raced the horse and wagon home with the wagon wheels touching only the high spots on the road.

Upon Michael's arrival in the early evening on Tuesday back in Kuldja, he informed Nadia of the grace that God had given him and that they had tickets for all his household. Michael was overjoyed with gladness and thanksgiving to God for providing transportation for him and his family.

Michael fed the horses and prepared for the long overnight trip back to Sujdun. The Ilyin family with all their precious belongings which they carried with them in their little bags, were loaded onto the britchka. Their goal was to reach the truck departure point in Sujdun before a scheduled 11:00 A.M. Wednesday morning departure.

They arrived late in the night on Tuesday and slept in the Muslim friend's barn where Michael had slept the night before. Wearied by the journey, they still made it in time to Sujdun. They had an unexpected guest follow them from Kuldja to Sujdun—the family German shepherd dog, Pirjat. They had tied their dog up when they left, knowing that in the morning their house would be a place of prayer for Christians in the neighborhood.

Nadia went to visit her very close friend, Duysia Sorokovsky, who lived close by and told her of the events that had transpired and bade her farewell. Nadia and Duysia felt God would bring them together within the near future as there was a destiny and plan God had for their lives. When Pirjat saw the Ilyin family leave, it was more than the dog could bear. Pirjat broke his restraint and followed them at a distance all the way to Sujdun.

As they pushed and prodded their way toward the truck, the truck driver and the officials that were there were opposed to taking this Russian family because they had children with them on the full-fare tickets; however, they finally made room on the truck. They hugged and squeezed their family dog sitting on the roadside, and it brought tears to Michael and the children. It was as if their dog knew he could go no further on this trip. The children in their hearts also knew that they would never see Pirjat again. The children cried, Michael cried and the dog cried, but their tears soon ceased as they heard the gruff orders of their fellow travelers to get on the truck.

There were four officials on this truck ride. Two were in the tractor and two were among the Christians in the back of the truck. As the truck moved down the bouncy roads, the ruts provided a great source of pain to Nadia who was about eight months pregnant. As she winced with pain, the four officials belonging to the Communist Party began to inquire why the sudden departure of this Russian family. The Christians made the classic error of mentioning God's leading, and they received sneers and mocking from the two officials sitting in the back with them.

Communism and atheism were synonymous, and these Chinese communists had no time for God and even less time for God's children. As the miles lengthened down the treacherous mountain passes, the two communists in the back conspired to return the truck back to Sujdun and across the border into Russia where they would turn in these Russian Christians and receive reward for their betrayal.

These officials persuaded the truck driver to turn the truck around in the middle of the road. In the process of the truck making a U-turn, the air filled with sarcasm and mocking by one of the outspoken officials. "We will show you the kind of God you serve. We will deliver you back to Russia where some of you will be taken into prison and others will return to your homes. We do not believe that there is a God. You are brainwashed by religion. There is no God!"

As the truck was making its abrupt turn, it flipped over on its side, throwing all its occupants and luggage in all directions. In moments like this, all one could do was cry out, "Jesus!" As the Christians called on His Name, the Lord was present with His host of angels to cover and to protect His children.

As the family flew through the air, all they saw was a flash of light, and they found themselves standing on the roadside with their entire family beside the overturned truck. The two men that had formerly sat beside the Christians had been the primary plotters of the treachery against the Believers were now buried by a barrage of luggage and baggage. Michael quickly began to unload the heavy cases off the two Chinese conspirators.

One of the men they pulled out from under the heavy load had been the primary instigator of this plan to return the Russians back to the Soviet Union. He also goaded the other communist officials to openly mock God. Little did that man realize that seconds later he would be standing before the Almighty God that he didn't believe in. This man would no longer say, "There is no God," as he was now before the Judge of all ages and the Creator and Savior of mankind Who lovingly pleads with every person to accept the Gift of Life, Jesus Christ, as Savior and Lord. Jesus will not force anyone to surrender their life to Christ, but each has the free will to make his and her own decision for their eternity.

Michael pulled this man's corpse out from under the luggage. The other official who had gone along with the plan was bruised and battered, but his life was still in him. As Michael was removing luggage, he saw a foot sticking out from beneath the pile of baggage. This was one of the Chinese officials who had called Nadia and Michael Russian spies and agreed with the communist official in their mockery of God. Seeing that Michael literally spared his life in spite of their sneering and treating them wrongfully, he was overwhelmed with awe.

When the communist official saw that the Ilyin family was barely harmed, he realized that there must be a God Who protects His Own. He asked Michael, "Why did you spare my life? The suffocation under the entire luggage would have killed me, but you came and saved my life." He continued to say, "Not only did you save my life, but I believe the God you have been sharing about is truly alive and through you He saved my soul."

The driver and his attendant had been thrown free from the truck when it rolled. Now here lay Nadia alongside of the highway in excruciating pain as she was about to deliver her second daughter. One of the Chinese officials whose life Michael spared hailed down a second truck that was going to Lan Chou. He helped the Ilyins with all their baggage to board this vehicle, thanking them again for sparing his life and bade them farewell.

Chapter Twenty-One
A SNOWBIRD IS BORN

In order to get to Lan Chou, there were many obstacles, barriers, and check-points to cross. Approaching one main Chinese checkpoint, everyone had to wait in line outside for the officials to check their documentation and permit to enter into this other Chinese province. As Michael stood in line, waiting patiently for their turn, he had some fear as they had no proper visa documentation that these officials were requiring. They had heard of some families being sent back to Russia by the Chinese authorities, and now the Ilyin family stood there with a dilemma. They began to pray quietly before the Lord, asking God to perform a miracle.

Before even finishing their prayer, one Chinese official came up to Michael and said, "What are you doing in this line? You don't belong here. This is for the ordinary people. You belong with the officials." Michael had never seen this Chinese official before. He asked Michael for some paperwork. The only thing Michael had was his fishing license, which he presented to this officer.

This Chinese official told the officer checking the documentation to put the Chinese seal on this document, allowing the issuance of a permit for the entire family to be able to get to their destination in China. Once the officer put an official Chinese stamp on this fishing license, the Ilyin family was put onto another truck and sent forth with a salute and smile.

Prior to getting onto another truck, Michael searched to find the Chinese official who helped the Ilyin family with the documentation, but he was nowhere to be found. He had disappeared. Michael wanted to thank him for his help, but he couldn't find him. The Word of

God says in Hebrews to be hospitable to strangers for some have entertained angels unaware.

As the Ilyin family arrived to the train station in Lan Chou, Nadia went into labor. A Chinese woman official came over to the Ilyin family. Seeing Nadia in labor, she rushed over to her workers, giving them a command to watch the Ilyin children. With the children secure, she took Nadia and Michael, accompanying them to the hospital. Upon her departure to the hospital she quickly gave her servants the following orders. This guardian angel assigned her help to cordon off a safe place and feed these little Ilyin children, with a clear directive for her servants to remain there even if it took all day.

The hospital was reluctant to receive these strange Russians who had come from a different province. That particular hospital had no room for delivery, as there were thousands of refugees, the product of a local civil war. These victims of war had saturated to overflowing the hospitals and clinics of that area due to their war wounds.

Finally, the Chinese official woman found a hospital where she demanded they make room for Nadia to deliver. Late that night Nadia delivered little baby Natasha. Later in her childhood, the kids affectionately named her "China Doll" or "Snowbird."

Due to birth complications, Nadia was in the hospital for one week. Michael would come and visit his wife daily, taking a rickshaw, while the children remained at the train station, being taken care of by the woman's servants. Talk about going the second mile, the one day of caring for the children had elapsed into an entire week. Yet the help of strangers and their compassion had not diminished.

When Nadia was able to leave, the Ilyin family had to purchase train tickets to Shanghai. In order to purchase these tickets, they had to present a visa from the communist officials with their seal. However, this Chinese woman official purchased first-class tickets and put the family on the train. She prayed over the family, blessing their journey and asking God to protect the children and the Ilyin parents. She then hugged every Ilyin child, and upon departure, tears flowed down her cheeks. She said, "God will be with you all the way through to Shanghai, and none shall harm you."

Traveling three days on the train, the Ilyins had a comfortable sleeping berth and a basin to wash themselves in. This was luxury beyond their wildest dreams and a far cry from the hard floor and a corner in the train station where they had camped out for a week. As the train would stop at different cities and stations, Michael and Nadia would buy food from vendors to feed their children. The children were overwhelmed at the scenery outside the window as the train moved quickly through central China's landscape. They finally arrived in Shanghai, the largest city they had ever seen.

Their entry into Shanghai was the beginning of another chapter in their lives. Here they would reside for nearly three years before their final exit visas were approved and sponsors were found in the West.

Meanwhile, the government of China issued them a settling area well outside the city limits. The Ilyins found a barn that once belonged to a well-to-do family and renovated it into a little home, making it as warm and homey as possible with their limited resources and a lot of "elbow grease." Part of the communist regime program that was taking over the cities of China was to control its population by food rationing. If a person knew their next meal came at the mercy of the state, they were less likely to revolt against the authorities. Ethnic groups other than Chinese were at the bottom of the rationing ladder.

Each family was issued a small measure of flour, rice, dried fish, and several other foods. For a growing child, these meager supplies were desperately inadequate. Not knowing where their next meal would come from, Sara would hide little crusts of bread under her pillow, so when her stomach rumbled in pain, biting a few morsels of bread would settle her growling stomach.

It wasn't long before Natasha, at this time a two-year-old, found her sister's secret. Just after Sara would hide her bread crusts, Natasha would go into the bed area in the corner of the room and from under the pillow and steal her sister's dried bread. When Natasha was asked who took the bread, she would rub her tummy and say, *"Tyut, tyut,"* which means in the Russian slang, "gone, gone."

The Ilyin children and the other Russian Christian neighbor kids had no playground or school to go to, so they made the local cemetery their playground. With its tall stone monuments, it made the ideal place to play hide and seek. One day while hiding behind the tombstones, their game was interrupted by a funeral procession. It was then that they noticed for the first time that bowls of rice and assorted vegetables were left on the tombstones of the recently departed. It seemed the Chinese family wanted to appease the spirit of their deceased ancestors, thinking the best way to do that was to feed them well.

When the funeral procession departed, the Russian children couldn't believe the bounty they had left in food. The more the children ate, the more the Chinese family members would replenish their supply with additional rice and vegetables, believing their ancestors were very hungry. In essence, little Russian kids hiding behind the tombstones became the "little ancestors" devouring the food that God had provided for them.

This plan went quite well for quite some time until one day the children were caught eating a fresh provision at one of the gravesides. The Chinese man that caught them cut off a willow switch from a nearby tree and unmercifully beat the children across their bare legs. The angry Chinese mourner reported the incident to the local authorities.

One day the unexpected alarmed them. Dusya Sorokovsky, one of Nadia's best friend and prayer partner in Kuldja with her family composed of five children and her husband came from Kuldja to Shanghai. Dusya passionately implored the Ilyin family for a place to refuge under their roof. The government had forbidden the issuance of any additional permits for Russian families settling in that region. When the local authorities found out that the Ilyin family had gladly taken in their good friends and prayer partners from Kuldja, things began to go down quickly.

With just enough flour, yeast, eggs, and other ingredients to be able to bake only one loaf of bread for her family alone, the Ilyin family prayed that God would multiply the bread baking in the little Dutch oven behind their hut. To their amazement, that night the bread miraculously had grown to satisfy both families' needs. When Nadia dipped into the earthen vessel, retrieving all the ingredients one more time to make bread the second day, to her shocked amazement, there was enough bread for the second day supply for the seven in the Sorokovsky family and for the seven in the Ilyin family.

This miracle of God's multiplication went on day after day until government officials came to the house and began to inquire, "Where are you stealing the food from?" Angry orders were barked out by the communist command. "We will not give you any portions of ration as long as you have the second family with you in your home."

What could a Christian do in a situation like this? If we close up our heart of compassion when our brothers are in need, how can we call ourselves true followers of Christ, especially if it's in our capability to make a difference?

Miraculously for an entire month, the cruse of oil failed not, the flour did not diminish, and all the ingredients for bread, like the mercies of God, were renewed fresh every morning.

At the end of thirty days, the government finally relented and issued the Sorokovskys a permit to stay in Shanghai. The same day the Sorokovsky family left for their own accommodations, the government reinstated its rationing to the Ilyin family. It was the same day the miracle provision of God's continued bread ingredients ceased. For over a month, the Sorokovsky family had used the kitchen counter and floor for sleeping their family. The one bedroom floor space with rolled-up mats was the sleeping area for the Ilyins. God had blessed their obedience together and made these family life-long friends for decades to come.

Chapter Twenty-Two
SHANGHAI: A NEW EXODUS BEGINS

A distant city park on the outskirts of Shanghai was the place that Paul Ionko, a young man from the Russian Christian group, would train the children how to read and write the Russian language. These Russians found themselves more and more isolated, both culturally and linguistically. This meant that the Russian children had no Chinese friends and very few places to call their own. With the cemetery as their playground, they were careful now not to eat the food of the ancestors for the fear of being beaten by the Chinese people.

One day while playing at the cemetery, an incident occurred that would be burned on Sara's memory forever. Sara had hid behind the tall tombstones as she saw some people coming to the cemetery. Communist authorities had brought a man bound hand and foot and tied him to a stake standing by the cemetery gate. As they placed wood at his feet and lit this man on fire, his face began to shine with the glory of God's presence. He did not yell out in pain, but with his head tilted back and his eyes lifted heavenward, he stood there like a lamb for the slaughter.

Somehow, Sara knew that this man was feeling no pain and that his accusers were disappointed they had not gotten him to deny his faith. Truly Christ is merciful in our hour of testing. Perhaps like Stephen of old when he was being stoned, this man, too, was seeing Christ standing at the right hand of God the Father receiving His son home.

Whatever had transpired that day invoked a vow in Sara's heart and spirit that if she was ever free from this communist country, she would never, ever, ever return to work among communist nations. However, we never say "never" to God, for just the thing that we fear; God allows to come upon us. In the process of finding God's perfect love, our fears are conquered and the tyranny of the enemy's control is destroyed. Truly *"...He who is in you is greater than he who is in the world"* (1 John 4:4).

Shaken by this encounter, when the communist guards finally left, Sara ran like a little scared rabbit back to her home and into the arms of her mother. Her heart pounded a thousand miles an hour. Her mind reeled with the impact of what she had just witnessed. This experience would forge her reluctance to minister to people in communist lands for many years to come.

It's only after God changes our hearts that we are able to perceive things from a divine perspective. God tells us to love our enemies and to pray for those who despitefully use us. That call is contrary to human nature and can only be implemented by the help of the Lord Jesus Christ and His love in and through us.

An unsettled stirring once again filled the hearts of the Ilyin family. Although settled for just a couple years on the outskirts of Shanghai near the sea, its gentle waves lapping against the shore provided little peace in their hearts that were filled with turmoil. It was more than communism having conquered the whole nation, but Mao Tse-Tung's regime was entrenching itself at every turn. It was a spiritual event exploding in their hearts. Despite the fact that they spoke numerous languages, somehow words fell empty to the ground.

In such turmoil, there's only one source of wisdom, direction and peace, and that is the throne of grace. The Ilyins began to pray. By the urging of the Holy Spirit once again through the prophetic, Nadia was directed by God to go to the highest authority of the city and ask the release of her family and friends in the Shanghai area, just as she had done in Kuldja.

In Shanghai, the Russian Christian population had grown dramatically as hundreds of families had followed the leading of the Lord from North-western China. The Word declares, *"...by the mouth of two or three witnesses every word may be established"* (Matthew 18:16).

Nadia solicited another brave sister to make the journey into the "lions' den."

In a nation that despised women, would they receive the same rebuff that they received in Kuldja? The answer was an emphatic *yes!* The guards at the consulate office in Shanghai seemingly were more brutal than any Nadia and the sister had encountered. Perhaps they were proven veterans of the revolutionary war that had just swept through China, or perhaps there was just merely a demonic encounter with God's daughters of righteousness. Whatever the case, they were unable to get by the gates.

With no appointment and no authority other than the Lord, they began the lengthy process of starting at the bottom and working their way from one bureaucrat to another until, by late afternoon, they finally succeeded in getting an audience with the consulate general. If they thought the guards were harsh or the diplomats were abrupt in Kuldja, that had been mere preparation for the rage and anger they encountered at the consulate general's office here in Shanghai. He was so infuriated that two women stood before him individually and had gone through all the tiers of command, that he threatened them with deportation as well as other Russian Christians in the province with expulsion back to Russia.

The threat of deportation to Stalin's Russia was internationally known as being some of the most brutal pages of history. Millions having died in the Gulags of Siberia and other millions died on the farm-fields of their labor as surf's to a communist ideology. They had no credence or value in their individuality but only in the collective good, your total obedience and cooperation afforded.

The consulate general's final shout resounded in their ears as they fled his office in terror: "If I see you women again, I will send you all back to Russia!" Like Pharaoh of old, God gave this modern dictator a short time and season to repent and turn away from his obstinate and wicked ways. Nadia and her Christian sister in the Lord returned home, feeling they were utter failures. They returned to the throne of grace and found their consolation and encouragement because of their obedience in the arms of God.

God had spoken of their Exodus; and despite man's resistance, all that would transpire would be a platform and an occasion to manifest the might of God. Steps of faith were stirring in Nadia's and Michael's hearts to expedite an exit for which they had no paperwork. From the feeble earnings of Michael sharpening knives and scissors in the Chinese neighborhood, coins and paper currency gradually began to accumulate.

A gigantic step of faith happened when Nadia and Michael decided to buy Michael a suit, as it seemed inappropriate to go to church in his everyday clothes. These two poor little church mice went to a second hand consignment store in Shanghai and purchased the least expensive suit they could afford. Michael was ready for the Lord's Day and ready for his immigration to come.

When we try to help God out, sometimes God allows our assistance to be frustrated and empty. That Sunday, Michael and Nadia decided to get on their Sunday-go-to-meeting best. They started early to a large Chinese church to join God's people in worship. Mao's focal attack had not yet singled out the churches and their leadership in some areas. So Michael and Nadia decided to join the Chinese brothers and sisters in worshipping the Lord in His house.

Things went rather well until it was time to pray. Of course, praying isn't praying unless one is kneeling down, and especially in a Chinese and Russian culture those rules hold true. When Michael got on his knees, before he could say a word, he audibly heard a ripping sensation in the back of his slacks. When he felt a draft, he realized what had happened. Nadia, kneeling beside him, took off her shawl from her shoulders and wrapped it around her husband's waist like a south island sarong. It covered the immediate problem at hand and made an interesting fashion statement as Michael and Nadia exited the service that evening.

Fortunately, a church of that size in Shanghai was blessed with indoor bathrooms. Michael made a beeline for the men's toilet and handed his torn pants to his wife through the door. Nadia found the church office which was able to assist her with a needle and thread, and the mending process of Michael's slacks and his ego were dually satisfied. That was a service they would never forget, and I am sure the Chinese will remember the skinny little man who had the Russian wife wearing a shawl around his waist. It is strange how in a place of solemnity, God allows humor to brighten our souls and gladden our hearts.

The consulate general sent one of their officials to Michael and Nadia's home, demanding Nadia and her friend's audience again after a six months' absence. Nadia had a time of prayer with her family. She did not know what she was facing, being called to the general consulate's office. She remembered his threat of returning her and other families back to Russia, but to her shock and amazement, the magistrate in the consulate was almost warm to his two guests. He told the women if they could find sponsors in the West that their exit visas would be granted.

The Chinese government required sponsors from foreign countries to under-write the cost of exit travel and accommodations in transit to countries in the West.

Nadia waited for the "other shoe to drop." She was wondering what the catch was and when were they going to send them back to Russia as they had done that with several Russian non-Christian families already. It was only after having a cup of tea together with the consulate general that she realized the favor God had given them was supernatural. The Word declares, *"The government shall be upon His shoulders..."* and *"...of the increase of His government and peace there will be no end"* (Isaiah 9:6-7). The ultimate authority is God's, and sooner or later all of His creation will bow down before the King of kings and Lord of lords, Jesus Christ.

Chapter Twenty-Three
A DOOR TO FREEDOM IS OPENED

Miraculously, Russian Christian immigration out of China swept the land like a prairie fire. Several torches were used by the hand of the Lord to ignite its flames. The Assemblies of God missionary, Rev. Claire Scratch, in the late 1950s, was one of those bringing the news out of the heart of China. Where missionaries were fleeing for their lives, leaving years of their labors behind, and in some instances with merely the clothing on their backs, Brother Scratch heard a mandate from Heaven to go inland into China instead of fleeing to the nearest seaport.

While Brother Scratch was obeying the Lord, he collapsed with dehydration and fever on a hut floor, unable to complete his journey. At the same hour, a Russian brother deep in a season of prayer made his way to the same hut. Led of the Lord by a vision from Heaven, the Russian brother found the reason for God's leading him to this particular place. Crumpled on the floor before him, Pastor Scratch lay semiconscious. The Russian brother dropped to his knees beside Pastor Scratch. As he laid hands on him and prayed in the Holy Spirit, Brother Scratch's fever was immediately broken and his ailment lifted by the power of Jesus Christ.

Returning to his knees, brother Scratch and the Russian brother grasped each other in a warm Christian bear hug. Squeezing each other in the Lord, they both invoked a string of praise and gratitude from their perspective hearts and mouths. It wasn't until after they hugged and shared their common expression of thanksgiving to Jesus Christ their Lord that they realized there was a language barrier that seemed insurmountable; but if God could lead them this far by the miraculous, He was able to take them the rest of the way.

As the Russian brother unburdened his heart for the multiplied hundreds of Russian Christian families trapped in China and needing sponsorship to the West, a strange phenomenon occurred in Pastor Scratch's hearing. Miraculously, he understood every word that was spoken to him in the Russian language, although he had never studied any of the Slavonic tongues.

When Brother Scratch began to speak in English, a second miracle occurred in the Russian brother's hearing. God gave the Russian brother an understanding heart, so he perceived everything that was said to him in English. The conversation went on for quite some time, back and forth, until hot salty tears were rolling down the faces of both men as they began to perceive the miracle that God had accomplished. *"And how is it that we hear, each in our own language in which we were born?"* (Acts 2:8). On their knees in prayer, a covenant agreement was made to share the plight of the Russian believers needing sponsors to leave from behind the Bamboo Curtain.

Some weeks later, Brother Scratch spoke at a Pentecostal Assemblies of Canada event in Toronto, where he related the events of his last days in China. He finished his presentation with an impassioned plea for sponsors to be raised up to bring God's people out of captivity. A young man in the audience hearing the presentation was arrested by the hand of God and, like a torch bearer running through the darkness, carried the call of the need for sponsorship across Canada, America, and Australia. Pastor George Derkatch was a catalyst in releasing thousands of Russian believers from China.

Sara and I had the honor of working over a decade with him and World Christian Ministries, which he founded. Many years later, we met the intercessor that had been awakened in the middle of the night and had groaned in the Holy Spirit, seeing Pastor Scratch's life in jeopardy as he was convulsing with a fever in a hut in China. She prayed until she felt the burden lift and had the occasion to tell Pastor Scratch personally the account of her vision as Pastor Claire Scratch became her pastor at Neighborhood Assembly in Bellevue,

Washington, for some years. It's this intercessor that brought us the details of this encounter. I don't believe that Brother Scratch ever realized the magnitude of his mission. Thousands of Russian Christians before the throne of grace will rise up and call him "blessed." Each of us plays a role, and when our obedience is complete, we reap great reward here and now and an everlasting reward in the world to come.

Seasons of prayer are posts-scripted by God speaking to sponsors across the Free World. We thank God for all the ambassadors who carried the message of sponsorship and immigration needs; but most of all, we thank the Lord for touching the heart cords of hundreds of families by sponsoring Russian believers, enabling them to come out of China's darkest hour.

Freedom of religion and expression were eroded daily. Mao's armies conquered and controlled every major segment of society. Media, civil government, and even informants on the streets were on Mao's payroll or control list. It wouldn't be long before the church would be focused on as a major target of Mao's fury. Rumors of arrests in some cities had reached the ears of the believers in Shanghai. When sponsorship was finally raised, it wasn't a moment too soon. The year 1959, just six months after Nadia's trip to the consulate, was a banner year of victory for the Russian redeemed of the Lord.

Leaving all their belongings behind and only carrying satchels and a few small suitcases, the Ilyin family boarded the train in Shanghai that would take them almost two days' journey to Hong Kong. This train run was totally different than their train travel previously. There were no first-class tickets, no sleeper berths—just a crowded train with every corner accounted for.

Upon arrival in Hong Kong, the Ilyins stepped off the train and onto free soil for the first time in decades. Their wanderings in China had been in excess of 25 years, and now they found themselves in FREEDOM like they had never known. Was this the fulfillment of the prophetic word they had heard in Shanghai, or did God have something much more for them in mind? In Shanghai, they heard the word of the Lord that they would enter a land of great freedom, a land flowing with milk and honey. There they would be able to worship the Lord God in spirit and in truth and they would raise sons and daughters in the admonition of the Lord. This next generation would be raised up that would hear and heed the leading of the Holy Spirit and pursue the calling of God to the ends of the earth.

All those immediate thoughts faded away as they stood on the platform, lonely and forlorn. Auntie May, as she was affectionately called, had heard from Heaven that a group of God's children needed her care and covering. The traffic in Hong Kong had delayed her arrival. Well after the entire train was unloaded and all of its passengers had left the platform, the Ilyin family huddled together, praying softly under their breath.

Auntie May was a missionary who shuttled between Shanghai and Hong Kong as a liaison in the release of these hundreds of Russian Christians. Truly, Auntie May had an open ear and a heart toward heaven as she responded to the direction of the Lord and fulfilled God's leading and desire. Her directions from the Lord carried her directly to the Ilyin family whom she had never set eyes on before.

Before long, they saw running to embrace them a little white-haired angel in shoe leather. Despite the language barrier, the Ilyins immediately perceived that this was one of God's choice servants and stood before them as a direct answer to their prayer. Like a mother hen, Auntie May gathered up the little "chicks" under her arms of love.

Down the long platform they went, through the busy train station in Hong Kong and into waiting vehicles that whisked them across the city to a nearby hotel. Here rooms were secured for the family. Immediately upon checking in, the Ilyin family was urged to come down to the ground floor to a restaurant and eat a meal that seemed like an endless banquet table of God's bounty. They were told they could eat as much as they wanted.

This was good news to little Sara in particular because she was down to her last crust of bread in a pocket of a makeshift dress that was sewn together by her mother. After blessing the meal, how delicious the food tasted as tears of gratitude and thanksgiving rolled down the cheeks of the least to the greatest.

Food was so much a part of their survival that each meal was prefaced by prayer and post- scripted at the close of the meal with standing up and giving thanks once again to the Lord for His provision. Truly, God is the faithful Father who loves and cares for His own.

After they were able to wash up and have a good night's sleep, Auntie May again came to the rescue. That morning at breakfast, an American sea captain, who had accompanied Auntie May the day before to the train station, came to the hotel to make sure that all the room costs and meals were covered for the Ilyin family.

During their three-week stay, the American captain would show up often to make certain of the welfare of the Ilyins. He would pick up Fred and put him on his shoulders and put Sara on his feet as they waltzed around the large ballroom attached to the restaurant. Then he would switch and take little Natasha and dance with her.

This was the first American that the Ilyins had ever met. His kind eyes, gentle touch, and generous spirit made the Ilyins desire to someday go to the land of this man's origin. If all the Americans were like this, America must be "Heaven on Earth," as God's gracious goodness was expressed by this stranger at every turn. Auntie May and the sea captain helped with the paperwork to arrange for the passage on the Queen Elizabeth II from Hong Kong to Sydney, Australia.

This ship voyage on one of the World's luxury Liners was the experience of a life-time. From the drab huts of China to a state room, lavished with polished brass and crystal clear mirrors, the Ilyin children were not sure whether this was a reality or whether they had entered into some dream-land where their wildest imagination were abated and satisfied.

"Every good and perfect gift comes down from the Father of light in Whom there is no variable or shadow of turning".

Chapter Twenty-Four
OPEN DOOR TO AUSTRALIA

T he voyage on one of the premier luxury liner of that day was an adventure the Ilyin family never forgot. Two weeks on the high seas with grandeur and food like they had never seen was more than just a feast to their eyes; it was a great satisfaction to their appetites and desire to learn.

They were entering a whole new world, a door of freedom of choices, a door with endless opportunities, and a door with many unanswered questions. What would their future hold in Australia? Was Australia the end of their journey? Was this the land that God had spoken of flowing with milk and honey and freedom of worship?

When the large passenger vessel anchored in the Sydney Harbor, another chapter in their lives had begun. Their sponsor, a single man living in Adelaide, Australia, was responsible for paying their ship passage. His generosity, however, was not a gift, but rather a loan—a loan which he constantly reminded the Ilyins was due him.

The weeks seemed to drag on, and Michael found work some distance out of town on a construction site. The heat, however, was so intense that Michael often returned with a bloody nose to have cold compresses put on him. This procedure was repeated the following day. He had to make a living for his family, and that was paramount in his heart and mind. His own personal comforts did not figure into the equation.

One day, a remedy was found. Nadia stirred the children awake early in the morning and took them to a nearby military range that was the site of target practice for the Australian military. The soldiers would shoot all day; and at five o'clock in the morning before chores and school, the Ilyin children were rousted from their beds to collect the spent brass casings from the bullets fired before.

A little oven was made in the backyard, and these casings were smelted down and the copper sold, creating a new stream of income for the Ilyins. Within several months, their bill to the bachelor was paid, but like Laban in the Bible, this bachelor changed the amount owed numerous times. He calculated the use of his vehicle; the gas that was put into his car, the wear and tear on the vehicle, and all were added to the bill. When the sum was paid in full, he still wasn't satisfied and was often known to grumble about his sacrifice to the church community.

One afternoon when the Ilyin parents attended a nearby prayer meeting, Sara decided to bathe her little sister, Natasha, in a bathhouse adjacent to the house. This separate room had no electricity and used a coal-fired stove to warm the water. When the water temperature was just right, Sara gently put Natasha into the large tub.

After thoroughly washing her, she wrapped little Natasha up in a cozy bath towel. Unfortunately, the kerosene lamp that was sitting nearby was knocked over in the process. When it fell, shattering to the floor, a fiery flame kicked up the kerosene spill into a blaze. Sara, taking her sister with the towel wrapped around her, ran outside the bathhouse, yelling in Russian, *"Pazhar! Pazhar!"*("Fire! Fire!"), but nobody understood her or called for help. Walter, returning home from a store on a bike, translated his sister's cry into terms all the neighbors could understand as he yelled "Fire!" in English.

Someone summoned the fire department, and they came to put out the flames. By the time the fire department arrived, severe damage was done to the bathhouse, and some smoke damage was done to the adjacent kitchen. When the Ilyin sponsor saw this, he took a willow switch and began to beat on the back of little Sara's legs without mercy. Blow after blow came across her little calves and ankles.

By this time, Michael and Nadia had arrived home from their prayer meeting. Nadia, her motherly instincts aroused, threw herself between Sara and the sponsor telling him, "It's enough!" The harshness of her voice and the restraint of her hands on his shoulders settled him until he could process his anger. All the while Sara was being beaten; she was trying to tell her sponsor that it was an accident, that she had not done it on purpose. She begged him, saying, "Please, forgive me!" His response through gritted teeth of anger was "I will *not* forgive you." Nadia kept telling him to forgive, or there would be consequences before God for his unforgiveness.

The hand that he had used so unmercifully against Sara was stricken shortly afterwards with a strange infection. Doctors had no cure, and it seemed the hand grew worse day by day. After prayer and the application of aloe cacti leaves for several weeks via Nadia's treatment and prayer, his hand finally began to recover; however, the sponsor did not forgive Sara until he bumped into her on our honeymoon in 1971. In a store aisle he said, "I have not forgiven you for burning my bathhouse all these years." Sara replied, "I have pled for your forgiveness, and you have not heard me. If you don't forgive me, you will not make it to Heaven because God will hold you unforgiven in your sins. If you can't forgive your brother or sister, then God cannot forgive you." He responded reluctantly after a twenty-year period with the words, "I forgive you."

This bathhouse incident at the time of its happening in Australia was the straw that broke the camel's back; and when a Yugoslavian co-worker with Michael offered a barn on his land, Michael jumped at the opportunity to move out of this unbearable situation. It wasn't long before Michael turned the barn into a beautiful love nest for his bride and his family. This interim housing would be a staging area. Months later, with a loan from some Russian Christian brothers, the Ilyins put a down payment on a house in Adelaide, South Australia, with a mortgage of $10,000. The Ilyins were all hard workers; and despite the house being too small, they paid off the mortgage within several years.

This house became a point of blessing as intercessory prayer ascended from it to the heavens. Mrs. Yuza Tula, Mrs. Dehtiar, Marczewskis, and a few other families frequently would assemble in the Ilyin house where it became an open window to the heavens. Mrs. Tula and Mrs. Dehtiar would agree in prayer for their unsaved husbands relentlessly, believing for the salvation of their spouses. Many years later, God answered their prayers. Due to the kindred spirit of intercession, some of these friends remain close to the Ilyin family to this day.

Many Russian believers who had come from China began to assemble for prayer at the Ilyin household. They prayed for God to use them in this new land of freedom so that somehow they would affect their community for Christ. They would pray for the local church and for the future leading of the Lord in their lives. Some of these friends were new acquaintances in Australia—such as the Marczewskis, Lipins, Tula, Dehtiar, and many others—while some of their old friends from China were gradually settling in Adelaide as well.

There were always prayer meetings, youth gatherings, and other Christian functions at the Ilyin home. Sara enjoyed walking with some of her dear friends into town, as this new sense of freedom was overwhelming to her. To see such beautiful homes, gardens, people laughing, enjoying life—and they seemed to have a purpose in life. The Golin girls, Nina and Lucy, Maria and Olga Dehtiar, Nida Vinaeva, along with Sara and many other girls from church would enjoy one another's fellowship.

The young people were enthralled by the ocean, as the water was very warm, swirling with beautiful blue colors, and the shore tapered gradually into the sea. This was unlike any waters in China. One afternoon they were having fun swimming in the ocean until they heard sirens. At first, they thought that the sirens were to alarm people of war activity, which they were used to in China. They asked the people on the beach where they should run to and what was happening.

To their amazement and relief, the Australian friends laughed and said that the siren is to warn people to get out of the water because there had been a spotting of whales swimming nearby. They were surprised and wanted to see what these whales looked like, although only from a distance. There were times they were able to see these beautiful creatures swimming and splashing in the deep sea waters.

On numerous occasions the shriek of sirens warned of much more ominous predators, among which was the infamous great white shark. During these times, the lifeguard made sure that everyone was out of the water. What a sight that was, and never to be forgotten.

Childhood pranks were the memorable form of entertainment the kids played with their friends. While the parents were praying, Richard Tula, along with Sara, Fred and Natasha, would play games with their neighbors. One of those games was throwing figs from a tree in their backyard across the fence to the neighbor's yard, which was filled with tall grass and scores of rabbits. The object of this game was to hit as many rabbits as they possibly could, and those who hit the most rabbits ran up a high score. The figs, of course, didn't hurt the rabbits as they were more than delighted to eat the sweet treats that bombed them from the skies. It was hard to tell who was having more fun: the kids on the fence or the rabbits eating figs.

Sara was also spoiled by Richard Tula taking her on his famous bike to the local little store where she was treated with delicious sweets that she had never seen in China. He would also tutor Fred and Sara, trying to teach them to speak English properly. That was quite a task; however, they would forever tease him, saying something in Russian rather than speaking English; whereas, he would rebuff and speak Polish to them. Now this was a new language that they had never heard before in China. There are many similarities between the Russian and Polish languages, but there are certain words that have totally the opposite meaning. Sara, Fred, and Natasha would play this game with Richard as well. Richard became their very dear friend for life.

The family loved their humongous house with many bedrooms and a large yard with a vegetable garden, fruit trees, and a lattice work covered with grapevines. Not only did the grapevines provide delicious treats at the close of their growing season, but their leafy foliage provided shade from the hot Australian sun. On hot summer nights, it became their favorite place to sleep out for the kids after the lattice and grapes were covered with mosquito netting. Many nights were spent outside, lying on their beds and looking at the skies, wondering what the future held.

Letters began to arrive from America as the families of Shevchenko, Marusia and Joseph Lockteff, Lena who married Anatoly Kozachuk, Vanya and Sophia Ilyin, and many others had immigrated from Paraguay to the San Francisco Bay area of California. Family members there told them about the freedoms of this great land of America and how God had drawn many hundreds of Russian Christians to this region from China. They mentioned how they missed the Ilyin family and would love for them to join them in America.

This truly was the fulfillment of God's prophetic promise so many years in the past. The Lord would lead them to a land flowing with milk and honey, where there would be no restraints or restrictions on their worshipping the Lord in Spirit and in Truth. The stepping stone of Australia was not their final resting place as God was leading them on.

The restlessness in the spirit of the Ilyins' hearts began to stir them to seek the face of the Lord again. Was it their natural desire to be with their family and friends, or was this the country of God's leading? They arrived in Australia to a church that was Full Gospel in name only; but due to the influx of hundreds of Russians led prophetically; this church took on a new DNA. Could they leave what they had seen grow while living in Adelaide, or was God leading them to something far better? All these questions were to be answered in a few weeks' time.

Chapter Twenty-Five
AMERICA, LAND OF THE FREE

The time had at last come when the world-wide wanderings of these children of God would enter its last stage. Selling their belongings, house and car, the Ilyin family paid for their passage on the SS *Oriana* for the long trip from Sydney, Australia, to San Francisco, California, United States of America.

Despite the fact that this ship was one of the fastest passenger vessels of its day, being able to maintain speeds of 30.64 knots, it took what seemed like forever to get to San Francisco. The halfway stop in Fiji was a welcome break from blue waters of the Pacific that seemed to go on forever beyond the horizon. The fact that Nadia was pregnant with Ruth who would be born in San Francisco didn't help. Later, God would give the Ilyin family one last child: Elizabeth (Liz), who would also be born in San Francisco.

As the SS *Oriana* came to dock under the Golden Gate Bridge at the pier of its mooring, the Ilyins entered into a final chapter of their wanderings. In America, they would taste FREEDOM in a new way. The rarified air of freedom tasted sweet to those that had lived in bondage all their life long. The cost of that freedom was the blood of many brave men and women who fought for the basic human right that all men are created equal under God to pursue life, liberty, and happiness.

San Francisco was a new world for the Ilyins. With family and friends all around them, a strong Russian Full Gospel Temple that was started by Alexander Shevchenko upon his arrival from Paraguay was such a tremendous blessing to the Ilyin family. Under Pastor Alexander Shevchenko's supervision and under the hand of the Lord's blessing, a new church building was constructed at the base of Russian Hill in the Portrero region of San Francisco. This church with over 500 members in the early 1960s was one of the strongest Russian Full Gospel churches on the West Coast. For many years, it broadcasted gospel radio back to the Soviet Union over world-wide translators in South Korea; Quito, Ecuador; Radio Malta; and Lisbon, Portugal. Their quality broadcast was a lifeline to millions of believers trapped behind the Iron Curtain. Thousands came to know Christ personally through this Russian church's evangelism efforts. The choirs of the church led by Joseph Lockteff became a source of blessing to the church and to multiplied thousands that would huddle around their radio sets behind the Iron Curtain to hear the good news in music and the Word.

This beacon of light was a source of inspiration and encouragement to many people whose heads hung low in hopelessness because of Soviet communism. To listen to a gospel broadcast in the former Soviet Union meant you were an enemy of the state and, if apprehended, could be imprisoned. Despite this threat of peril, thousands risked the consequences just to cloister around the radio and be comforted by the anointed ministry they heard from the Russian Temple.

Michael and Walter sang in the choir with their tenor voices while Sara, Fred, and Natasha sang in the youth choir. There seemed to be something for everybody. The whole church was swept up into a precious time of visitation from Heaven and bonded as a family in God. The youth of the church began to perceive that God had no grandchildren, but all His children must be born of the Spirit, and every generation had to make a personal confession of faith in Christ Jesus.

Tommy Hicks, having just returned from an awesome revival in Argentina, became one of the speakers at the Russian Full Gospel Temple. Unorthodox as he was, there was no denying the heavy anointing on the man and his ministry. In one of the services, as he spoke of the Holy Spirit, he took some of his water and sprinkled it out across the youth in the congregation. As the water touched many scores of young people, they were filled with the baptism of the Holy Spirit with the evidence of speaking in tongues.

However, prayer meetings continued in the adjacent room to the sanctuary after the services were finished. There were young people who had not received the infilling of the Holy Spirit in the services, lingered in prayer afterwards, pursuing God to baptize them with His Power. One of the Christian sisters who also came out of China, Ruth Shevchuk, would pray with and for the youth to be baptized in the Holy Spirit. It was in one of these meetings that through Ruth's tenacious prayers over Sara, God baptized her with the baptism of the Holy Spirit, with the evidence of speaking in tongues. Missionary calls were birthed in many hearts, and a passion for the lost was a byproduct of the Holy Spirit's infilling.

In this supercharged environment, I was invited to speak at the Russian youth camp. This invitation came about as the Russian Temple choir had visited Seattle, Washington numerous times and specifically, the Slavic Full Gospel Church where my father served as a preaching elder. I considered it a high honor for Pastor Alexander Shevchenko to invite me, Richard Michalski, a young adult of twenty, to speak to their youth. It was after one of these camps that I was given the honor to speak in the Russian Full Gospel Temple in California on a Sunday morning service.

Four rows from the front, I spotted a sixteen-year-old, long-haired, doe-eyed brunette, Sara. She caught my eye as she sat and worshipped the Lord with her friends that sat around her. My seeing Sara for the first time does not mean however, that she noticed me, despite the fact that I spoke in her church that Sunday morning. My message that morning obviously had very little impact on her mind and heart. It wasn't until some years later that my casual glances of her turned into romance as I got to converse with her and know her heart. Little did I realize that in three short years, in a different season and in a different city that little princess would become my precious bride?

Sara and her family were visiting Seattle after travelling through Canada and the World's Fair in Montreal in 1968. This opened a new chapter of our relationship together.

The invitations kept coming by Pastor Alexander Shevchenko to speak at different events in their church, and of course with more than just spiritual interest, I gladly accepted the invitations to come to California. After one of my visits from Seattle, I went out with the youth at the close of the service and had a chance to walk on the sands of Half Moon Bay in San Francisco with Sara and some of her girlfriends. This was subsequent to my meeting her entire family some months before. It is there at Half Moon Bay in San Francisco that I held her hand for the first time. Upon returning back home to Seattle, I began to write Sara poetry and letters on a regular basis. The US Postal Service probably made it in the black that year due to the constant letter writing between Sara and me!

At long last all my immediate prayers were answered when Sara's family moved from San Francisco to Seattle. I frightened off most of the young men that were interested in Sara due either to my leadership as youth pastor or my prowess as a weightlifter and an athlete. Meanwhile, Sara had some growing up and maturing to do. I definitely had a lot of growing up to do as well.

An indicator that we were not willing to give up our childhood was found in the way Sara treated her younger sisters, Natasha, Ruth, and Liz. In the narrow two-story townhouse on Shotwell Street, where they lived in San Francisco, was a tall uncarpeted staircase, excluding a narrow runner down the middle. After much persuasion, Sara and Fred convinced their little younger sisters—Natasha, Ruth, and Liz—to one by one crawl into the newly acquired cardboard box for the ride of their life. As each of the young sisters got into the box, the lid being held tightly by their older sister, they were given a gentle push. As they slid down the long staircase, bumping on each step, the crash landing on the bottom of the staircase was punctuated with screams and howling.

It took more persuasion for the other sisters to follow suit. However, Fred and Sara insisted their little sisters take their turns. They persuaded each one that the previous run was a fluke with the harsh landing at the bottom and that their run would be full of fun. Each obediently took their turn with the same disastrous results. It was not the fall that hurt them; it was the abrupt stop at the end! This ride of their life became a ride that they nearly did not live through!

When Dad and Mom Ilyin got home, proper corporal punishment was issued to the two offending culprits, who after their spanking had a hard time sitting down. It's amazing how quickly we learn when the board of education is applied to the seat of learning!

While Sara was maturing and becoming a lovely young lady, God was working a mighty work in my heart through his association with Pastor Peter Kerychuk's sons, Gary and Allan. Sister Gene Kerychuk, Pastor Peter's wife, said to me one day, "You have slept in every bed in our house except our own bed." When Sister Gene gave birth to Sherri, their youngest daughter, their bed became my accommodation for several nights. The reason for this is that there were so many guests visiting Pastor Peter's house that there were no other beds available. Since Pastor Peter and sister Gene were at the hospital, I took the only bed available that was not occupied by friends or family. My trips to Vancouver, Canada, became a frequent shuttle as I found true friendship with Gary and Allan.

Having the common ground of being PKs (preacher's kids), the only moderating influence in the Kerychuk house was Patricia, affectionately known as Pat, the oldest sister who seemingly was the only one that could put controls on her younger brothers.

When Gary's voice began to change as he matured through puberty, he delighted to use his deeper voice to play pranks on the phone. It started simply enough with calling somebody randomly from the telephone book and asking them if their refrigerator was running. If they answered yes, Gary would respond in a deep baritone voice, "Go catch it!" One day, they called Hertz Rental Car and the agent answered, "Hertz." Gary and Allan on separate lines both retorted at the same time, "If it hurts, put a Band-Aid on it!" Then, they would quickly hang up.

The favorite victim of their pranks was a boarder named Albert. He rented a suite in the attic in the Kerychuk home. Let's be gracious and say that Albert was "simple." One day on the extension phone, Gary disguised his voice and called Albert pretending that he was the

RCMP (Royal Canadian Mounted Police). They told Albert that his car had been found and was at the RCMP impound lot on Frazer Avenue (with a fictitious street number) and that he was to go and claim it. Albert raced down the steps from his upper bedroom apartment, jumped in his car in front of the house, and drove two blocks before he realized that he had been had. He returned to the house and yelled at the Kerychuk boys, calling them "Dilbert's," to which they responded, "You yo-yo!" Needless to say, Pat had her hands full.

Add me to that mix, and we outnumbered Pat three to one. All these pranks were practice ground and would be very effective against the KGB in the years to come with our work in the former Soviet Union, not to mention being a great tension reliever from the constant surveillance that Sara and I found ourselves in many years later. It's amazing what you can learn in Christian circles!

The Kerychuk home became my home away from home and a staging area for my visiting Sara when she attended North Vancouver Pentecostal Assemblies of Canada Bible College. My parents, Roman and Olga, trusted the Kerychuks to keep me under control, as I would use any excuse possible to visit my little princess over two-and-a-half hours away from Seattle where she resided for over a year.

Not only was Pastor Peter Kerychuk gracious and hospitable to our family, but he often gave my father and me a pulpit to preach from. He would regularly invite me to speak at banquets and youth gatherings and other church functions. Pastor Peter believed in me and my calling when I had a hard time believing in myself. I will eternally be grateful for the discernment and the great heart of compassion I found in Pastor Peter and Gene Kerychuk.

In 1968, during a summer break from Bible school my calling was forged in that season of opportunity. Upon my return from ministry in Poland at the age of nineteen with my parents and my sister, Monica, my burden for missions was undeniable. My calling was set with a passion for missions and the lost without Christ. While spending four years at Northwest Bible College in Kirkland, Washington, from 1966 to 1970, many students were not sure of God's leading. With me that was never in question. Somehow, some way, I would make it back to Eastern Europe and to our people because I saw a thirst in them for the things of God that shook my lukewarm world. Sometimes the most radical of youth are the greatest instruments of God's grace. God takes our zeal and drive and, when our hearts are converted, applies it all to Kingdom purpose in the earth.

"Because the foolishness of God is wiser than men and the weakness of God is stronger than men. For you see your calling, brethren, that not many wise according to the flesh, not many mighty, not many noble, are called. But God has chosen the foolish things of the world to put to shame the wise, and God has chosen the weak things of the world to put to shame the things which are mighty; and the base things of the world and the things which are despised God has chosen, and the things which are not, to bring to nothing the things that are that no flesh should glory in His presence." (1 Cor. 1: 25-29)

Chapter Twenty-Six
CALLED OF GOD TOGETHER

"From the ends of the earth will I call my son." This prophetic passage of course concerns Jesus Christ; but in similar application, Sara and I experienced the same logistics of God's sovereign hand. God had brought my wife to me out of China, via Australia, Fiji, San Francisco, and finally to Seattle. Although my journey was shorter, God had brought my parents out of war-torn Poland, through displaced-persons camps in Germany, to reside in Seattle as well. Seattle has been our home ever since our wedding and in my case, since I was three-and-a-half years old.

Sara and I learned the dynamics of our calling as we took several short-term ministry trips together with teams from Northwest Bible College to Vancouver Island in British Columbia, Canada. These trips were a forging of our faith as we met the missionaries from Oregon, the Millers, who graciously gave me the pulpit on numerous occasions. The supervisor of missions for the island was a man of awesome relationship with God. On one occasion, while helping build one of the Native American churches on the Island, a young man from the Northwest College team fell off the scaffold. It was obvious this young man's leg was broken, and Brother Nyguard laid hands on the ankle. Before our very eyes, that broken bone was instantly made whole by the power of Christ.

I remember preaching in a basement of a church that was not yet complete, and the burden of the Lord had come so intensely upon me that tears flowed down my cheeks as the Holy Spirit cried out through me to the indigenous Indian tribe of that area. Our ministry in Nanaimo, Chemanis, and Duncan became a time of stretching and growth in our faith and walk in Christ. Finally, I received the ultimate honor to preach at an Indian camp. This meant numerous tribes from varied backgrounds would come together and have an old-fashioned camp meeting, Indian style.

They would whoop and howler, jump and dance, and have a freedom that I had never seen before. Everything was going quite well until the speaker of the camp was introduced and I stood behind a flimsy makeshift podium. A very large Indian squaw stood up from the front row and vehemently protested my speaking at the camp. Her protest was due to the glaring fact that I was a white man and no white man should preach at an Indian camp. The elders around her finally succeeded in settling her with the promise: "Give the lad a chance. If you think he can't preach after the first meeting, feel free to leave the camp."

Something happened that night that I cannot explain. A deluge of God's anointing poured on me, and for an hour and a half what I had to share was liquid fire from the throne of grace. After that first meeting, that squaw became my strongest supporter. I wish many times I could have taken her to dry, deadbeat services where eyebrows barely moved and to hear her from the top of her voice crying out, "HALLELUJAH! HALLELUJAH! AMEN!"

Needless to say, I fell in love with the Millers and the indigenous Native American people and have many times in many different locations spoken on their reservations. I love their sincerity and spontaneity. I think we have much to learn from other cultures, especially that we should not be stuck in our routines and ruts. My definition of a rut is a grave with both ends kicked out. If we don't get out of our religious traditions and be real before God, our "rut" will be our burial place. We serve a God of the living. Let's come alive to His dictates and directives in the Holy Spirit.

All these times together of ministry helped me realize what a precious gem God had given me in my fiancée, Sara. If it was preaching the Word, her head would drop in prayer; or if it was the prophecy, her eyes would meet mine, and I would realize in those moments that God had released the same words into her spirit that I was expressing through my mouth. This agreement in Christ Jesus would play a crucial role in our marriage and ministry for decades to come.

Chapter Twenty-Seven
WEDDING BELLS RING

The preparation for our wedding was conducted on a shoestring budget, but God helped us at every turn. Sara, some of her family and friends—Natasha, Sara's younger sister, Vera Ilyin, (John and Sonia's oldest daughter, and Sara's cousin); Nida Shevchenko, (Pastor Alexander and Ekaterina Shevchenko's youngest daughter, and Sara's cousin); Helen Lockteff, (Maria and Joseph Lockteffs daughter and Sara's cousin); Nida Pustobaeff, (the sister in law of Walter Ilyins, Sara's oldest brother who married one month earlier to Vera Pustobaeff). Monica Michalski (Richard's only sister and sibling) and some of the other bridesmaids—made favors from discounted materials, while others made floral arrangements which they hand crafted as boutonnières and bouquets.

The groomsmen were hand-picked of an inner circle of life-long friends: Ruben Lockteff, my best man was the son of Maria and Joseph Lockteff and a cousin through marriage. It was hard picking other groomsmen, not wanting to offend any one of them as I felt that they were all best men in my life. Gary Kerychuk, (Pastor Peter and Gene Kerychuks oldest son. There was a string of cousins and family members that included: Peter Lockteff, (Maria and Joseph's oldest son); Peter Ilyin (John and Sonia's son) and Vera Ilyins younger brother; and Victor Ilyin (Sara's oldest brother). Fred Ilyin (Sara's younger brother) and Victor Karpiak were junior attendants for the wedding.

Last but not least, Liz, (Elizabeth), Sara's youngest sister and Paul Darafeev were flower girl and ring-bearer respectively. This time, once again, her injuries were inflicted by Fred's coaxing her to swing on a plumbing pipe in the basement of their newly acquired home in Seattle. This incident resulted in Liz's arm being broken upon her fall. Liz almost didn't make the wedding due to this breakage.

For some awkward reason, Liz and Paul got in a verbal disagreement during their marching procession down the aisle of the wedding ceremony. To the gasp of all the audience, Liz settled the disagreement by decking Paul, the ring-bearer with her full length, arm cast. Needless to say, any tension in the room was broken by the giggles and humor of this scene.

We thank God for the host of friends and family that sacrificed in bringing to pass that which God had initiated in our lives. The Northwest College chapel and its cafeteria were rented to us for a nominal fee. All this played a part in making this wedding possible. Pastor George Derkatch presided over the wedding and later became the mission's director we worked with for more than ten years

It is difficult enough to make an adjustment in the beginning months and years of marriage, but to Sara and I, that adjustment had far greater ramifications. It is one thing to settle in an environment in a house or a rental to plan and work out your life together; it's quite another thing to adjust to each other while on the "run" from the KGB in Russia. The glue of this marriage was Jesus Christ and our joint calling to missions and ministry.

We worked with a mission whose base was in Toronto, Canada which was first called, Christian Mission Publishers and later became known as World Christian Ministries, directed and founded by Rev. George Derkatch. Their first printings of Halley's Bible Handbook, a one volume Matthew Henry Commentary, an unabridged Bible concordance and hundreds of thousands of Bibles in both Russian and Ukrainian became the legacy that the Derkatch's left behind. Their sowing of seed in the form of Scriptures, smuggled into the Soviet Union became the life-blood of the Church. The revival and Church growth we are seeing now in Eastern Europe is a result of the sacrifice of many ministries and pioneers that laid their life down and paved a highway of holiness that millions are now able to walk upon.

Thank the Lord for both Pastor Peter Kerychuk and Pastor George Derkatch who gave Sara and I the opportunity to deliver Scriptures back to our own people trapped behind the Iron Curtain. How often the pressures of the hour forced us to our knees to cry out to the Rock that is higher than us and then have the rush of God's presence bring His comfort and consolation in the absence of friends and family. He, the Comforter, promised never to leave us nor forsake us, and it is He that is guiding us ever deeper into our love and devotion to Christ and for each other.

Sara never thought what would be a honeymoon of a month's duration in Europe would escalate to multiple years and hundreds of visits over the span of more than four decades. Upon our brief returns to the home front in Seattle for me and to Vernon, British Columbia, where Sara's parents and family moved shortly after our wedding, we found support and comfort.

Oftentimes my mother would pull me aside privately; and if she said it once, she said it a hundred times: "Richard, you have a good woman for a wife. Cherish and love her." *"She's a keeper."* I never quite knew what my mother meant by this expression because divorce was never considered or this was a fishing and game term, none of which applied to our relationship. I always felt welcomed by Sara's warm family, and our marriage has always been more than just the merging of two lives, but also the integration of two families.

God blessed our blending together with constant covering of prayer and intercession availing before the Lord from both sides of the families, the Ilyins and the Michalskis. We still enjoy the agreement and prayer covering we receive from remaining family members to this very day.

Chapter Twenty-Eight
CHILDREN, A HERITAGE FROM THE LORD

Sara and I were married for six-and-a-half years; and due to complications in our RH negative and positive, as well as other problems, we were not able to have children. One day during one of our many return trips home, a little sister at Cedar Park Assembly of God Church in Bothell, Washington, laid hands on Sara's stomach and commanded the womb to be open and the barrenness of her womb to cease. We thought that was a peculiar prayer, only to have it answered some months later when we had returned to minister in England.

While in England, Sara was taking fertility tests when the doctor came out perplexed one day and gave us the news: "I don't think further fertility tests will be needed as, Mrs. Michalski, you are PREGNANT!" Oh how we rejoiced at the hearing of those words! God had finally answered our prayer. Sara jumped up and down, shocking the doctor as she shouted, "HALLELUJAH! HALLELUJAH! HALLELUJAH!"

Our joy, however, was short lived as we found complications had set in and an ultrasound revealed that Sara's pregnancy was a tubular pregnancy. The doctor insisted aborting the child because of endangerment of the life of the mother. The complication was further exasperated in that I was in Poland at that time, delivering $1,500 dollars to pay a fine against the Sosulski's church in Krakow. Communism was still alive and well and their arch enemy are the followers of Jesus Christ. Fines and surveillance and threatening, both privately and in the media were common place by the Soviet KGB.

On such short notice, the only fare available was a package deal with a week's stay at a hotel in Southern Poland. This packaging meant I was unable to return back to England for an entire week. I was accommodated at the Francuski Hotel, off the central square in Krakow, Poland. I had left Sara in good hands in the home of Rev. Hugh and Iris McGowan, our British director for Christian Mission Publishers. I was unaware of the complications that Sara was suffering.

That week was sheer misery for Sara and me because we could not communicate one with another for a total of seven days. Telephones and telegrams were all controlled by the Secret Service in Poland, and personal phone calls to a foreign country were not allowed except from a post office that was especially wired for the KGB to eavesdrop on the conversation. There was also the added complication, in that many times one had to order their phone call and pay for it in full two or three days in advance. How much has changed from those years to now!

Sara had left me with only one request and that was to bring a thermos of Mrs. Sosulski's heavenly chicken noodle soup from Poland. I delivered the funds in the first days of my visit, attended the Sunday service, and was bored without anything productive to do during the middle of the week. My boredom caused me to take walks late at night around the large city block that housed the Francuski Hotel.

With the streets clear after ten o'clock in the evening, due to an enforced semi official-curfew that was imposed by local communist officials, it was obvious I was being followed. Westerners were exempt from this curfew in that they brought hard revenue to the nation and the communists did not want the West to hear how restrictive their society was.

The doorman of the hotel would unlock the triple lock of the front door, releasing me to my routine of circling the block, and let me in again after my walk was concluded. With the streets clear after ten o'clock in the evening, it was obvious I was being followed as I could hear steps on the cobblestones behind me near the midnight hour. The second night, I decided to give my followers a little Christmas present. They had been summoned by the doorkeeper of my hotel and alerted to my routine. I had bought the stickiest guest chocolates I had ever seen, wrapped the box of chocolates in butcher paper, and wrote on the outside in Polish: *Merry Christmas and Happy New Year!*

Under my overcoat, unseen by the doorman, I tucked this box carefully under my arm. As I walked around the first corner at the end of the block, I found the ideal location to place my treasure. Behind a large, downspout of over twelve inches wide and four inches deep, I tucked the box with its wrapping on the bracket holding the pipe.

That night, I made one complete circle of the block and came around the second time to find my box of chocolates had disappeared. The KGB had bitten my "bait." I turned around, went back to the front door of the hotel, and laughed myself into a fitful night's sleep. I could visualize the KGB not accepting the pure simplicity of my message of *Merry Christmas and Happy New Year!* They would start with thinking that it was some kind of code, and then they would check every "i" being dotted, suspecting a microdot. When they would come to the conclusion that there was no ulterior motive to the message, they would then in their paranoia begin to dissect each chocolate within the box, looking for microfilm or some kind of espionage communication from the West.

In the morning as I sat at breakfast, the doorman joined me at my table. His eyes were bloodshot; as it was obvious he had not slept the night. When I saw the chocolate under his fingernails and that some had run down between his fingers, it was all I could do to refrain from bursting out laughing over the top of my lukewarm, coffee. His constant inquiry to me was "When are you leaving?" I surprised him and said, "I've enjoyed my stay so much, I have thought of extending my visa." He said something in Polish that I was not used to hearing, hammered the table with his fist and stomped off, leaving a deposit of chocolate on the white linen tablecloth that had been shaken off in the impact of his knuckles.

That morning, I decided to pay the $50.00 fine for an early departure and return to the United Kingdom, because I felt this to be the prompting of the Lord. Little did I know that Sara had passed out several times due to blood loss, and was strongly urged by the doctors in England to abort her tubular pregnancy. She kept delaying the doctors by saying, "Wait until my husband comes." The doctors replied, "It is critical that we remove the child right away. Your life is in jeopardy if you do not respond immediately."

Sara persuaded the doctors to wait one more night. As Pastor Hugh and Iris McGowan paced the floor in prayer for Sara's pain and groaning that they could hear coming from her room, they were interrupted by a phone call from Heathrow Airport. I had landed Wednesday night in a plane filled with Polish people coming to England to celebrate Christmas with their friends and family. Due to the nearness of the holiday, there were no customs officials to help them fill out their landing cards. When I finished assisting the entire planeload in filling out their landing documents, I then made the phone call to the McGowan's.

Stating the hour was late, nearly midnight, and that I would find somewhere to stay in London before traveling up north the next morning, Rev. Hugh McGowan, our British director of Christian Mission Publishers for whom we worked, urged me to get to Rotherham as quickly as I possibly could. All he said was "I have never seen Sara as near to death as she is right now."

I took my Opal Manta Rally Sport out of long-term parking and began to race north on the M-1 Motorway, making my way up to Sheffield and on to Rotherham. This was a little four-cylinder with ram air and specialized cam designed for Autobahn speeds, and so I sustained speeds upwards of 140 miles an hour, hoping to pick up a police escort, but to no avail. What would normally take me three-and-a-half hours in travel time, I trimmed by nearly an hour off my ETA (estimated time of arrival).

Rushing up the steps into the McGowan's home, Hugh and Iris met me at the door and took me to the bedside of my sick wife. Sara laid there pale white, curled up in a fetal position in excruciating pain. Hugh and I laid hands upon her and began to pray. Iris joined us as we cried out to the throne of grace. Just minutes after our gut-wrenching crying to God for His mercy and healing, Sara's groanings ceased and she settled into a deep, restful sleep.

The next morning when Dr. McKenzie examined her, using ultrasound and other devices, he came out of the room scratching his head. He asked us, "Have you been on your knees in prayer?" We asked, "Why?" He said that in all of his medical years of a gynecologist, he had never seen this happen before. He said the child had moved from the fallopian tube on its own accord and attached itself to the uterine wall in a perfectly normal pregnancy. In Dr. McKenzie's own words, "This is a miracle!"

Dr. McKenzie registered the medical report with the miraculous designation in it. With all the difficulties that Sara and I had known, being naturalized citizens of United States of America, we wanted our children to be born on American soil. As Sara was feeling much better, arrangements were made for our return back to Seattle, Washington, to our home. At full term, Sara later gave birth to our first son, Jeremy Joshua Michalski. Then we took the newborn child over to one of our key intercessors in our lives, Sister Martha Dubeck. We rang the doorbell. As she swung the door open, there was no salutation or greeting, but merely a powerful prophecy broke through her lips.

She declared that this son would be a prophet of The Most High and that he would be used mightily of God in his generation. This 86-year-old sage of the church walked in a realm of the Spirit that few people find. As she covered us three times a day in prayer, we tangibly felt the presence of God drop on us as she called on the Name of the Lord Jesus Christ on our behalf.

At the age of 96, Martha Dubeck went home to be with the Lord; her intercessory prayer has been greatly missed. There are few people in one's lifetime that play such a key role of standing in the gap in prayer like the "old saints" who knew how to pray. They called it, "praying through." Sometimes I am frustrated by hearing people pray around their problems or avoid their problems altogether. These saints— distinguished themselves from many others. These prayer warriors like Michael and Nadia Ilyin, Martha Dubeck, my parents, Roman and Olga Michalski, and a host of others—prayed until the problems were shattered and God was glorified. They took hold of the horns of the altar of God and would not let go until God had answered by fire. These are life lessons that many of our younger generation need to learn.

The children came fast and furious after our firstborn. Leah Rachelle Michalski was born 16 months after Jeremy and became our one and only daughter who I kindly refer to as "Princess." Three years later, God gave us Jonathan David Michalski, whom we call our sweet "Singer of Israel." Eighteen months later, Sara was pregnant again with our last precious child, Jason Richard Michalski.

When Sara was four months pregnant with Jason, the doctors urged us to abort him because they said that he would be badly deformed or stillborn. We told Dr. Charles Bell that abortion was not an option to us as believers. We would rather believe for a miracle from our living God in Whom we trust. God heard our prayers and gave us our miracle.

The last two months of Sara's pregnancy with Jason was spent at University Hospital of Seattle where the doctors took the amniotic fluid samples periodically from her womb to diagnose at what level the child development and maturing process was. They used ultrasound each time with this process to make sure the baby would not be punctured in this procedure.

The doctors kept insisting that abortion was the only option. We persisted in praying for the Heavenly option. One day during the procedure, the specialist used a dull spinal needle and punctured too large of a hole in the womb, piercing the amniotic sack and causing the fluid to seep out.

We were in our van on our way to Portland, Oregon, for services when Sara began to seep fluid drastically. We had to turn the van around and went straight to the doctors while Sara was convulsing with pain. They checked her into the hospital where she remained bedfast for the final two months of her pregnancy.

I went on to take one week of services, leaving the children behind with Sara's mother and some of her sisters. We so desperately needed the revenue that I couldn't cancel the three-week itinerary. In just over a week and a half, I cancelled the final ten days and returned to the bedside of my wife.

During one of my frequent visits to Sara's ward, I found she was not in the room, but they had wheeled her to the ultrasound room down the hall. I asked the nurse receptionist where my wife was, she gave me instructions how to get to the ultrasound ward. When I entered the room, the doctors immediately pulled me aside and gave me the bad news. The placenta within Sara's womb had begun to detach itself from the uterine wall. This, of course, is the main supply of nutrients and oxygen to the growing baby.

They said, "Mr. Michalski, in just eight minutes your child will have permanent brain damage due to lack of oxygen. We must abort in order to save your wife's life." I asked the doctors kindly to leave me with my wife for just a few minutes and to close the door behind me. We had been in a similar situation here before with Jeremy, and now we were in need of God's miracle again.

As I reached deep down within my inner being, a groaning in the Holy Spirit broke loose in depths I had never known. As I gently laid my hands upon Sara's stomach, I heard a shriek come from the other room. I had no idea that there was a second monitor for the ultrasound in the adjacent room. Two doctors and a nurse watched as the miracle transpired before their own eyes. The placenta had reattached itself to the uterine wall at the command of the Spirit of our living Savior, Healer and Lord, Jesus Christ.

The doctors and nurses were too shaken to say much to me upon my exit from the room. They sent an orderly to talk to me, assuring me that my wife would be okay. We had gone through such a struggle in those two months. Well-meaning Christians had come to us, telling us to confess our sins and that if I was a real man of faith, my wife would not be in this predicament. In times and seasons like this, a person asks in desperation for the Holy Spirit to cleanse every recess of the soul. But everything we could confess to God had been confessed. Still, they insisted it was our lack of faith that had brought this upon us.

During Sara's two months' stay at the University Hospital of Seattle, she led a Muslim janitor to Jesus Christ and saw him gloriously filled with the Holy Spirit before she left the hospital ward. She led the Unitarian pastor's wife to Christ, saw a marriage reconciled, and led one more roommate to the Lord who calls us once in a while, telling us of her growing faith in Christ as well as that of her husband who was serving God in a local Baptist Church.

We believe the fruit was evident, but we were there by divine appointment. When we left the University Hospital, we owed over $36,000 in medical bills. After paying monthly installments for almost two years, we had worked the bill down to $30,000. When I came in to make that month's installment, the bookkeeping department of the University Hospital asked me why I was there. I told her I came to make a payment on my medical bill. She informed me that it had been paid in full.

When I inquired saying, "By whom?" she replied, "By an anonymous donor." To this day, we are not certain whether one of the doctors paid the bill who was a witness to the miracle or some other benefactor covered the entire amount. I asked for a print out verifying the full payment, and she gladly printed me a copy. You wouldn't believe the joy and laughter that came on Sara's face when I told her that the medical bill had evaporated and that heavy burden was GONE! We jumped for joy, holding hands and rejoicing in Jesus for what He had done.

Our whole life has been a string of miracles because we live with the Miracle Worker, or more accurately, He lives in us; and His Name is Jesus Christ, the Lord God, our Savior and Sovereign.

When Dr. Charles Bell delivered Jason and found him a perfectly healthy, normal baby, he made a vow that he would never commit another abortion unless it was critical to the mother. What might be even more important, Dr. Bell, who delivered all four of our children, received Jesus Christ as his personal Savior.

Sara's sister, Ruth, worked for Dr. Bell for many years as a receptionist and affirmed the commitment he made to Jesus and the vow he had made not to abort children unless the mother's life was in danger.

Our oldest son, Jeremy, met Dr. Bell at a Safeway store many years later, and Dr. Bell mentioned the miracles from the medical reports from Dr. McKenzie from England who had more letters of degree behind his last name than I have in my entire name. The medical report used the word "miracle. What broke Dr. Bell was the eyewitness account of Jason's miraculous healing and birth.

Each of our children has a unique calling on their lives. Before they were born, we sang to them in the womb and read the Word of God. Whenever I would preach during Sara's pregnancy with Jeremy, he would jump for joy. So severe was his jumping that Sara's ribs became bruised and troubled her for two years after her delivery.

Jeremy is called to be a Christian business administrator and enjoys organizing Christian events through the Church, advancing the Kingdom of God. He has also organized our mission's short-term ministry teams that we take to Russia and Ukraine to work in planting churches and with orphanages in these countries.

Leah, our only beautiful daughter is compassion in shoe leather, especially when it comes to children and orphans. There has been many a little child helped, comforted, and blessed by Leah's love and compassion for the little ones. Her burning passion is to build orphanages in Ukraine, Russia and other nations that truly reflect the love of our Heavenly Father.

Jonathan is our sweet Psalmist and a profound teacher of the Word. In Siberia, his teaching of the Word was so anointed that he captured his Russian Bible School audience for hours on end and made it seem like minutes in the presence of the Lord. God has called and gifted him to share Truths from the Word, captivating his audiences, having God transform people's lives for eternity.

Jason is our "fire brand" evangelist that rocks the boat wherever he goes. From the Philippines to the Ukraine, from Africa to North America, there is a trail of testimonies of God's saving grace and miraculous healings wherever he has gone in God. God's calling in his life for nations is being fulfilled by the power of the Holy Spirit with signs and wonders.

We have always asked God for only two things: that our children would serve the Lord and that they would be healthy. God has more than abundantly answered our prayers with many tens of thousands of souls in numerous lands being affected by their ministries. How faithful our Lord and Savior is to complete that which He has begun in us, even unto the Day of the Lord.

We have been blessed with three Christian daughter-in-laws who love God and have already graced us with one grandchild, Grace Elizabeth Michalski and prayerfully, others on their way. We are just asking our other children to get with the program and give us tons of grandchildren! They are a lot more fun than your own kids; you can spoil them and leave the consequences with their parents. It's God's way of retribution with your children for all the trouble they have caused you in their growing years and adolescence.

We are trusting God that not only our children and their spouses, but also all the grandchildren, and great grandchildren will be mightily used by the hand of the Lord as a fifth generation redeemed, walking before Christ in faith and in the fear of the Lord, leading many to the saving knowledge of the Lord.

Chapter Twenty-Nine
MISSIONS IMPOSSIBLE

"Now Lord, look on their threats and grant to Your servants that with all boldness that they may speak Your word by stretching out Your hand to heal and that signs and wonders may be done through the name of Your holy Servant, Jesus." (Acts 4:29-30)

Due to the overwhelming waves of God's faithfulness, our minds would often drift back on the tides of reflection. Sometimes this flood of memories took us back years to milestones of God's mercy. One of these moments that stands out in our minds happened early in our years of ministry to the Iron Curtain.

A lot of the renovation work on many of our vehicles was done at the Neugraben Christian Fellowship in Hamburg, Germany. Its team of mechanics and tools provided an invaluable help in modifying stock vehicles into Bible courier transporters. The greatest help from the Neugraben Fellowship was not that of the mechanical assistance or even their sacrificial financial giving, but that of the pure prophetic word that we heard in their midst.

I don't think Sara and I have known any other fellowship that had been blessed with so many mature gifts of the prophetic in their ranks. Names, addresses, cities, times of departure and border crossings were not a mystery to God. Our Lord Jesus Christ through the Holy Spirit would give us clear directions through His saints. As the Neugraben Church family would fast and pray with us in preparation for our next assignment, the Lord would through the prophetic of the Holy Spirit often answer the deep inquiries of our heart.

This next mission would be no different. This time there came a warning from the Lord that all of our Bibles would be confiscated. Another sister in Christ saw a prophetic vision of a nail-scarred hand reaching down and taking the Bibles out of our control and distributing them to the points of greatest needs in Russia.

With this austere warning in mind, Sara and I both agreed that we would not take any Bibles on this particular run. We couldn't imagine the precious "loaves of the Living Bread" of God's Word being taken from us. What made it doubly horrifying to our hearts was the fact that often we heard that Soviet guards burn the Bibles they confiscate. On other occasions, the confiscations of God's Word would be taken and sold on the black market in Russia. In either case, the outcome was unacceptable as the hunger for God's Word was so acute at that time.

Sara and I switched gears in our thinking and decided logically that if the Bibles would be confiscated, the simple solution would be not to take any Bibles on this trip into the Soviet Block. We would merely collect finances to leave the impoverished Christian families whose breadwinners had been placed in prison for their Christian faith. It was a cardinal rule that one never takes money and Bibles on the same trip; for if they were confiscated, the authorities would have an open and shut case against them for selling contraband to the Soviet public.

This provided an even clearer determination to only take our personal Bibles. The task at hand was that we desperately needed hard currency from the West to help the persecuted church. In some instances, a one-year's earnings fine was placed against believers for teaching their children in the ways of God. In other cases, parents were placed into labor camps, separated from loved ones and family for years, leaving Christian families behind void of all support. Other Christians that would try to help them would in turn be heavily fined themselves.

Funds from the West were a crucial lifeline, especially to the unregistered church and its embattled leadership. Our hearts were made up and our plan was set, but we had not considered that God's ways are higher than our ways and that He rules in the affairs of men and nations.

A grandmother and grandfather in the faith near the Russian border became our frequent stopover point before piercing the inner chambers of the Iron Curtain. Their faith and joy in the Lord disguised their eighty-plus years of age. Like young kids, they delighted in their calling in God. Shortly after their printing, every new edition of Scripture, concordance, and hymnbook found their way into this couple's house as a staging area before being bridged into the U.S.S.R.

Upon first meeting this wonderful couple, their house tradition was to drop on their knees and pray with their guests. We as family had done this many times with them before. However, on this occasion after a season of prayer, they asked us a burning question. "How many Bibles are you taking on this run?" With the backdrop of the prophetic ringing in our ears that we had just heard at Neugraben some days before, we told this couple in sheepish terms, "None."

Their look of amazement was as though someone had doused them with ice water. They repeated the words in questioning tones: "None?" to which we responded, "No, we are just taking our personal Bibles." Now it was our turn to be shocked when they both responded by saying that if we did not take Bibles to help the Christians in Russia, we would be sinning. They said the Scripture in James 4:17 to us: "...to him who knows to do good and does not do it, to him it is sin." We didn't want to be sinning, so we surrendered to their constant urging and let them put a few Bibles in our car.

That night as we slept, this precious elderly couple worked with the zeal of the Lord because their version of a "few" and our version of a "few" were two completely different things! At morning light after prayer and breakfast, we took our overnight bags out to our car, which was showing distinct signs of sagging under its heavy load.

With already several visits to Russia under our belt, in our youthful zeal we thought of ourselves as veterans. Nothing, however, could totally prepare us for the surprise attacks the devil throws against those that defy his kingdom. Picking up a load of Bibles in Poland one more time with hearts prepared by intercession, we were ready again to pierce the Iron Curtain.

Our Opal Rekord (German GM vehicle) was loaded to the gills. Special air shocks had been previously installed to stabilize the back end from dragging. However, this load was extremely heavy; and despite the air shocks, the rear tires definitely revealed the reality of the excess weight.

The Polish couple's final word to us was "Until we meet at the throne of grace, before the feet of our Lord and Savior, Jesus Christ. He is faithful and we will be praying for you." Little did we know then, but those would be their final words ever to us before we meet them again in Heaven. As we drove off, more accurately limped off, I thought to myself sarcastically, "Yeah, you can be praying for us, but you're at home here in Poland with minimal risk, and it's us that are putting our lives on the line."

We were told on the outskirts of Pszemysl to pick up one of our Bible couriers who would take us right up to the Russian border and then, from a distance behind the low shrubs, observe our entrance all the while covering us in prayer. Our courier had to shove Bibles over on the back seat to make room for him to sit; and now with his additional body weight, it meant every rut in the road provided an occasion for the tires to rub inside the wheel wells.

Although it was early in the morning, an eerie fog had settled over the hilly terrain approaching the border. Our immediate thought was, "*this fog was Heaven's way of camouflaging us.*" This valley was often filled with seasonal fog in the shallow trench, housing the road to the city of Brest, Belarus.

With the border crossing in view, we slowed down some two or three hundred meters from "no man's land" without coming to a full stop. We heard our courier open the back door and roll out into the grassy ditch covered with occasional large green shrubs. In one smooth action, he vacated our vehicle and slammed the door shut, whereupon we began to accelerate once again.

The courier had used the shrub covering to hide himself from the ever-searching field glasses that were issued to the guards in the towers before us. He would remain there watching and praying as we proceeded into the lions' den. Every trip was different. We never quite got rid of the butterflies that seemed to fill our stomachs.

These natural fears and reservations helped us reach deeper into God; and as if on cue, Sara and I both began to speak in tongues. Praying in the Spirit does two things simultaneously: It builds up the spiritual man, and the spirit prays not after the will of man, but after the will of our Heavenly Father. If it wasn't for this gracious gift from Heaven, I am sure we would have burned out long before.

We entered the first outer perimeter, and a gate locked behind us as we proceeded toward the guard booth. Just in front of the hood of our car, a young uniformed officer stepped out, commanding us to stop. With our window rolled down, he demanded to see our passports and visas. As he took both of our passports and separate visa slips into the booth, he was out of sight for what seemed to be more than half an hour. In actual fact, it was more like ten to fifteen minutes.

The young officer marched up to our car, returned our passports and visas, and with a salute, commanded us to go on. In less than fifty yards, a secondary gate closed behind us, and this time two officers with a police dog on a short leash came toward our vehicle. Passports and visas were asked for a second time as the dogs circled the car smelling for drugs. We were waved on after some time to a third gated area where several cars before us had been partially dismantled by the young customs team.

Our knees like Belshazzar's, once again began to have "fellowship one with another" because of our nervous tension. There was no time to pray now. We had to trust God that our relationship with Him was deep enough to endure the trial of the hour.

Several members of the customs team approached our vehicle, demanding we exit the car and sit on the nearby bench. They thoroughly went through our vehicle, poking the upholstery with a long heavy-gauge wire, looking in the glove box, under the seats, under the hood, and then they opened the trunk.

It was as though God had blinded their eyes. We had seen this happen many times before, and its mystery never seemed mundane.

Seeing eyes could not see; trained inspectors saw open boxes before them, but seemingly they were blinded to the fact that each of the open boxes was filled with *Svyataya Bibliya* (Holy Bibles).

The back seat of the car and part of the floor boards were covered with Bibles without boxes. The only thing that was enclosed on the seat of the car was two small personal overnight cases which had all of our clothing and toiletries for the short trip into Russia.

Sara reached out, grasped my hand, and squeezed. Without saying a word, our eyes met, and we realized God had delivered us from "round one" of this multi-bout battle with Satan's servants. A third examination of our passports and visas and a second team of customs officers re-examined our car. We had survived "round two." At this moment, we were quite confident that somebody was interceding for us in the West and that God was giving us a repeat performance of His grace and mercies in the blinding of these guards.

At the commencement of "round three," the young officer who was part of the first search stood there with a perplexed look on his face. In a gruff voice, he demanded us to come from the bench and explain what "these" were. As we made our way to the trunk area of the vehicle, he pulled out a Bible in his hand, reading the cover, "*Svyataya Bibliya*" out loud.

In an instant fit of rage, he flung the Bible to the ground. His gesture invoked an immediate response from Sara, saying, "Yes, that is the Holy Bible, and it must be the most powerful book in the world because you can't even hold it in your hands for a few seconds." The veins in the officers neck stood out as his face turned flaming red with fury. He yelled for his subordinates nearby to come to his assistance.

With his barked orders, one officer took Sara by the arm, shouldering his *Kalashnikov* on the opposite shoulder. Two officers took me in a different direction. We would not see each other again for eight hours.

At one end of the interrogation ward sat an officer behind what looked like an old oak school desk. The interrogation ward smelled foul with cigarette smoke and urine. Sara's one arresting officer was now joined by a second subordinate officer with a superior officer seated, hands folded across his chest. Sara, being the weaker vessel, was preyed upon at the level of her emotions.

The superior officer began his interrogations by stating, "Your car and personal belongings have been removed to a detonating area. You are looking at a minimum of ten years in prison at a hard labor camp. You will be all alone, and you will not see your husband again." Somehow, the issue of motive came into play and the interrogating officer asked Sara point-blank, "Why did you do this?" The unction of the Holy Spirit now came upon Sara in a whole new dynamic and dimension. She replied, "Every man should be given a chance to choose faith in God or absence of faith. In your country that does not allow the choice, we are simply delivering God's Word, the Bibles, to help your people in the decision-making process. Besides that, the Word of God declares that *"We will all be directly judged by God; and in that day, every knee will bow and every tongue will confess that Jesus Christ is Lord to the glory of God the Father."*

The head interrogator yelled back with a retort, "But there is no God! If there is a God, His children are confused because they adhere to so many religions." Sara responded by declaring, "Religion has never saved anyone. It is only when we have a personal relationship with our God through His Son, Jesus Christ that we can come into the knowledge of His mercy."

With that declaration still lingering in the air, the officer stood up from his chair to his full height. He towered over Sara's slight five-foot-two frame. He must have weighed in excess of over 300 lbs. His large arms and barrel chest showed that he had been a body builder for many years. Anger now etched the lines of his face. Out of tightly pressed lips and eyes full of Satan's dancing delight, the words roared out from his angry soul: "In that judgment day, I will ring Christ's neck!" Sara reiterated, *"Every knee will bow and EVERY tongue will confess that Jesus is Lord."* "You won't be able to touch Christ, but you will be bowing in the dust before Him." That triggered a rush of demonic rage as the man pulled back his right arm ready to plow it into Sara's face. As he began to throw his furious punch as hard as he could, the authority of Heaven came upon Sara. Like a lightning bolt, a boldness that was not her own took over this situation as Sara declared, "In the Name of Jesus Christ, I command you to stop!"

As the officer's fist began to hammer down on her face, it was not able to hit its mark. Instead, his arm and hand went paralyzed in mid-flight just inches away. Now with terror on his own face, Sergey, the head interrogator, attempted to speak, but God had denied him of that power. The two subordinate officers in the room kept on yelling, "Sergey, what's wrong? Hit her hard!" However, Sergey was not able to respond or answer verbally. God had once again intervened because someone out there had covered us in intercessory prayer.

"Now when they bring you to the synagogues and magistrates and authorities, do not worry about how or what you should answer or what you should say, for the Holy Spirit will teach you in that very hour what you ought to say." (Luke 12:11-12)

An explosion of scriptures cascaded into Sara's mind and flowed like a stream out of her mouth. The selection of the Word God had quickened to Sara dealt with salvation and the cross. The barrage of Scripture after Scripture finally abated, then ceased after nearly half an hour.

The interrogators in that room stood paralyzed, both physically and spiritually. For the first time perhaps in a lifetime, they had heard the declared message of the power of God to save. Truly the word of God is sure and faithful in saying, *"He will put a word in your mouth in that day, and it will shut the gainsayers' mouths."* Silenced were the agnostics and the atheistic babblings of those that did not have a personal relationship with God. Filling that room was the glory of God in His majesty and power.

The Lord spoke clearly to Sara's heart to pray for her interrogators, stating, "God will heal you when I pray, to show His great mercy for you and His eternal desire to see you repent and accept Christ as your Savior." Just a few words into Sara's prayer, Sergey's paralyzed hand fell limp to his side, with total mobility restored. His mouth opened; and with a strong commanding voice, he summarily dismissed the two subordinate officers from the interrogation ward.

With the door being shut after the exit of the last officer, Sergey fell back into his chair, his hands on his face, with elbows resting on the desk. He began sobbing like a little child and began to unveil the story of his heart and life. He was merely eight years of age when his father was taken to prison for his faith in Christ. His mother had been verbally warned by the KGB not to instruct her children in the Bible. An unsaved neighbor had informed the KGB that this interrogator's mother had continued to teach her children the Word of God and prayed with them every night. As a good mother, she taught the children well, knowing her relationship with Christ was the key to their lives and eternity to come.

One morning without warning, with their black-paneled van with no windows, the KGB pulled up to the little house in the farming village where Sergey and his mother lived. Sergey's mother, holding Sergey by the hand, met the KGB officers on their front porch. As the KGB ranted and raved, they began to rip Sergey out of his mother's grasp. The mother tenaciously held onto her son until her weakened arms could no longer hold her child from the pull of the three officers standing before her.

As they carried off Sergey, he heard his mother's words: "I will pray for you every day of my life. I will pray for your salvation!" Those were the final words that Sergey remembered since he was not allowed to see his mother for almost thirty years.

Until his eighteenth birthday, Sergey was moved from one foster home to another. All of the homes were decidedly atheistic, and so Sergey grew up an atheist, a loyal communist—and now the head interrogator at the Brest border.

Through the tear-stained fingers of his hands on his face, Sergey spoke to Sara, stating that the Scriptures she had used about salvation were the same Scriptures that he had heard out of the mouth of his mother many years prior. He went on to say that there was nothing he could do with the court proceedings that would follow this interrogation.

Sergey promised to take the Bibles from us and deliver them to the village of his mother. We had heard promises from atheists before and were extremely skeptical that he would follow through on his word. After all, with no God to give account to on their part, lying and deception were the norm in many agnostic and atheistic hearts. This was part of their nature as lost souls separated from God and His laws. Shortly after this encounter, they released Sara and she walked down a long corridor to join me in a room adjacent to the judge's chamber.

Chapter Thirty
THE CHAINS OF BONDAGE BROKEN

My interrogators had used a different approach with me. They used a softer touch, thinking it would be the best approach to open me up and have me respond to their interrogations. When they asked a question, I gave the same answers Sara was giving her interrogators over a hundred yards away at the opposite end of the building. In separate interrogation wards, they asked, "Who sent you?" Our joint answer was "Jesus Christ."

They continued to ask, "Where did you get the Russian Bibles?" Our answer was "From the sacrificial giving of God's people in the West."

"Give us names and addresses of your accomplices." We replied, "We don't know any names, as these Bibles are destined to those in greatest need of the Word." This infuriated the interrogators.

Then my interrogators surprised me, giving me six sheets of tan-pulp paper. They then told me to write on that paper every grievance that I had against the Soviet government and communism. I heard the voice of God speaking to my spirit, saying, "Answer them with the Word."

I carefully used both sides of the six sheets of paper. Starting from Genesis, I worked my way through to Revelation, giving every key Scripture I could remember on salvation through our Lord Jesus Christ. A flood of Scriptures that I had not memorized, but had read many times in the past, were now spilling into my spirit as I filled page after page with salvation references.

My head interrogator considered himself a man of great authority, but he was not able to resist the heavy anointing that was deposited on me during my hours of interrogation. As I was writing my lengthy dissertation, the man in charge nervously lit a cigarette to calm himself. The smoke in the small, smelly room immediately got my attention. Lifting my head and eyes from the task of writing, I saw the man in charge light a second cigarette, but his shaking and trembling would not cease. Of all the training that these professional interrogators had received, nothing prepared them for encountering the heavy presence and power of God, which they were told did not exist.

When my interrogator lit his third cigarette, as he shook like a leaf in a violent wind, I asked him kindly, "You already have one cigarette in each hand. Where will you place the third one?" Unable to give me a reasonable answer, he crushed all three cigarettes on a musty old ashtray on the nearby table.

As I continued to write, there was an uneasy silence in the room as the cat-and-mouse game had ended with the mouse chasing the cat; for in God, giants still topple, kingdoms are still shaken, and the Lord is glorified in the earth. Our God has all power and authority in Heaven and in the earth. Through His Word and the salvation of Christ's blood, He gives his children the power of attorney to speak in the full authority of His Name. Demons tremble, and the kingdom of darkness languishes in fear and pain at the power of the Name of Jesus Christ, Who rose with the keys of death and hell and gives His gifts unto the sons of men.

I wrote every Scripture on salvation I could possibly think of—every single text that would lead them to Calvary and make them understand the cost of the cross, and then turned around and signed the grievance papers: *Your loving brother in Jesus Christ.* Where these papers would end up, how many officers had to clear this paperwork, and how many times that it must be read before it is finally thrown away, God alone knows; but the Word being the Word will not return void; it will bear fruit. The Word bears forth 30-, 60-, or 100-fold return in this life and in the life to come.

As Sara and I met in the room before the judge's chamber, we united for a few minutes after the ordeal of more than eight hours of interrogation. Behind closed doors, the prosecutors had an open-and-shut case against us due to the sure volume of the Bibles that we had carried. This "kangaroo court" did not allow us into the same room of our own trial to say even one word in defense for our case.

What seemed to me like an eternity, later, more realistically was only about two hours, ended with the doors of the judge's chambers suddenly bursting open. The judge in his black robe was followed by a procession of court officials. In the two hours we waited for the verdict of our trial, Sara and I held hands together, quietly praying in the Holy Spirit.

Little did we realize that ten time zones away in Redmond, Washington, on a Sunday morning, our pastor, Richard Strum had stopped the proceedings of the worship and praise service and had announced with a strong declaration to his congregation that Richard and Sara were in trouble. "Let's pray for them now," he said, and some five hundred people stood up and joined him and prayed until they felt the burden lift. We were members of this church for almost twenty-five years.

At that same moment, ten time zones away, the Judge stood before us and said, "We don't understand why we feel lenient towards your case, but you are free to go." What a contrast from what we were told before the trial began that we were looking at ten years in prison in separate hard labor camps, accusing us of espionage! Now the words rang like a bell in the hearing of our hearts: "We don't understand why, but you are free to go!"

That last phrase, *"free to go!"* echoed in our minds and spirits. We knew why we had been released. Somebody had covered us in prayer, and we had received the benefits of hundreds of people simultaneously agreeing in intercession, bombarding the gates of Heaven on our behalf. We had the sensation of goose bumps racing down our spine, going north and south at the same time, colliding in the middle, electrifying our hands to the very fingertips. The hair on my arms stood on end. Prayer is tangible, and when you are on the receiving end of prayer from hearts that are unified, it's one of the most awesome experiences in the world.

We urge you to use every occasion when someone's name or face comes into your remembrance, to respond to the prompting of the Holy Spirit. Immediately drop everything you are doing and pray for that individual until the burden of the Lord is lifted from your spirit. You, like the congregation in Redmond, can be the catalyst of change that spares that individual's life and gives him or her God's mercy and grace in their time of trouble.

We were released that night with our car emptied of its cargo and returned to the Polish frontier. When the Polish officers saw the name Michalski on the passport, they in unison declared, "You're one of us. You're Polish?" They then asked me why the Soviets had expelled us. We told them that we were caught taking Bibles into Russia. They answered, "If there are any pagans that need the Bibles, it's definitely the Soviets!"

Without hesitation, these officers prepared a 48-hour transit visa for us that we could use easily for exiting Poland in a two-day timeframe. However, halfway across Poland, it dawned on Sara and me that we were in trouble because we had returned during a Catholic holiday in Poland. All the gas stations were closed.

We limped into the city of Legnica, where we knew the pastor who is an awesome man of God. Pastor Mankowski had suffered greatly for the cause of Christ under the Soviet occupation just after World War II. His persecution had given him a most tender spirit for people in need. He graciously offered us the pulpit the night of our arrival.

An elder in Pastor Mankowski's church was an instrument of God's grace, as he had been saving his gasoline coupons and purchasing extra fuel over the last six months. At the close of the service, he approached Sara and me and said, "The Lord told me to fill your tank." Our car was parked behind the church courtyard. In all our years of ministry in Poland up until that time, we had filled many other pastors' tanks with fuel, but no one was capable of filling ours. Due to the heavy rationing of fuel and its extreme cost, this young elder had made a deep sacrifice in order to obey the Lord.

The equivalent of several five-gallon "jerry cans" and a large Polish funnel would complete the task, and our tank was filled to the brim. It became a miracle tank of fuel. It took us to the Polish border and across the entire nation of East Germany. Without skipping a beat our miracle fuel took us all the way down to the Munich area in southern Germany. Here, it sputtered its last vapors of fuel in front of the home of Al and Carol Akimoff, directors of Youth With A Mission in that region.

A similar run of the same vehicle had consumed two tanks of gas, but God stretched out every cell in this gas composition by the touch of His miraculous hand until we arrived at the safe harbor of friends and family in the faith.

In the basement of Al and Carolyn's home, we collapsed in utter exhaustion. The weariness that we were experiencing was more than just the fact that we had not had an entire night's sleep, but the emotions of our hearts drained us further. I cried out to God, saying, "Lord, we failed You!" Sara had voiced that already in the car on the way, sobbing before the Lord, saying, "Lord, we have failed you. Our Bibles were confiscated; we did not make it in to deliver the Word of God to Your people. Lord, we are utter failures!"

However, we did not allow the devil to discourage us or stop the work God had called us to do. We continued to believe God to use us for His glory and for His kingdom in reaching the lost for Christ. We continued taking Bibles into the former Soviet Union through other border crossings as the hunger for the Word was so great.

It was about two years later, following multiple entries into the Soviet Union, before we dared venture across the border of Brest (now in Belarus). The chilling memories of our arrest at this location some years before still haunted our minds. We had come into Moldavia (new Republic of Moldova) into the Ukraine, cutting through the corner of Belarus, exiting out from the Brest border to Poland. While awaiting our exit procedure we were stopped by the officer, Sergey, Sara's interrogator. When we were dismissed from our vehicle, he ran toward us, embracing me, and asking Sara and me with his hand covering his mouth for fear of the border tower reading his lips, "Are you still doing a good work for Him?"

Both Sara and I replied to this officer: "Better than ever in the Name of our Lord Jesus Christ." We had never ever had a Soviet officer embrace us in the past. Beatings, yes, but never have Soviet officers embrace us. With his hands still covering his mouth, the officer said, "I am one of you." We responded by saying, "One of who?" Sergey gave us additional information, stating that he had taken all the Bibles which had been confiscated two years before. Shortly after our previous interrogation, Sergey was given a permit to visit his mother after not seeing her for thirty years. He was true to his word as he delivered all the Scriptures to his mother's village and region which, by this time, was being evangelized.

Sergey stated that he had never seen such spiritual hunger for the Word of God as he did in this community. The Bible quantity that we tried to bring in was sufficient for that village as well as the neighboring villages where each Christian family had received one Bible per family. He responded by telling us, "When I saw how these people hugged and kissed the Bibles, I was overwhelmed, and how, oh HOW they cherished the Word! This experience changed my life forever." He couldn't sleep that night even though he was in his own home visiting his beloved mother whom he had not seen all these years.

The scenes of tears and gladness at the reception of God's Word filled Sergey's troubled mind until he cried out to Jesus Christ for His mercy. That night, the Lord had answered a mother's daily prayer of thirty years when her prodigal son had come home—not home to her house, but "home" to the arms of Jesus Christ, the Savior of his soul.

Sergey, our former interrogator, became our greatest Bible courier. He submitted his work schedule to our teams in Poland, allowing us to drive vanloads of Bibles into the former Soviet Union. After our relationship was established with him, it began to be truckloads of Bibles; and even at times, train loads would be released under his covering and care. His authority level had been increased at the border, and no one questioned the commander when "contraband" in the form of Scripture or Bibles was found. We have no idea of how many hundreds of thousands of Bibles bridged into the Soviet Union were a direct result of his working with us. Little did we realize what an instrument in the hand of God this man would be; what a role of fulfillment this man would have in bridging one of the most difficult borders into the heart of Russia with the Word of God?

The vision from Neugraben came with a whole new clarity. The Bibles would be taken out of our control and by a "nail-printed hand" distributed to places where we could not go. The Scriptures would be distributed where the need was most acute. For two years, we had felt we had failed God in having this initial load of Bibles confiscated. Truly, God's ways are higher than our ways; they are as lofty as the heavens are above the earth, and even the foolishness of God is wiser than men.

Chapter Thirty-One
HEARING THE VOICE OF GOD

S ome years later, brother Sergey, the border commander and a co-labor in Christ rendezvoused with us and our small team at a border crossing train station. He had lost a lot of weight and lost hair as we all had over the years, but he said to us, "Do you remember me?" Now no longer having a beard, it was hard to recognize him. We had not seen him for many years as we were moving Scriptures through other frontiers and had released our connection with Sergey to other couriers. He said, "I am the officer whose hand was paralyzed." We responded, "Yes, we do remember that incident very well." He said, "Not only am I still your brother in Christ, I am a pastor of a church of over 1,500 believers."

Little was realized so many years before in the intensity and the heat of the interrogation, how God would use this Saul and turn him into a Paul. God still effects total transformation in the hearts of those who surrender to him.

Then He who sat on the throne said, *"Behold, I make all things new."*(Revelation 21:5)

By the grace of God, we still are being changed into new creations in Christ, with an instantaneous new birth and then the glorious process of sanctification, the separation from the world, and separation unto God. We are transformed more and more into the image of Jesus Christ.

God is still stretching forth His arm across the nations and across the generations. He reaches out to people who, in their blindness and in their hardness and confusion, cry out in desperation to Him. He hears and heeds that cry. The word of God says that in the last day

"...if you confess with your mouth the Lord Jesus and believe in your heart that God has raised Him from the dead, you will be saved. For with the heart one believes to righteousness, and with the mouth confession is made to salvation. For the Scripture says, 'whoever believes on Him will not be put to shame.' For there is no distinction between Jew and Greek, for the same Lord over all is rich to all who call upon Him. For 'whoever calls upon the name of the Lord shall be saved'" (Romans 10: 9-13).

What a high honor for us mere mortals of clay that we can communicate with the Creator of the Universe! He Who formed the galaxies with the mere word of His mouth, Who made all the species of animals and plants, each to produce after their own kind, and finally the pinnacle of His creation—*mankind*, made in His image and after His likeness so He can commune with His creation. Why would the God of the Universe condescend in the form of a man and in the person of Jesus Christ to live among us, die on the cross for us, be raised from the dead the third day, and be caught up in the heavens to be seated at God's right hand, ever to make intercession for us? Why would this same Creator and Savior, Jesus Christ, love us so much that He invites us into His courts via prayer? Is it perhaps that God is trying to restore the fellowship He had with Adam and Eve in the garden, but due to our fallen nature in sin, we are separated from God and need the blood covenant of Christ's cross to restore the position we've lost?

God desires to hear us when we pray. He also desires that we hear Him when He answers our prayers.

"For if our heart condemns us, God is greater than our heart, and knows all things. Beloved, if our heart does not condemn us, we have confidence toward God. And whatever we ask we receive from Him, because we keep His commandments and do those things that are pleasing in His sight. And this is His commandment: that we should believe on the name of His Son Jesus Christ and love one another, as He gave us commandment." (1 John 3: 20-23)

From this passage, we come to the understanding that hearing from God is in direct proportion to our heart's condition. If our heart does not condemn us because we are washed by the blood of Jesus Christ, we enter His throne room with confidence, clothed not in our own righteousness, but the righteousness of His Son Who redeemed us unto God by the blood of His cross.

If we walk in obedience to God's commands, then we have confidence that He hears us when we pray; and if we know He hears us when we pray, then we have the petition that we desire from Him. All that remains for us to do is worship Jesus Christ until the answer to our prayers is manifested.

Our sins have separated us from God. As the prophet Jeremiah said, *"The heart is deceitful above all things, and desperately wicked. Who can know it?"* (Jer. 17:9). The purging of our conscience and the cleansing of our heart can only be accomplished through Calvary.

If you are reading this book, my friend, and have never called upon Jesus Christ the Lord to have a personal relationship with Him, for the transformation by His blood washing away your sin; this is your moment, this is your day, and this is your opportunity to call upon the name of the Lord. Tell Jesus that you are a sinner in need of forgiveness. Tell Him that you need a Savior, a Lord that is able to change your life from the inside out. It is not a matter of turning over a new leaf. It is not a matter of pulling yourself up by the bootstraps. It is not a matter of vain self-effort. Jesus Christ can take the hardest and the vilest and those that have been atheists for years. He also takes the proud and the self-righteous who put their trust in their deeds or in their religion and commands to us one and all that *"You must be born again."* There is only one name given under Heaven that brings us salvation. Call on the Name of the Lord Jesus Christ. His Word says, *"that all those that come unto Him, He will not cast away"*(John 6:37).

* * *

Sara and I are living in the next chapters of an unwritten book. It is our personal venture of faith. We would like to thank every intercessor that has partnered with us in fervent prayer and finances in missions. Your obedience in Christ was the catalyst for the miracles in this book. The dimensions of your investments will be realized only in eternity. By the grace of God, we are still distributing Scriptures and Bibles to lands that forbid them. Impact Ministries continues to be a planter of churches as beacons of light in nations of darkness.

Through churches and conferences, we are seeing the balm of Gilead released. Jesus is our Lord and Savior, mighty to save and heal the sick and the infirm.

We would be remiss as a ministry if we did not in our sphere of witness touch the elderly, shut-ins, and orphans among the nations. This vital aspect of **IMPACT MINISTRIES** uses the indigenous local church to partner with us as they are most completely aware of the genuine needs of their region. Food, medical supplies, and hygiene kits are part of Impact Ministries' outreach to the **Former Soviet Union and its Republics** for more than forty years.

If you would like to partner with us, we need monthly support to help us continue the work of our calling. If God hasn't called you to be a monthly partner through your prayers and through your giving, perhaps you will consider making a targeted contribution to **IMPACT MINISTRIES** to advance the cause of Christ among the nations of our calling.

We look forward to hearing from you. If God is prompting you to have a part, please obey His voice and do what He is releasing you to do. You can contact us via mail or email, and you can also contribute online through our website.

Your friends and fellow servants in ministry and missions,

Richard and Sara Michalski

NOTE: With multiplied hundreds of families, each saw the events of this book through their own eyes and from their own perspective. Like the four Gospels, which often relate the same events but with different detailing in accordance with their personal emphasis, so this book represents only the transcripts of Michael and Nadejda Ilyin as they recollect the events as viewed through their eyes. To the best of their memory, the dates and events are accurate, but other individuals may have viewed the fulfillment of these occurrences with a slightly different perspective and time frame. Some of the detailing and accuracy of the years as well as the time lines may have faded somewhat. Each of these families could and should write their own story from their own perspective, but we have written the story to give glory to God as He led our parents from 'Bondage to Freedom.'

IMPACT MINISTRIES
P.O. BOX 2500
REDMOND, WA 98073-2500
U.S.A.

Email:impactmini@aol.com
Phone: (425) 882-0761
Fax: (425) 881-1851
Website: www.impactmin.org
Face book: Sara Michalski
Twitter: Impact Ministries

"Once again Thomas Greanias takes the Atlantis mythology and ties it to events stripped from today's headlines. LIGHTNING-PACED, DAGGER-SHARP, AND BRILLIANTLY EXECUTED, *The Atlantis Revelation* made me gasp out loud."

—James Rollins, *New York Times* bestselling
author of *Altar of Eden*

"A PEDAL-TO-THE-METAL thriller that combines good old-fashioned suspense with THROAT-GRABBING TWISTS.... Marvelous."

—Steve Berry, *New York Times* bestselling
author of *The Paris Vendetta*

The truth is *down* there . . .

RAISING ATLANTIS

A *New York Times* and *USA Today* bestseller and
#1 bestselling eBook

"A ROLLER COASTER THAT WILL CAPTIVATE READERS OF DAN BROWN AND MICHAEL CRICHTON, penetrating one of the biggest mysteries of our time."

—*The Washington Post*

"IT'S A LOT LIKE *THE DA VINCI CODE*, BUT I LIKE THE ENDING ON THIS ONE BETTER.... A gripping page-turner."

—Sandra Hughes, CBS News

"AN ENCHANTING STORY with an incredible pace."

—*The Boston Globe*

Also by Thomas Greanias

The Atlantis Prophecy
Raising Atlantis

THE
ATLANTIS
REVELATION

THOMAS
GREANIAS

POCKET BOOKS

New York   London   Toronto   Sydney

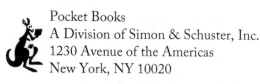

Pocket Books
A Division of Simon & Schuster, Inc.
1230 Avenue of the Americas
New York, NY 10020

This book is a work of fiction. Names, characters, places, and incidents either are products of the author's imagination or are used fictitiously. Any resemblance to actual events or locales or persons, living or dead, is entirely coincidental.

First Pocket Books paperback edition June 2010

POCKET and colophon are registered trademarks of Simon & Schuster, Inc.

For information about special discounts for bulk purchases, please contact Simon & Schuster Special Sales at 1-866-506-1949 or business@simonandschuster.com.

The Simon & Schuster Speakers Bureau can bring authors to your live event. For more information or to book an event, contact the Simon & Schuster Speakers Bureau at 1-866-248-3049 or visit our website at www.simonspeakers.com.

Cover design by Erik Hollander, HollanderDesignLab.com

Manufactured in the United States of America

10 9 8 7 6 5 4 3 2 1

ISBN 978-1-4767-8887-6
ISBN 978-1-4165-9746-9 (ebook)

Once again, for Laura

A river watering the garden flowed from Eden. . . .
And the LORD God said, "The man has now become
like one of us, knowing good and evil. He must not
be allowed to reach out his hand and take also from
the tree of life and eat, and live forever." So the
LORD God banished him from the Garden of Eden
to work the ground from which he had been taken.
After he drove the man out, he placed on the east
side of the Garden of Eden cherubim and a flaming
sword flashing back and forth to guard the way to
the tree of life.

—Genesis 2:10, 3:22–24

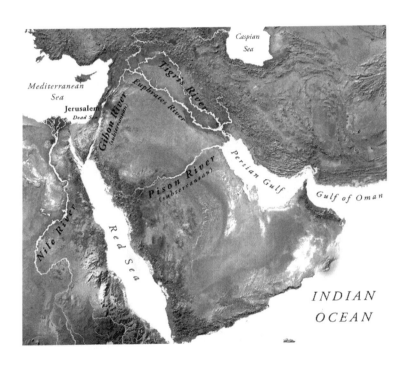

Caspian
Sea

Mediterranean
Sea

Tigris River

Euphrates River

Jerusalem
Dead S

Gihon River
(subterranean)

Pison River
(subterranean)

Persian Gulf

Gulf of Oman

Nile River

Red Sea

INDIAN
OCEAN

PART ONE

Corfu

1

The Calypso Deep
Ionian Sea

Conrad Yeats started having second thoughts as soon as they anchored the fishing boat *Katrina* over the discovery.

It wasn't just that he hated the water. Or that it was three miles to the bottom at the deepest part of the Mediterranean. Or that his Greek crew believed these waters were cursed. It was the words of a former U.S. secretary of defense warning that what Conrad sought didn't exist, but if it did, he was not to disturb it or else. *Maybe it's time you gave it a rest, son, and let the damned past rust in peace.*

But he had come too far on his journey to recover a real-world relic from the mythological lost continent of Atlantis to turn back now. And he would never rest until he found out exactly what kind of damned past everyone would just as soon bury simply because it threatened their own vision of the future.

Conrad pulled the black neoprene wet suit over his

shoulders and looked over at Stavros, his diving attendant. The big, strapping Greek had hauled up the sonar towfish that a team of sidescan sonar experts from the exploration ship had used to get a fix on the target only hours ago. Now he was fiddling with Conrad's air compressor.

"You finally fix that thing?" Conrad asked.

Stavros grunted. "Think so."

Conrad glanced up at Polaris, the brightest star in the constellation Ursa Major, and then at the silvery waters. This location wasn't on any charts. He'd found it by using ancient poems, ships' logs, and astronomical data that only an astro-archaeologist like himself would take seriously.

Yet he wasn't alone.

The black cutout of a megayacht loomed on the dark horizon. For a pleasure palace cruising the Ionian Islands on an Easter holiday vacation, the six-hundred-foot vessel boasted an impressive communications array, a helicopter, and for all Conrad knew, even a couple of submersibles. It was probably all for show, but Conrad still didn't like someone else with that kind of firepower near his find.

He planned to be long gone before the sun came up. "I need forty minutes of air to the bottom and back," he told Stavros.

Stavros threw out a small buoy tied to two hundred meters of line. "If she's still sitting on the edge of the trench, like the robotic camera showed, you'll be lucky to get twenty minutes of bottom time," Stavros said. "If she's slipped into the Calypso, then it doesn't matter. The Baron of the Black Order himself will grab you by the leg and drag you down to hell." He shivered and made the sign of the cross over his heart.

Conrad could do without a Greek chorus to remind him that tragedy haunted these waters. In the light of day, the surface of the Ionian was among the most serene for sailing in Greece, surrounded by easy anchorages and safe bays for cruise ships and private yachts alike. But in the darkness of its depths was one of the most seismic areas in the world.

There, three miles down at the bottom of the Hellenic Trench, lay the vast Calypso Deep. It was the point where the African tectonic plate subducted the Eurasian plate, pulling anything too close under the plates and into the earth's magma. Even, some had argued, something as big as a continent.

"You worry about my oxygen, Stavros. I'll worry about the curse of the Calypso." Conrad slipped on his full-face dive mask and stepped off the bow, fins first, into the sea.

The cool water enveloped him as he followed the anchored buoy line to the bottom. His high-powered Newtlite head lantern illuminated the way through the darkness. Halfway down he met a school of bottlenose dolphins. They parted like a curtain to reveal the startling sight of the legendary *Nausicaa* rising out of the depths, her 37mm antiaircraft guns pointing straight at him.

The German submarine was imposing enough,

which Conrad had expected. After all, it had belonged to SS General Ludwig von Berg—the Baron of the Black Order, as he was known to his friends in the Third Reich. Among other things, the baron was head of Hitler's Ahnenerbe, an organization of academics, philosophers, and military warriors sent to scour the earth to prove the Aryans were the descendants of Atlantis.

That mission had taken Baron von Berg as far away as Antarctica, where decades later, Conrad's father, USAF General Griffin Yeats, had uncovered a secret Nazi base and ancient ruins two miles beneath the ice. But any evidence of that lost civilization—Atlantis—was wiped away in a seismic event that killed his father, sank an ice shelf the size of California, and may well have caused the Indian Ocean tsunami of 2004 that killed thousands in Indonesia.

Ever since, Conrad had been trying to find some proof that what he had found under Antarctica wasn't a dream. Clues left by his father on his tombstone at Arlington Cemetery had told Conrad as much and more. Soon he had discovered that his father's successor as head of the Pentagon's DARPA research and development agency, Max Seavers, had developed a weaponized flu virus from the infected lung tissue of dead Nazis found frozen in Antarctica.

Those discoveries ultimately led Conrad to the mysterious Baron von Berg. Classified American, British, and German intelligence files from World War II recorded that the SS general's U-boat, *Nausicaa,* was returning from its secret base in Antarctica when it was sunk by the British Royal Navy in 1943.

Conrad's hope was that he would find on board a relic from Atlantis.

He kicked through the water toward the sunken submarine. The *Nausicaa* lay like a gutted whale along the cusp of the Calypso Deep with her tail broken off and her forward section jutting out over the abyss like a metal coffin.

Conrad swam to the mouth of the broken fuselage and studied its teeth. The British torpedo that had sunk the *Nausicaa* had taken out the entire electric motor room. But it wasn't a clean break. One little nick of his air hose would cut off his oxygen. He spoke into his dive helmet's integrated radio. "Stavros."

"Right here, boss," the Greek's voice crackled in his earpiece.

"How's the compressor?"

"Still ticking, boss."

Conrad swam into the abandoned control room of the forward section, keeping his eyes peeled for floating skeletons. He found none. No diving officers, helmsmen, or planesmen. Not even in the conning tower. Just an empty compartment with unmanned banks of instruments to his port and starboard sides. Had all hands managed to abandon ship before she went down?

The captain's quarters were empty, too. There was only a phonograph with a warped album. Conrad could still read the peeling label on the album: *Die Walküre.* Von

Berg had been playing Wagner's "Ride of the Valkyries" over the loudspeakers when the sub went down.

But no sign of Baron von Berg himself. Nor a metallic Kriegsmarine briefcase. Maybe the legend was true, and von Berg never carried secret papers with him, telling everyone instead: "It's all in my head."

Conrad's hopes of finding anything were sinking fast.

He swam up the cramped fore-and-aft passageway through the galley and officers' quarters. A creeping claustrophobia washed over him as he slipped through the open hatch into the forward torpedo bay.

At one end were four circular hatches—the torpedo tubes. The atmospheric pressure gauges, frozen in time, told him that the *Nausicaa* had fired off at least three torpedos and drained her tubes to fire more when the Brits sank her. Only the No. 4 tube was flooded. The Baron of the Black Order obviously had not gone down without a fight.

Conrad turned to the bomb racks and found a large protrusion. He fanned away the accumulated silt. An object took form, and he realized he was staring at a human skull with black holes for eyes.

The bared teeth seemed to grin at him in the eerie deep. The skull had a silver plate screwed into one side—the legacy of a bullet to the head in Crete, Conrad had learned in his research.

SS General Ludwig von Berg. The Baron of the Black Order. The rightful king of Bavaria. That was what the old top-secret OSS report Conrad had stolen had said.

Conrad felt a shock wave in the water, and the *Nausicaa* seemed to lurch.

"Stavros!" he called into his radio, but there was no response.

Suddenly, the black holes in the baron's skull glowed a bright red, and his skeletal arm floated up as if to grab Conrad.

Conrad backed away from the skeleton, figuring that the water was playing tricks on him. Then he noticed that the glow actually came from something behind the skull. Indeed, the Baron of the Black Order seemed to be guarding something.

Conrad's heart pounded as he brushed away more silt, revealing an odd hammerhead-shaped warhead. He shined a light on it and ran his hands across the torpedo's slick casing.

It had no markings save for a code name stamped across the warhead's access panel: *Flammenschwert.* Conrad's rudimentary grasp of German translated it to mean "Flaming Sword" or "Sword of Fire."

He recalled from his research that von Berg claimed to have developed a weapon that the Nazis were convinced could win them the war: an incendiary technology that allegedly was Atlantean in origin and could turn water into fire and even melt the ice caps.

Could this be the relic he was searching for that would prove Antarctica was Atlantis?

The mysterious glow was coming from inside the hammerhead cone of the torpedo, outlining the square access panel like a neon light. But this was no mere illumination. The light seemed to be consuming the water around the warhead like a fire consumes oxygen.

Conrad's dosimeter gauge registered no radiation, so he put the fingertip of his glove to the glowing seam of the access panel. It didn't burn his glove, but he could feel an unmistakable pull. The warhead was sucking in the water around it like a black hole.

He sensed another shock wave through the water and turned to see four shadowy figures with harpoon guns enter the torpedo bay.

They must be after the *Flammenschwert*! he thought. He'd rather sink the sub than let this weapon fall into anybody's hands.

He reached up for the blow valves above the four torpedo tubes and twisted the wheels, flooding three of them. The sub tilted forward toward the Calypso Deep, throwing the others back. The rumbling was deafening. Breathing hard in his mask, heaving as he kicked, he was swimming madly to escape the torpedo bay when a harpoon dart stabbed his thigh.

Grimacing in pain, Conrad grabbed his leg as three of the divers swarmed around him. He broke off the harpoon dart and stabbed in the gut the diver who had shot him. The diver doubled over as a cloud of blood billowed out of his wet suit. The other two had grabbed him, however, and before Conrad could tear away, their leader swam over, drew a dagger, and sliced through Conrad's lifeline.

Conrad watched in shock as silver bubbles rose up

before his eyes like a Roman candle, literally taking his breath away.

Then he saw the dagger again, this time its butt smashing the glass of his mask. Water began filling the mask, and he inhaled some against his will. His life flashed by in a blur—his father the Griffter, his childhood in Washington, D.C., his digs around the world searching for Earth's lost "mother culture," meeting Serena in South America, then Antarctica . . .

Serena.

His lips tried to repeat the prayer that Serena had taught him, the last prayer of Jesus: "Into Thy hands I commit my spirit." But the words refused to come. He could only see her face, now fading away. Then darkness.

When Conrad opened his eyes again, the phantom divers were gone. He wasn't breathing, but his lungs weren't filled with water, either—laryngospasm had sealed his airway. He would suffocate instead of drowning if he didn't surface immediately.

He looked out through his shattered dive mask to see the skull of SS General Ludwig von Berg smiling at him. The fire had gone out of the baron's eyes. Also gone was the *Flammenschwert* warhead, along with the shadow divers. But the divers had left behind something for him: a brick of C4 explosive with a digital display slapped next to the torpedo's open casing.

The numbers read: 2:43 . . . 2:42 . . . 2:41 . . .

On top of the C4 was a metal ball bearing that glowed like a burning ember from hell. It must have been extracted from the *Flammenschwert,* which probably contained thousands of these copperlike pellets inside its core. The bastards were going to verify the design by detonating just one tiny pellet, simulating on a small scale the device's explosive power. In the process, they were going to destroy him and the *Nausicaa.*

Conrad mustered the last of his strength and tried to swim out, but his leg caught on something—the skeletal hand of SS General Ludwig von Berg. The baron, it seemed, wanted to drag him to hell.

Conrad couldn't break free. The clock was down to 1:33.

Thinking quickly, he grabbed the baron's steel-plated skull with both hands and broke it off the skeleton. Slipping his fingers into the eyeholes as if the skull were a bowling ball, he brought it down on the finger bones clasping his injured leg and smashed them to pieces.

He was free, but his fingers were now stuck like a claw through the skull as another shock wave hit the *Nausicaa.*

The entire forward torpedo bay dropped like a broken table—silt and debris sliding past him to the front, further tipping the submarine over the edge of the Calypso Deep. Conrad's back slammed against the bomb rack, and he saw the compartment hatch and entire fore-aft passageway beyond rising like a great elevator shaft above him.

The *Nausicaa* was about to go down nose-first into the Calypso. Conrad had only seconds left. He positioned himself under the hatch, forcing himself to resist the temptation to panic. He held his body ramrod-straight, like a torpedo, his hands arched together with the skull over his head. Then he closed his eyes as everything collapsed around him.

For a moment he felt like a missile shooting up out of its silo, although he knew it was the silo that was sinking. Then he was clear. He looked down into the Calypso Deep as it swallowed the *Nausicaa* with the tiny pellet from the *Flammenschwert* still inside its belly.

The powerful wake of the plunging sub began to pull him down like a vertical riptide. He knew if he fought it, he'd go down with it. Instead he made long scissor kicks across the wake and over the rim of the crater, putting as much distance between him and the abyss as possible. There was a flash of light behind him, and the water suddenly heated up.

Conrad looked back over his shoulder in time to see a giant pillar of fire shoot straight up from the depths of the Calypso. The sound of thunder rippled across the deep. Abruptly, the flames fanned out and seemed to assume the form of a dragon flying through the water toward him. Conrad started swimming as fast as he could.

He surfaced a minute later into the dim predawn light of day, gasping for breath. Finally, as he was on the verge of passing out again forever, his larynx opened, and he coughed up a little water from his stomach as he desperately inhaled the salty air.

His groan sounded like jet engines in his own ears.

He was sure he was experiencing some kind of pulmonary embolism from coming up so fast. Several deep gulps of air cleared his head enough for him to scan the horizon for his boat. But it wasn't there. In the distance loomed the silhouette of a megayacht, its decks stacked like gold bullion in the glint of the rising sun, turning away.

Debris floated around him—the remains of his boat. Poor Stavros, he thought. He swam toward a broken wooden plank to use for flotation. But when he got there, he realized it wasn't wood at all. It was the charred carcass of a bottlenose dolphin, burned to a crisp.

The horrific nature of the *Flammenschwert* sank in.

It works. It really turns water to fire.

Conrad stared at the dolphin's blackened rostrum and teeth. He felt some stomach acid rising at the back of his own throat and looked away. All around him were incinerated bottlenose dolphins, floating like driftwood across a sea of death.

2

Sister Serena Serghetti clutched the metal box containing African rice seeds to her chest as she walked down a long tunnel blasted out of the arctic mountain. High above her, fluorescent lights flashed on and off as she passed embedded motion detectors. Close behind, a choir of Norwegian schoolchildren held candles in the flickering darkness and sang "Sleep Little Seedling."

Their heavenly voices felt heavy in the freezing air, Serena thought, weighted perhaps by the tunnel's meter-thick walls of reinforced concrete. Or maybe it was her heart that felt so heavy.

The Doomsday Vault, as it was called when it opened in 2008, already housed more than two million seeds representing every variety of the earth's crops. In time it would house a collection of a hundred million seeds from more than 140 countries here on this remote island near the North Pole. It had been built to protect the world's food supply against nuclear war, climate change, terrorism, rising sea levels, earthquakes, and the ensuing collapse of power supplies. If worse came to worst, the vault would allow the world to reconstruct agriculture on the planet.

But now the vault itself was in danger. Thanks to global warming, the shrinking ice caps had spurred a new race for oil in the Arctic. It was the next Saudi Arabia, if someone could figure out a way to extract and transport all that oil through a sea of ice. A few years earlier, the Russians had even planted a flag two and a half miles below the ice at the North Pole to claim its oil reserves. Now Serena feared they were preparing to start mining.

She passed through two separate air locks and into the vault itself, blinking into the glare of the TV lights. The Norwegian prime minister was in there somewhere, along with a delegation from the United Nations.

Serena knelt before the TV cameras and prayed silently for the people of the earth. But she was aware of shutters clicking and photographers' boots shuffling for better shots of her.

Whatever happened to finding a secret place to pray, like Jesus taught? she wondered, unable to shake a guilty feeling. Did the world really need to see Mother Earth arrayed in high-definition piety 24/7? As if the prayers of the Vatican's top linguist and environmental czar counted more than those of the anonymous humble field laborer whose hands culled the seeds she now held.

But this was a cause greater than herself and her tormented thirty-three-year-old soul, she reminded herself. And her official purpose here today was to focus the world's attention on its future.

As she knelt, tightly gripping the box of seeds, a feeling of dread came over her. What the vault meant, what it was built for: the time of the end, which the Bible had prophesied would come soon. The words of the prophet Isaiah whispered in her ear: God is the only God. He will draw all people to Himself to see His glory. He will end this world. And He will judge those who reject Him.

Not something TV audiences wanted to hear.

She felt a nagging sense of hypocrisy about her performance. A disturbing thought began to bubble up, a thought she couldn't quite formulate. Her dread began to take shape in the words of Jesus: "If therefore you are offering your gift at the altar, and there remember that your brother has anything against you, leave your gift there before the altar, and go your way. First be reconciled to your brother, and then come and offer your gift."

She didn't understand. She had plenty of people angry with her at the Vatican—for being a woman, for being beautiful, for drawing cameras wherever she went—and that was just within the Church. Outside, there were the oil and gas companies she chided, and diamond merchants, and the exploiters of children.

But that wasn't what this word from God was about.

Conrad Yeats.

She fought to push his face out of her mind and felt the slightest tremor as her knees pressed against the concrete floor.

That rogue? That liar, cheat, and thief? What could he possibly have against me? Other than I wouldn't sleep with him?

But she couldn't get his face—his handsome unshaved face—out of her mind. Nor could she forget how she had left things in Washington, D.C., a few years back, after he had saved her life. She had promised to leave the Church and be with him forever. Instead she had stolen something priceless out from under him and the U.S. government, leaving him with nothing.

But Lord, You know it was for Conrad's own good and the greater good.

When she opened her eyes and rose to her feet, she surrendered the box of African rice seeds to the Norwegian prime minister. With solemn fanfare, he opened the box for the cameras, revealing sealed silver packets, each labeled with a special bar code. Then he resealed the box and slid it onto its designated shelf in the vault.

After the ceremony, she went into the main tunnel and found her driver and bodyguard, Benito, waiting for her with her parka. She slipped it on, and they started walking toward the main entrance to the facility.

"Just as you suspected, *signorina*," he told her, handing her a small blue device. "Our divers found it at the bottom of the arctic seabed."

It was a geophone. Oil companies used them to take seismic surveys of the earth's subsurface in search of oil, in this case the earth two miles beneath the ice and water of the North Pole. Her visit to the Doomsday Vault had been a cover for her to meet with divers who could investigate for signs of drilling.

"So someone is planning to mine the bottom of the Arctic," she said, watching her breath freeze as they stood before the facility's dual blast-proof doors. Slowly and heavily, the doors opened.

The arctic air slapped Serena in the face as she stepped outside, where a van with tanklike treads was waiting to take her to the island's airport, the northernmost in the world with regular flights. Behind her, the exterior of the Doomsday Vault looked like something out of a science fiction movie, a giant granite wedge protruding from the ice.

The Norwegian island of Spitsbergen had been chosen as the location for the seed vault because it was a remote region with low tectonic activity and an arctic environment that was ideal for preservation. Now oil exploration posed a direct threat to this environment. It would also accelerate global warming's melting of the ice cap, threatening coastal cities around the world.

So why was she thinking of Conrad Yeats?

Something is terribly wrong, she thought. *He's in danger.*

But she couldn't put her finger on why and blamed her gloomy thoughts on the sweeping vista of endless ice and water spread out before her. It brought back memories of her adventure with Conrad in Antarctica years ago.

Benito said, "Our divers say there are thousands of them, maybe even tens of thousands, below us."

Serena realized he was talking about the geophone in her hand. "It will take them at least six months to map all the underground formations," she said. "So we still have some time before they decide where to start drilling. That might give us a chance to stop them."

"The Russians?" Benito asked.

"Maybe." She flipped the geophone over and saw the manufacturer's name: Midas Minerals & Mining LTD. "But I know who can tell us."

3

CORFU

If Sir Roman Midas loved anything in his life, it was his prized superyacht. Named after his one true love—himself—the *Midas* had a two-thousand-square-foot gym, two two-person submarines, and two helicopter pads, one for his chopper and one for guests. At 595 feet, the *Midas* was longer than the Washington Monument was high and, by design, resembled a shining stack of sliced gold bricks. Today those bricks sat atop the sparkling blue waters of the Ionian Sea near the Greek island of Corfu.

Not bad for a Russian orphan turned British tycoon, Roman Midaslovich told himself as he stood on the aft-deck helipad. He watched while a winch transferred the unmarked crate to the awaiting helicopter, its blades whirling for takeoff.

Midas's London-based trading firm, Midas Minerals & Mining, had made him the world's richest trader in minerals and metals futures, and his patronage to the art world had won him a knighthood from the queen. It had also made him a top lieutenant inside the

Alignment, a centuries-old organization whose leaders fancied themselves the political if not the biological descendants of Atlantis. *Utter rubbish,* Midas had thought when he first heard the Alignment's claim to have orchestrated the rise and fall of empires across the ages. He alone was responsible for his rise from a Russian orphanage and the mines of Siberia to the trading pits of Chicago. But then the Alignment had orchestrated his entrée to the jet set of London and awarded him seats inside some of the international organizations that truly set the world's agenda: the Club of Rome, the Trilateral Commission, and the Bilderberg Group. Now he was a believer.

He waved off the pilot and watched the chopper lift into the sky. Then he turned to see Vadim Fedorov, his number two, standing before him in all his steroid-pumped muscularity. "They're waiting for you in the decompression chamber, sir," Vadim said.

"They" were two of the other divers from the *Nausicaa* extraction, Sergei and Yorgi. As far as everyone else was concerned, they were the only people who had seen the *Flammenschwert* besides himself and the pilot of the submersible, whom he had already dispatched to the ocean depths. Meanwhile, the helicopter would carry the crate to the airstrip on Corfu, and Midas's Gulfstream V private jet in turn would fly it to its intended destination.

"Is everything set?" Midas asked.

Vadim nodded. "You were right. They are FSB. Sergei

sent a text message to Moscow almost immediately after they surfaced."

"They never really went away, you know."

Midas was speaking of Russia's ancient secret police, which, after the czars, had become the Soviet Union's feared KGB. After the collapse of the Soviet Union, Russia's first president, Boris Yeltsin, had dismantled the KGB and renamed it the Federal Security Service, or FSB.

Many deeply disillusioned agents, such as Sergei and Yorgi, had gone into the private security business, ultimately supplanting the mafia in running Russia's "protection" rackets. Others, such as Russia's former president and prime minister Vladimir Putin, had penetrated the government. Today in Russia, three out of four leading politicians boasted a background in the security forces, and almost every large Russian corporation was run by ex-KGB executives with personal ties to Putin.

Sergei and Yorgi, despite their employment agreements with Midas Minerals & Mining, were Putin's men and as such no longer of any use to Midas. "Tell them I'll be down in a moment. First I owe Sorath a progress report," Midas said. Vadim nodded.

Midas entered his stateroom and poured himself a drink while he waited for the coded signal to connect. Right now Sorath was just a code name to a voice on the other end of the phone. Midas had no idea who Sorath was or if they had ever met. But all his questions would be answered soon enough.

"This is Xaphan," Midas reported as soon as a light told him he was on a secure connection with Sorath. "The sword has been removed from its sheath and is en route to Uriel. A successful test has proved the design is safe for deployment and that the device's criticality formulas are correct."

"What of Semyaza?" the voice demanded, referring to Yeats.

"Dead."

"Those were not your orders." There was anger in the voice.

"It couldn't be helped," Midas said, and quickly moved on. "We're on schedule. T minus eight days."

"Keep it that way."

The line cut out, and Midas stared at the images of Conrad Yeats on the large flat-panel screen of his computer. He zoomed in on one in particular—of the archaeologist's DNA. There was nothing remarkable about it save for one thing: It spiraled to the left. All indigenous life on earth has DNA that spirals to the right. To the Alignment, that bestowed Yeats with some mystical meaning, as if the freak of nature somehow possessed some lost pieces of Atlantean blood in his genetic makeup.

Midas could care less. He closed the image on his screen and, with a few taps on his keyboard, connected with his trading firm mainframes in London. Then he went down to the lower decks and the yacht's submersible launch bay.

Next to a double-domed "deep flight" Falcon submarine, designed to fly underwater like a private jet through the air, was the decompression chamber, its hatch wide open, with Sergei and Yorgi waiting for him inside.

Yorgi didn't look too good, his stomach hastily patched where the late, great Dr. Yeats had stabbed him with his own harpoon dart.

"We could have been decompressing instead of waiting for you," Sergei complained. "Are you trying to kill us?"

Midas smiled, stepped inside the chamber, and allowed Vadim to close the hatch on the three of them. The air compressor started to hum and raise the internal air pressure to rid their bodies of harmful gas bubbles caused by inhaling oxygen at higher pressure during their dive for the *Flammenschwert.* The two divers were rubbing their itchy skin and sore joints. They were clearly displaying symptoms of the bends—their lungs alone were unable to expel the bubbles formed inside their bodies.

"I wanted us to decompress together," Midas said, taking his seat opposite the two FSB men. "But first I had to see off the *Flammenschwert.*"

Sergei and Yorgi looked at each other. "The arrangement was for us to take it back to Moscow," Sergei said.

"*Nyet,*" said Midas. "I have other plans for the *Flammenschwert,* and they don't involve the FSB."

"You are a dead man if you betray Moscow,

Midaslovich," Sergei said. "Our organization spans the globe and is as old as the czars."

"Mine is older," Midas scoffed. "And now it has something yours does not—the power to turn oceans into fire."

"The deal was to use it in the Arctic and split the oil," Sergei pressed.

"Like the deal you did with British Petroleum in Russia before you stole their operations and ran them out?" Midas answered calmly as the air inside the chamber started to smell like bitter almonds. "Fools. Higher oil prices may have fueled your regime, but you don't know how to manage production. So you nationalize it and penalize real producers like me. Now that production has peaked, you have no choice but to stick your noses south into the Middle East and make war. You could have been kings instead of criminals."

Sergei and Yorgi began to cough and choke. Sergei said, "What have you done?"

Midas coughed twice. It would have been easier to throw them into the chamber, crank the dial, and blow their guts out. But it also would have been a mess to clean.

"As a child in the gold mines of Siberia, I was forced to extract gold from finely crushed ore," he told them calmly, like a firefighter lighting up a cigarette in the middle of an inferno. "Unfortunately, the only chemical up to the job is cyanide. It's stable when solid. But as a gas, it's toxic. I can see you are already experiencing rapid breathing, restlessness, and nausea."

Sergei began to vomit while Yorgi crumpled to the floor in convulsions.

"As for myself, my body developed a tolerance to the immediate effects of cyanide. But rest assured, I am experiencing all that you are to a lesser degree, and my doctors inform me that my long-term prognosis is the same as yours. We can't all live forever, can we?" Midas knew he didn't have to bother with theatrics in order to kill his enemies, but somehow he felt it was deeply important to show them that he had not only beaten them through his cleverness, but he was also, in his physical and mental evolution, inherently superior to them. "As your blood pressure lowers and heart rate slows, you will soon experience loss of consciousness, respiratory failure, and finally death. But you died a hero to the people. Too bad they are the wrong people."

The two were already dead by the time Midas had finished what passed for a eulogy. A minute later, he emerged from the chamber. The cyanide dispersed into the air, and two crewmen coughed. He left them to dispose of the bodies and took an elevator topside to the deck.

As he stepped into the sunlight and blinked, he reached for the sunglasses in his shirt pocket and glanced at his hand, which trembled slightly. It was the only visible neurological damage caused by his long-term exposure to cyanide poisoning as a child. So far.

He enjoyed watching death—it made him feel so alive. Like the salt that he now smelled in the sea air.

Or the sight of Mercedes sunning topless in her chaise longue that he drank in on the foredeck. He made himself a vodka martini and stretched out next to her golden body, looking forward to tonight's party on Corfu and letting all thoughts of Nazi submarines and American archaeologists fade away like a bad late-night movie.

4

Conrad Yeats stared at the skull of SS General Ludwig von Berg inside his suite at the Andros Palace Hotel in Corfu town overlooking Garitsa Bay. The balcony doors were open wide, and a gentle early-evening breeze blew in, carrying with it music from the town green below.

He took another swig from his bottle of seven-star Metaxa brandy. His leg smarted from the harpoon dart, and his mind still reeled from the events of the morning: the *Flammenschwert*, the loss of Stavros and the crew, and the image of Serena Serghetti filling what he'd thought were his dying moments.

There was a knock at the door. Conrad put down his Metaxa, picked up a 9mm Glock from under the sofa pillow next to him, and stood up. He moved to the door and looked through the peephole.

It was Andros. Conrad opened the door, and his friend walked in. Two big security types with earpieces and shoulder holsters were posted outside.

"We have a problem," said Andros, closing the door behind him.

Chris Andros III, barely thirty, was always worried. A billionaire shipping heir, Andros had squandered several years after Harvard Business School dating American starlets and hotel heiresses from Paris Hilton to Ivanka Trump. Now a consummate international business-man, he was bent on making up for lost time and owned the Andros Palace Hotel, along with a string of high-end boutique hotels around the Mediterranean and the Middle East. It was Andros who had helped Conrad find the *Nausicaa*. Andros claimed the sub was named after his grandmother, who, as a young nurse in Nazi-occupied Greece, had been forced to help the Baron of the Black Order recover from his gunshot wound to the head.

"Let me guess," Conrad said. "That superyacht I saw belongs to Sir Roman Midas, and your friends at the air-strip have no idea what was on that private jet of his that took off today or where it was going."

Andros nodded and saw the laptop computer Conrad had used for his research sitting at the bar, its screen filled with news and images of Midas. He seemed about to say something else when he saw the skull of SS General Ludwig von Berg on the table. "That's him?"

"Silver plate and all."

Andros walked over and studied the skull and its metallic dome. He made the sign of the cross. "I cannot tell you how many nightmares this baron gave me grow-ing up. My parents told me stories about what happened to those who crossed the baron—or children who didn't listen to their parents. Being a naughty boy myself, I had nightmares of his skull floating in the air and hounding me to Hades."

Conrad said, "I didn't find a metal briefcase with any papers."

"Of course you wouldn't," Andros said. "Von Berg always liked to say—"

"'It's all in my head,'" Conrad said, completing the sentence. "I know. But what, exactly?"

Andros shrugged. "At least you confirmed he's dead."

"Along with Stavros and the rest of the crew of your boat," Conrad said. "All at the hands of Sir Roman Midas. So now we plot revenge. Isn't that what you Greeks do?"

A cloud formed over Andros's face. "I'm but a humble billionaire, my friend, and barely that. Roman Midas is that many times over, and far more powerful. Especially if he has this weapon you say he took from the *Nausicaa*. Look outside." He walked out to the open balcony.

"I saw it," said Conrad, limping over with the Metaxa and looking out at Garitsa Bay.

To their right the sun was setting behind the old town, its colonnaded houses dating back to the island's days under British rule. To their left the stars were rising above the old Venetian fortifications.

"Look closely," said Andros.

Conrad set the bottle of Metaxa on the balustrade and picked up a pair of Zeiss binoculars. Beyond the stone fortifications of the Old Fort, the superyacht *Midas* was anchored in the bay, with small boats ferrying well-dressed men and barely dressed women to and from shore.

"Looks like he's celebrating his catch of the day," Conrad said. "Any way I can get a closer look?"

"Not a chance. Greek coast guard boats are maintaining a perimeter. And the island is crawling with security."

"Why's that?" Conrad swept the deck with the glasses and noticed the chopper had returned.

Andros said, "The Bilderberg Group is holding their annual conference at the Achillion."

Conrad looked at the ornate palace atop a hill opposite the bay.

"Ironically, it was Baron von Berg's headquarters during the war," Andros told him. "Built by the empress of Austria and later bought by Kaiser Wilhelm II of Bavaria as a winter retreat. It's a fanciful place, with whimsical gardens and statues of Greek gods all over the place. I deflowered many a girl there myself."

"What's the structure next to the palace?"

"The House of the Knights," Andros said. "The kaiser built it to house his battalions. There are nice stables, too, for the kaiser's horses. For all its romance, the Achillion has a long history of military staging. It was strafed by Allied planes in 1943 during the baron's stay and then turned into a hospital after the war. Later, it became a casino featured in a James Bond movie."

"And now?"

"It's a museum, used on occasion as a spectacular backdrop for meetings of the G7 nations, the European Union, and apparently, the Bilderberg Group."

The Bilderbergers. Conrad knew a few of them, including his late father, who had attended a couple of the conferences back in the 1990s when he was acting head of the Pentagon's DARPA research and development agency.

Officially, the Bilderberg Group brought together European and American royalty in the form of heads of state, central banks, and multinational corporations to freely discuss the events of the day away from the glare of the press. Unofficially, conspiracy buffs suspected the Bilderbergers set the world's agenda, orchestrating wars and global financial panics at will to advance some totalitarian one-world government that would arise from the ashes.

"I'm thinking Midas is a member of the Alignment," Conrad told Andros.

Andros looked at Conrad as if he were talking about Atlantis, which in a way he was, as the Alignment considered themselves to be the custodians of the lost civilization's mysteries. "I'll have the doctor check the oxygen in your blood again."

"The Bilderberg Group is the closest real-world equivalent to the Alignment that I know of," Conrad said. "If there are any Alignment members left on the planet, it stands to reason that at least a few of them would be members of the Bilderbergers and use the group as a proxy to advance the Alignment's agenda."

"Just as the Alignment used the Egyptians, Greeks, Romans, Knights Templar, Freemasons, USA, and Third Reich?" Andros said, holding up the half-empty bottle of Metaxa with a knowing smile.

Conrad put down the Zeiss glasses and looked Andros in the eye. "I think I know a way into the party tonight."

Andros frowned. "Who is she?"

"According to Google, she's his latest girlfriend, Mercedes Le Roche."

"Of Le Roche Media Generale?"

Conrad nodded. "Her father," he said. "She used to be my producer on *Ancient Riddles*."

"You're crazy," Andros said. "Put this insane idea out of your head. Get off the island before Midas figures out you survived. Get out while you still can."

"I have to find out what Midas intends to do with that weapon," Conrad said.

"Maybe sell it?"

"He doesn't need the money. He's Midas."

"True," said Andros. "You say this *Flammenschwert* is Greek fire?"

"No, you said it's Greek fire. I said it's a weapon that turns water to fire."

"Greek fire," Andros repeated. "But we Greeks have always called it liquid or artificial fire. We used it to repel the Muslim Arabs at the first and second Sieges of Constantinople in the sixth and seventh centuries. That's how Europe survived Islam for over a thousand years."

"But how did Greek fire work?"

"To this day, nobody really knows," Andros said. "The ingredients and manufacturing process were closely guarded military secrets. The emperor Constantine VII Porphyrogenitus even warned his son in a book to never give away three things to a foreigner: a crown; the hand of a Greek princess; and the secret of liquid fire. All we know is that Greek fire could burn on water and was extremely difficult to extinguish. The sight of it alone was enough to demoralize the enemy. My father always suspected that it was petroleum-based and spiked with an early form of napalm."

"Maybe," Conrad said. "But I think that the petroleum jelly your forefathers used was a crude copy of something far more devastating. Something that used a uranium-like ore that could actually consume water like oxygen, not just burn on its surface. Where did you say Greek fire came from?"

"I didn't," Andros said. "But tradition says it was cooked up by chemists in Constantinople, who inherited the discoveries of the ancient Alexandrian chemical school."

Conrad nodded. "Who inherited the discoveries of the Atlantean school. Only the Alexandrians didn't have access to *Oreichalkos*."

"*Oreichalkos*?" Andros looked mystified.

"The mysterious ore or 'shining metal' mined by the people of Atlantis, according to your ancient philosopher Plato," Conrad said. "Plato called it 'mountain copper.'

He described it as a pure, almost supernatural alloy that sparkled like fire. I've seen it before."

"In Antarctica," Andros said with condescension. "Pish. Atlantis was the Greek island of Santorini. I have a hotel there."

"Let's not get into that debate now," Conrad said. "The point is that this technology is older than mere Greek fire. I witnessed what a speck of it can do. I think Midas could fry oceans with it. But which one?"

"My grandfather said Hitler wanted to use it in the Mediterranean," Andros said. "The Nazis wanted to protect Fortress Europe with a moat of fire and burn the warships of the Allied invasion fleet before they could land. Von Berg, however, wanted to use it to dry up the Mediterranean and proclaim its one million square miles as the new Atlantis."

"Too big, I think, and this is a new century." Conrad shook his head. "Where else in today's world?"

"Where it can do the most damage," said Andros confidently. "The Persian Gulf."

Conrad paused. Here Andros, whose family's tankers brought oil to and from the Persian Gulf, knew what he was talking about. "Go on."

"Midas is in deep with the Russians, and they're running out of production. Best way to boost prices is to cut supply—preferably somebody else's. Especially when the Americans depend on it. What better way to disrupt oil shipments through the Persian Gulf than to set it on fire? Who knows how long it would burn with this weapon?"

"Pretty good."

"I think so," said Andros. "So now you tell your friends at the Pentagon and call it a day."

"Or you get me into the Bilderberg bash."

Andros looked at the imposing Achillion on the hilltop beyond the bay. "My money reaches the Greek police. But the Bilderbergers bring their own security. Even I can't get into that club."

"They publish their guest lists. Maybe I can go as somebody else before they show up. Say hello to Mercedes, get something out of her before Midas knows what's going on."

"And kills you?"

"In front of all the other Bilderbergers? No. I know guys like Midas. Appearances and respectability are paramount. He won't lay a finger on me in front of Europe's rich and powerful."

"No, he'll simply kill you as soon as you step foot out of the palace."

Conrad studied Andros. "What's going on? I say Midas, and your knees start shaking. The guy blows up your boat, kills your crew, and almost kills me, your good friend. Odysseus would have had three arrows in this guy's throat by now."

Andros, in turn, studied him. "You were not always so vengeful. I want to meet the woman who hurt you so badly. So I can introduce her to my rival shipowners in Athens."

Conrad looked out at the lush green esplanade of

Corfu town and thought of Serena. "When you find her, let me know. Because she's not taking my calls."

"Forget her," Andros said. "How did you leave things with Mercedes?"

Conrad said nothing.

"I thought so," said Andros. "Why should she tell you anything about Midas or his operations? More important, what makes you think Midas would have told her anything of value that she could pass on to you? My rule is the less a woman knows, the better."

"Which explains the women you go out with," Conrad said. "Look at that boat he named after himself. You know that the richer a man gets, the smarter he thinks he is. Midas is an arrogant bastard, and I'm willing to bet that in his hubris, he's let Mercedes see more about his operations than he's realized."

"Are you willing to bet your life?"

"I did that a long time ago. Midas took his shot this morning. And I'm still here."

"So is he, my friend. And he has an inexhaustible supply of henchmen and money. You are only one man."

Conrad poured some of the brandy into a glass, gave it to Andros, and then held up his bottle in a toast. "What about my buddy the Greek tycoon, who is going to get me into that Bilderberg party tonight?"

5

There were lights and music coming from the Achillion Palace that evening, but no crowds of onlookers, no paparazzi to snap photos as the guests stepped out of their limousines and entered the palace. And the glamour quotient took a distant backseat to the power quotient. Everything was understated and discreet, save for the music: Coldplay live in concert. Actually, it struck Conrad as odd—a bit of contemporary fizz thrown on a very old-world gathering.

Conrad sat in the backseat of his limousine in an Armani tuxedo as Andros played the part of his driver, nudging the sedan forward in the line of black chariots at the main gate where U.S. Marines stood.

Andros, whom Conrad had never seen more nervous, pressed a button to unlock the trunk and then lowered his window for the Marines and spoke in Greek. "His Royal Highness Crown Prince Pavlos."

One of the guards flashed a light at the rear passenger

window as Conrad lowered it for them to get a better look at his impression of the Greek royal. The guard matched the name and face to the computerized clipboard while three others with extended mirror plates examined the underside of the sedan and the trunk. Conrad's resemblance to Pavlos was close enough for the Marine, who got the all-clear from the bomb squad and waved the limousine through.

Andros let out a sigh of relief as they rolled down the drive to the entrance of the palace and looked up in the rearview mirror. "This was a bad idea."

"We got through the gate, didn't we?"

"Only because U.S. Marines don't know what Pavlos really looks like up close and in person. His family isn't even of Greek descent. The monarchy was originally imposed on Greece by the Bavarian ancestors of these Bilderbergers. Trust me, the cabinet-level Greeks and *Evzoni* at the entrance will know on sight that you're an impostor."

Conrad knew that Andros was referring to the Greek security detail dead ahead. They were members of Greece's elite ceremonial presidential guard who, besides guarding the Hellenic Parliament and Presidential Mansion in Athens, guarded the reception of foreign dignitaries. Dressed in traditional light infantry uniforms, they wore scarlet garrison caps with long black tassels and red leather clogs with black pompons.

"They're just for show, Andros. Men in kilts."

"And carrying M1 Garand semiautomatic battle rifles with bayonets."

As they pulled up to the columned facade of the palace, Conrad saw four members of the Bilderbergers on the front steps welcoming guests: Her Majesty Queen Beatrice of the Netherlands; His Royal Highness Prince Phillipe of Belgium; Microsoft founder and the world's richest man, William Gates III; and a man Andros said was Greece's minister of finance.

Andros said, "We're cooked."

"Just remember, buddy. You're richer than half of them and better than the other half."

Andros stopped the limousine, and an *Evzoni* opened Conrad's door as another ceremonial guard announced his arrival in English. "Dr. Conrad Yeats, USA."

They knew all along it was me, he thought with a start.

He glanced back at Andros, but the *Evzoni* had already waved off the limousine to make room for the next arrival, leaving Conrad alone to face a smiling Queen Beatrice, who coldly shook his hand.

"So good to meet you, Dr. Yeats. I'm so glad you could come at the last minute as a substitute for Dr. Hawass from Cairo. We're looking forward to hearing your perspectives on archaeology and the geopolitics of the Near East."

"My pleasure." Conrad smoothly shook hands with Prince Phillipe and then Bill Gates. He knew he was a fool to have believed he ever would have slipped anything past these people. They had let him know it and were about to make him an exhibit for public viewing at their little gathering.

"I heard your talk about astronomical alignments and Washington's monuments at the TED conference in Monterey a couple of years ago," Gates told him. "I remember thinking you were either completely nuts or archaeology's equivalent of the world's most dangerous hacker."

Conrad couldn't tell if that was a compliment or indictment as Queen Beatrice indicated he should take her arm and they walked up the three flat marble steps through the main entrance.

Inside the reception hall, arrivals had gathered at the base of an impressive staircase flanked by statues of Zeus and Hera. At the top of the stairs was a grand mural that showed Achilles dragging the dead Hector behind his chariot before the walls of Troy. Conrad hoped it wasn't a prophecy for the evening and that the courtesy of his hostess would be extended to him by the rest. "Why the special treatment, Your Majesty, if I may ask?"

"All of our guests tonight are special, Dr. Yeats."

Conrad watched the crowd move up the grand staircase to the second floor, which opened onto the terrace and gardens outside. The guest list he had seen numbered 150 names—about a hundred from Europe and the rest from North America. Mostly government, finance, and communications types.

One of them, the new publisher of *The Washington Post*, he instantly recognized in front of him. Unfortunately, the tall, thin blonde saw him, too.

"Conrad Yeats, what the hell are you doing here?" she said. "Stepping into your daddy's shoes?"

"Hello, Katharine," he told her. She was wearing her white watch with the rhinestone skull-and-bones face. He had never seen her without it. "You seem to have filled your grandmother's pumps nicely." He watched her move toward the bottom of the grand staircase, where her party was waiting.

"Ah, you know Ms. Weymouth," Queen Beatrice said.

"Just a dance or two in high school," Conrad said. "I thought media was banned from this event."

"Not at all," the queen said. "We have several American and European news organizations represented here. But our participants have agreed not to report on the meeting or to grant interviews to outside press about what transpires. It would defeat the purpose of this forum."

"Which is?" Conrad pressed.

The queen smiled and clasped his hand with both of her own. They were small but firm. "Simply and only to allow world leaders to speak their minds freely."

"I'll do my best," he said, and turned toward the staircase.

"Before you do, your friend and sponsor for tonight would like to speak to you in the kaiser's room," Queen Beatrice said.

"Sponsor?" Conrad repeated, stepping toward the room to the right of the reception hall before the queen tugged his arm.

"That's the chapel. You wouldn't want to go there. Maybe later. The iconography is unparalleled. But the kaiser's room is this way." She gestured to the short hall on the left of the grand staircase. "It was a pleasure meeting you, Dr. Yeats." There was an unnerving finality in her voice.

Conrad bid adieu to the queen, who moved back toward the front steps while he walked down the hall to the kaiser's room and entered the study. There stood a short, barrel-chested penguin of a man in a tuxedo: Marshall Packard, former U.S. secretary of defense and now acting head of its DARPA research and development agency.

"Hell, Yeats, is there any woman alive you don't have a past with?" Packard said.

Packard must have seen his little run-in with Katharine back in the foyer, Conrad realized. "You're violating the Logan Act, Packard, you know that," he said. "You and every American here who discusses anything pertinent to the national security of the United States with foreign powers."

Packard walked behind the kaiser's old desk and made himself comfortable in the leather chair. "Spare me the lecture, Prince Pavlos, and shut the door."

6

Conrad sat down in the kaiser's study and looked at Packard—"Uncle MP," as Conrad had known him growing up, when he was his father's old wingman in the air force.

Packard and his father, the onetime Bilderberger, had been best friends until his father's first ill-fated trip to Antarctica as an *Apollo* astronaut on a Mars training mission. Four astronauts made the mission, but only Griffin Yeats returned alive. The Griffter was profoundly changed by the mysterious affair, confounding those who thought they knew him, including his own wife. When the Griffter introduced four-year-old Conrad to the family as an adopted son immediately thereafter, the suspicions only grew.

Conrad knew that his adoptive mother had enlisted Packard's help to get to the bottom of the story. But Packard never did. Nobody did. Not even Conrad. Not until the Griffter recruited Conrad for a last-ditch, no-holds-barred military expedition to Antarctica, where he said he had found a young Conrad frozen in the ice. That Conrad, in fact, was an Atlantean, and the U.S. government had the DNA to prove it: Whereas the DNA strand of every indigenous species on earth spiraled to the right, Conrad's spiraled to the left.

Ergo, he was not of this earth.

Conrad almost bought the story, except for the reality that in every other way, his DNA and life were extraordinarily ordinary. Outside of Conrad being of interest to the Alignment types, and the mystery of his alleged Atlantean roots, Uncle Sam really had little use for him beyond his expertise in megalithic monuments, astronomical alignments, and ancient mysteries.

Conrad took another look around the kaiser's study and said, "The Bilderbergers let you do this—go off and have closed-door meetings away from everybody else?"

"Hell, Yeats, that's all we do at these things. Wake up," Packard said, and got down to business. "You need to find out where the hell that *Flammenschwert* went and what the Alignment wants to do with it."

How on earth did Packard know about the *Flammenschwert* or that Midas had it? Conrad wondered. But it took only a second for him to come up with the answer. "So Andros gave me up?"

Packard nodded. "Your boy's family goes way back with us in Greece. He knows who your true friends are, even if you don't."

Conrad said, "Did Andros also tell you he thinks

Midas might want to use the *Flammenschwert* to set the Persian Gulf on fire?"

"Hell, I'm worried the Alignment is going to use it in the Caspian Sea and destroy Russia's ability to ship oil," Packard said. "That's twelve trillion dollars' worth of oil right there. Trillion! It's the only thing keeping the collapsed Russian economy going. They lose that, and they won't bother with their Arab proxies. Their tanks will sweep into the Middle East, and we'll respond, and then we've got nuclear Armageddon."

It was a hellish scenario, to be sure. "So you're sure the Alignment is behind Midas?"

"They made him," Packard said. "And since you helped us smash their network in the U.S., they're using the EU as their cover and base of operation. What do you think this bullshit European summit about the fate of Jerusalem next week on Rhodes is all about? You really think European bureaucrats are ever going to agree on anything remotely resembling a 'coordinated, comprehensive peace plan' for the Middle East? It's all a cover. While the French and German presidents preen for peace, the Alignment will be conducting business as usual. They bankrupted the Russians in the nineties. Now they've bankrupted the United States. All that's left for them is to get our armies to knock each other out so they can unite the rest of the world."

Conrad had heard it all before from his father. "How is one man like me going to change any of that?"

"Maybe seeing you tonight will shake Midas up,

knowing that you're on to him. Maybe he'll make another mistake."

"Another?"

"You survived your first encounter with him, didn't you? How did you do that?"

"Atlantean blood, remember?"

Packard gave him a funny look, as if he half believed it. *These guys at DARPA,* Conrad thought, *always looking for any way to create the perfect soldier.* "You do realize that I don't work for you anymore, Packard, don't you? I'm under no contract to the Pentagon or anybody else."

"Only your pledge of allegiance to the United States of America, Yeats. And that's worth more to me than all the promises of a U.S. senator. They can be bought, or at least rented. Not you. Now, tell me how you found the *Nausicaa.*"

Packard seemed genuinely interested, so Conrad obliged.

"Same way I helped the Greeks here fix April 15, 1178 B.C., as the date of King Odysseus's return from the Trojan War and his slaughter of his wife's many suitors," Conrad said. "I aligned clues about star and sun positions from Homer's ancient Greek epic poem *The Odyssey* and contemporary German and British captain's logs to pinpoint the location of the *Nausicaa* when it sank."

Packard frowned. "The same astrological mumbo-jumbo the Alignment swears by?"

"Not quite," Conrad said. "According to Homer, the goddess Calypso had bidden Odysseus 'to keep the Bear on his left-hand side' until he reached this island of Corfu. I let Ursa Major be my guide."

Packard, satisfied yet again that Conrad was the right man for this job, said, "So you knew the *Flammenschwert* was on board the sub?"

Conrad shook his head. "All I knew was that the sub was returning from Antarctica. I was hoping it was carrying some relic from Atlantis."

"From the pit of hell, for all it matters," Packard said. "This *Flammenschwert* is a game-changer. The world is seventy-five percent water. Whoever rules the waves rules the world. You've got to stop Midas from using this thing or, worse, figuring out how to make more of them."

"How do I do that?"

"Just throw yourself in his face," Packard said. "I told you. Midas thinks you're dead. Maybe the sight of you will prompt him to double-check something with regard to the *Flammenschwert*. Now that we're monitoring him with every conceivable electronic surveillance on sea, land, and sky, we might catch him before it's too late."

"And what do I get?" Conrad demanded. "Just because I can't be bought doesn't mean I wouldn't enjoy some spoils of war."

"You didn't get enough from Uncle Sam for those two Masonic globes you dug up under the monuments in D.C.?"

Packard was referring to Conrad's last adventure with Serena Serghetti, which began at his father's funeral in Arlington Cemetery. Conrad had discovered that his father's tombstone was encoded with Masonic symbols and astrological data. It was yet another riddle wrapped in an enigma for Conrad to solve and Packard to go ballistic over. That tombstone turned out to be the key to a centuries-old warning built in to the very design of Washington, D.C. In the deadly race to decode that warning, Conrad and Serena had discovered two Templar globes of murky origins that America's first president, George Washington, had buried beneath the capital city—one terrestrial and one celestial.

It was the document inside the terrestrial globe that exposed the Alignment's plot to destroy the American republic and ultimately led Serena to steal that globe and take it with her to Rome, leaving the Americans with only one of the Templar globes. Meanwhile, the suspicion at the Pentagon that the globes worked together in some mysterious way probably explained the glare now coming from Packard and his cigar.

Conrad said, "The almighty American dollar isn't what it used to be. I used up my reward from the globes to find the *Nausicaa*. So, again, what do I get?"

"How about answers to all your questions?" Packard said. "Atlantis. Your father. Your birth. Hell, maybe we'll even get to the bottom of those globes."

"I've been to the bottom and back," Conrad said. "I know more about those two globes than anybody."

"Enough to explain how you let one of them slip away to the Vatican with your old girlfriend?" Packard said, lifting his eyebrows and his glass of brandy.

"I'm beginning to hate you as much as I did the Griffter, Packard."

"Then we're all good." Packard got up and ushered him to the door.

Conrad said, "That's it?"

"Text me when you find something," Packard said. "You've got my number. Just say the word and I'll send in the Marines."

"Last time the Marines tried to kill me."

"For all our differences, Yeats, you and I are on the same side. We don't buy any of this 'post–American world' bullshit the One-Worlders are here to propagate. Power and evil abhor a vacuum. We can't let the Alignment fill it."

Packard opened the door, and they walked into the reception hall, where a few late arrivals were making their way upstairs to the terrace.

"Just be yourself," Packard said softly as they started up the grand staircase. "Midas, like you, is a fringe player here—you by virtue of specialized knowledge and him by virtue of his oil billions. He wants to make a good impression on his Alignment masters, whoever they may be. Just seeing you walking around will rob him of that confidence."

They paused at the reception chamber at the top of the steps, in front of the *Triumph of Achilles* fresco. Conrad took a closer look at the gates of Troy in the background and saw a swastika. He knew it had been an ancient symbol of Troy long before the Nazis misappropriated it. But given the circumstances of the evening, it creeped him out just the same.

"What makes you think he's scared of me?" Conrad asked.

"He's not scared of you. He's scared of anybody in the Alignment who sees you here tonight," Packard said. "He'll know that we know he's got the *Flammenschwert* and that we can tie him to whatever happens with this thing. More important, he'll know his friends in the Alignment know it and that you just made him their fall guy."

They were on the second floor, which led outside to a sweeping veranda and the gardens overlooking the bay. This was where the lights and music were coming from, as the women in gowns and men in sleek tuxedos mixed among the life-size statues of Greek gods.

A floating tray with drinks came by. Packard grabbed two and handed one to Conrad. It was a Mount Olympus. Conrad tasted it. Not bad. He nodded and took another sip. They walked outside into the gardens, preparing to separate, and Conrad scanned the faces for Mercedes.

Packard seemed to read his mind. "Looking for her?"

"Gotta play my best hand if Midas is holding all the cards," Conrad said.

"Her Highness is even more of a player than when you last saw her," Packard said. "Never looked better, or more powerful and influential on the world stage."

Conrad knew Mercedes was thin, rich, and French. But "Her Highness" and power and influence never quite fit his picture of her, even when she was his producer playing with her papa's money.

"There's Midas," Packard said, gesturing outside. Conrad couldn't see through the small crowd of Bilderbergers. "He's talking to Her Highness right now."

Conrad wondered which royal princess Packard was snidely referring to. Then two guests parted like the Red Sea to reveal Midas holding court with several admirers around a stunning brunette in a backless black dress.

It was Serena.

7

Serena stood by the bronze statue of the dying Achilles, having traded her parka in the Arctic for a backless Vera Wang. To her left was Roman Midas, the man she had come to meet, representing the Bilderbergers' back channel to Russia. To her right was General Michael Gellar of Israel. Neither man was particularly pleased with the other, as Gellar had essentially accused Midas of providing the uranium for a Russian-built nuclear reactor that Israeli jets had bombed the month before. Now the mullahs in Tehran were threatening to attack Israel through their Palestinian proxies in Gaza and the West Bank.

"Any direct attack on Jerusalem or Tel Aviv will invite a devastating response on Tehran," said Gellar, his hawklike, craggy face looking like it had been cut from the rocks of Masada. "Israel has a right to exist and to defend herself."

Serena eyed Midas as he calmly sipped his vodka and

nodded. She had been invited by the Bilderbergers as a Vatican back channel between both of them in hopes of averting the latest Middle East crisis. But she also wanted to get Midas alone to press him about his mining in the Arctic.

"As you know, General Gellar, I'm a Russian expatriate often at odds with my homeland." Midas affected an odd British accent that Serena thought made him sound like a roadie with Coldplay. "I can vouch from personal experience that there are thugs running Russia now. The government itself is a mafia-like criminal organization. They are looking for any pretext to punish Israel through their Arab allies. If you attack Tehran, you will be handing them that pretext. And then what are you going to do? Nuke Moscow?"

"If our existence as a state is threatened, of course," Gellar said.

"Then Russia attacks America, and we have Armageddon," Midas said. "No more oil. And I'm out of business." He was trying to make a joke out of it, and Gellar grudgingly cracked a half-smile.

Seeing an opening, Serena made her move. "I hear there's always oil in the Arctic," she said, looking at Midas.

"I think the ice would have something to say about that," he said. "But I'd be there in a second if we could drill and ship. It would be the fifth-largest field of oil in the world."

"But what about the damage to the environment?" she asked.

"Moot point," he said. "By the time we ever drilled the Arctic seabed, the ice cap would have already melted completely, and we'd be drilling to fuel the rebuilding of whatever was left after the global floods." As an afterthought, he added: "Global warming is a tragedy."

"Nothing that fossil fuel consumption in the form of oil has anything to do with, I suppose?"

Midas smiled and pushed the conversation back at her. "That medallion," he said, noticing the ancient Roman coin that dangled just above her gown's sequined neckline. "What is it?"

"Oh, it's a coin from the time of Jesus," she said, touching it with her fingers. The medallion designated her status as the head of the Roman Catholic Church's ancient society Dominus Dei, which had started among the Christian slaves in Caesar's household near the end of the first century. It was also a sign, she was convinced, that as head of the Dei, she was one of the Alignment's legendary Council of Thirty. She had begun to be more public in her display of the medallion in an effort to ferret out the faces of others in the council. "My order's tradition says that Jesus held it up when He told His followers to give to God what is God's and to Caesar what is Caesar's."

General Gellar said somewhat dubiously, "That's supposed to be the actual coin?"

"You know some traditions," she said, smiling. "There are enough pieces of the cross for sale at churches in Jerusalem to build Noah's ark."

Gellar nodded wanly.

So did Midas. "Jesus suffered terribly at the hands of the Jews."

Oh God, Serena thought, watching for a sign of outrage on Gellar's face, but there was none. His face was a craggy slab of stone. But then Gellar had fought anti-Semitism from the Nazis, Russians, Europeans, Arabs, and regrettably, even the Church his entire life. He had mastered the art of overlooking the small offenses and forgoing the small battles so long as he won the war. And he had never lost one.

Midas, meanwhile, seemed delighted with the direction the conversation had taken and asked with feigned earnestness, "Tell me, Sister Serghetti, what is Caesar's and what is God's?"

Serena sighed inside, having realized she was foolish to believe Midas would be a gusher of information about his Arctic expeditions. "Basically, Jesus said to pay our taxes but give God our hearts."

"See, this is the problem with the world's monotheistic religions," Midas said quite passionately. "And I include the Russian Orthodox Church. They demand people's hearts. Then they demand people's hands. Then wars start. The world would be better off without religion."

"Wars rarely start over religion," she said diplomatically. "Usually, they start over something two or more parties want."

"Like land?" Midas asked.

"Or oil?" Gellar echoed.

"Yes," said Serena. "They simply use the cloak of religion to disguise their naked ambitions."

"Then let's remove the masks and solve the problem. Like I am doing. By creating more oil."

All at once Midas had made himself and technology the uniter of the world and Serena and her presumably backward faith its divider.

"Technology is no cure for evil, suffering, or death," she reminded Midas. "It is but a tool in the hands of fallen men and women. It cannot redeem the human heart or reconcile the peoples of the earth."

At that the blood drained from Midas's face, as if he had seen a ghost, and the hair on the back of Serena's neck stood on end even before a familiar voice behind her said, "Gee, Sister, how *does* reconciliation happen?"

Slowly, Serena turned to see Conrad Yeats standing before her in an elegant tuxedo, holding a drink in one hand and a cigar in the other. She blinked and stared at him. There was a smile on his lips but hatred in his eyes. She had no idea what he was doing there, only that with Conrad Yeats, there was no telling what he would do, and she was genuinely frightened.

"Dr. Yeats," she faltered. "I didn't know you were a Bilderberger."

"Oh, they'll let anyone join these days," he said, looking at Midas before locking his hazel eyes on her. "So you just forgive and forget?"

There was a pregnant pause, and Serena could feel his gaze on her, along with everybody else's. Except for Midas.

His ice-blue eyes, wide with shock, stared at Conrad in disbelief, and in that split second she grasped that Midas had thought Conrad was dead.

"Forgiveness isn't the same as reconciliation," she answered, sounding detached even though her heart was racing faster than her head. "You can forgive someone, like a dead parent, without resuming the relationship. Reconciliation, however, is a two-way street."

"Interesting," said Conrad. "Go on."

"Well," she said, pursing her lips. "The offending party first must show remorse and ask for forgiveness."

"And then?"

"Next the offending party must pay some kind of restitution. After he met Jesus, the tax collector Zacchaeus repaid everybody he ripped off four times over to show his remorse."

"Sounds good to me," Conrad said, puffing on his cigar. "Is that it?"

"No," she said. "Last, the offending party must show a real desire to restore the relationship. That takes trust. And trust takes time."

Conrad nodded and blew a circle of smoke into the air. "What if the offending party doesn't give a rip or return your calls?"

Serena took a deep breath, aware that Midas and Gellar were gone and the circle had broken up, leaving her alone with Conrad, who was ruining everything. "Then you should forgive them but not resume the relationship in hopes of reconciliation."

Conrad looked around and acknowledged that they were speaking privately. "Thanks for clearing that up, Serena. I thought I had just one reason to hate you for the rest of my life after you stole from me and then ditched me in D.C. But you keep giving me more."

"What are you doing here, Conrad?"

"I was going to ask you that very question," he shot back. "I thought Jesus hung out with the poor, the oppressed, the sick. Not the rich and powerful."

"It's not like that, Conrad."

"Then enlighten me, please."

She told him. "I think Midas is helping the Russians mine the Arctic. I want to stop them."

"Interesting," Conrad said. "Midas tried to kill me this morning."

"Really?" she said, hiding her concern. That meant both Midas and Conrad knew something she didn't. It had to be something terrible to bring together two such extreme men in her life. "I hope he has a ticket. The line seems to get longer each year."

"Lucky you," he said, looking over her shoulder. "It looks like my number is up."

At that moment Sir Midas's girlfriend, Mercedes, waved and headed toward them with a smile. "Conrad!" she called out.

Serena whispered into Conrad's ear: "Squeeze her for information. She might confess some things to you that she wouldn't to a nun."

He looked at her with contempt. "You want me to

sleep with her because your vows keep you from sleeping with Midas?"

"Something like that," she said. "You were going to anyway, weren't you?"

The look in his eyes told her that she had hurt him, and she hated herself for it. But it was better than him harboring any hope for her, as much as she was dying to be with him. Because there wasn't any hope as long as the Alignment lived.

"You're just a cast-iron bitch with a crucifix, aren't you?" he said.

The words pierced Serena's heart as Mercedes arrived, but she forced a smile.

"Professor Yeats!" Mercedes said, giving him two air kisses on each cheek.

Serena said innocently, "I forgot you two worked together."

"Truth be told, Professor Yeats worked for me until he didn't work out at all," Mercedes said, and gave her a wicked wink. "Sister Serghetti, if you'll excuse us, I'm going to have to take the professor away and spread him around."

Serena wanted to reach out and grab Conrad's arm to keep him from walking away with the woman. But she could only nod politely as she stood by herself next to the statue of the dying Achilles.

8

Conrad knew that he had come tonight to see Mercedes, whom he reluctantly followed past security down some stone steps into the lower gardens. But the sight of Serena had so thoroughly thrown him that Mercedes could have stripped off her snug gown and invited him to skinny-dip with her in the sea and he still would have passed on the opportunity in order to get back to Serena. Or get back *at* her. He wasn't sure.

Mercedes, meanwhile, looked incredibly if artificially well sculpted in her silver halter dress. Her forehead and facial features, however, seemed a bit too tight when she turned to him in the dim light of the lower gardens. Sure they were at last alone, she slapped him across the face.

"You bastard!" she hissed. "You stranded me in Nazca with a stolen artifact and a dozen Peruvian soldiers."

He rubbed his stinging cheek with his hand. "You got out okay, didn't you?"

"And how do you think I managed that?" she said, tearing up. "You think those pigs cared who my father was?"

It dawned on him what must have happened, the favors she was forced to offer to get out while he was off in Antarctica with Serena. He couldn't tell her he'd had no choice, because in hindsight, he had. It hadn't been necessary to leave her on that plateau. He could have insisted that the U.S. military take her and drop her off somewhere safe before proceeding. And he hadn't.

Conrad said, "You told me later that all was forgiven and forgotten."

Her eyes turned into black slits, the moonlight giving them an otherworldly glow. "Because I had to," she said. "I was hoping you'd come back. But you didn't, did you?"

Conrad, realizing that Mercedes's feelings toward him were the same as his own toward Serena, felt horrible and gave her his full attention. "I'm here now."

"No, you came to see *her*," Mercedes said, referring to Serena.

"Actually, I came to see your boyfriend," he said, surprised that he was actually telling her the truth.

She believed him, it seemed, and said nothing for a couple of minutes as they walked down more steps to the beach. There was a tiny Greek fishing village there, with some modest homes behind whitewashed walls. She removed her stiletto sandals, and they walked along the sand to the old stone bridge jutting out into the water.

"This is the kaiser's pier," she said. "He used it to go back and forth from his yacht."

"Like Midas?"

Her slits for eyes softened into a worried look. "What's your business with Roman?"

"He stole something that belonged to me."

She forced a smile. "I doubt that."

"That he stole something?" Conrad asked.

"That whatever he stole belonged to you. What was it, Conrad? Some Greek statue at the bottom of the sea?"

"Something important enough for Midas to blow up my boat and kill my crew over." He was as serious as he had ever let her see him.

She paused. "And so you decided to come back for more?"

"Did you hear me, Mercedes? Your boyfriend killed people today. You don't seem surprised. And that surprises *me*. What are you doing with a monster like Midas?"

"All men are animals." Her eyes narrowed back into slits. "But Roman is an adult, Conrad, not a child like you. He understands power and money and politics in a way you never could."

"All I understand, Mercedes, is that Midas seems to have moved on from oil to arms."

Mercedes sniffed. "I don't believe you. Midas doesn't need anything in this world. He's as rich as, well, Midas. He doesn't have to steal anything. He can buy it."

Conrad said, "Then tell me what he's buying these days besides megayachts and art."

A shadow passed across her face, betraying the fact that, yes, Midas had bought something interesting lately.

"You haven't changed, Conrad," she said. "You're looking for links that don't exist. The great conspiracy is that there are no conspiracies. Everybody is out for himself. Life is a big black hole. There is no meaning."

"Your existentialism used to have some romance, Mercedes. What happened?"

Her phone beeped, and she glanced at a text message and shook her head. It must have been from Midas, Conrad thought. "Romance is dead," she told him. "And so are you if you go after Roman."

She took his hand to lead him back to the party when two security men came down the steps, talking softly into their radios. "You fool, it's too late," Mercedes said, sounding genuinely alarmed.

Conrad looked over his shoulder past the kaiser's stone pier. A light in the distance grew closer, and soon a dinghy emerged from the mist around nearby Mouse Island, like a boat from the River Styx, with a large, muscular colossus of a man standing at the prow.

"You've got to be kidding me." Conrad had started to turn back to Mercedes when he felt the stab of a needle in his neck and blacked out.

9

A bucket of freezing water brought Conrad to life. He blinked his eyes open. He seemed to be inside the submersible launch bay of the superyacht *Midas*. The hatch was open wide over the surface of the water. Moonlight reflecting from the sands beneath the yacht bounced around the hold. He was sitting in a chair, his feet bound together at the ankles and his hands tied behind him to the back of the chair.

"What is the four-digit code, Professor?" said a voice with a thick Russian accent.

Conrad looked up to see a bodybuilder type towering over him. Behind him stood two security men and a giant basin of water. They were leaning against a double-domed deep-flight Falcon submarine. Midas must have used the Falcon to transport the *Flammenschwert* from the *Nausicaa* to the yacht, Conrad thought.

"I don't know about any four-digit code," Conrad said, trying to quickly make sense of his predicament. He should be dead. Maybe Midas hadn't found everything he was looking for in the *Nausicaa* and was hoping Conrad had. "But I'm sure glad you told me about it."

The Russian held up an electric shock baton. Conrad recognized it as the type favored by the Chinese police in torturing Falun Gong practitioners. "Maybe this will jog your memory," the Russian said.

Conrad shivered as the picture came into focus: He was drenched in water in order to intensify the three hundred thousand volts of electricity this thug was about to apply to him.

"I know you," Conrad told him, and he realized where he had seen the face. "You're that ex-KGB guy turned fitness guru with the kettle ball infomercial."

The Russian paused, seemingly pleased at the recognition. "It is true. I am Vadim."

"Too bad your website sucks. Bet your online sales of those Vadimin supplements do, too. Is this your day job, or do you have another one at some health spa?"

Vadim cocked his thick head. Conrad was clearly getting inside it, and the Russian didn't like it. He plunged the electric baton into the fresh harpoon wound in Conrad's leg.

Conrad gritted his teeth as the voltage shot up his thigh and throughout his body. For a second he thought his head would explode. When the wave of devastating pain finally passed, he dropped his head and saw that the baton had reopened his harpoon wound, which oozed blood.

"Utter a sound, Dr. Yeats, and I'll shove this baton

into your mouth and shock you with a thousand root canals at once until you black out."

Conrad could smell his own burned flesh. It would take weeks for it to fully heal. Not that Vadim was intending for him to see that day. The Russian pressed the wound with the baton until a shard of harpoon protruded up through the blood. Conrad moaned in agony.

"Go easy on the lad, sport," one of the other guards said in a British accent. "Midas wants to get the code out of him before he dies."

So the other two were Brits, Conrad thought. Private security. For all Conrad knew, Midas also employed former Navy SEALs and American mercenaries in his private global army. Who said capitalism was dead?

"Shut up, Davies," Vadim told the Brit sternly while he trained his eyes on Conrad. "Von Berg's code," he repeated. His breath was foul. "Four digits. Like your hand after I cut off your thumb." He pulled out a cigar cutter. "Or maybe I'll cut off something else. Now tell me where the code is."

"Of course!" Conrad cried out. "It's all in my head!" He started to laugh uncontrollably, despite the pain. It was crazy, but by rephrasing his demand for the code in terms of "where" instead of "what," Vadim had triggered an epiphany for Conrad. Now Conrad understood why nobody had found a metal briefcase containing secret codes inside the sunken sub. The paranoid Baron of the Black Order never carried secret papers in a briefcase or on his person on land, sea, or air. Von Berg knew he'd be dead if anybody found them. So he kept the code in his head, literally. And that head was back in Conrad's room at the Andros Palace Hotel.

Vadim and the Brits glanced at each other. "You find this funny, Dr. Yeats?"

Conrad nodded. "Let me guess. This code Midas wants. You don't know what it's for, do you?"

Vadim said, "You will tell us?"

"Hell, no. But Midas is going to assume I did. And then you guys are dead."

Vadim's nostrils flared. "What are you talking about?"

"I know what Midas stole from the sub this morning. Don't you?"

It was clear from Vadim's expression that he did not.

"Oops," Conrad said. "Maybe you're not as tight with the boss as you thought."

Vadim's eyes dilated at the truth of Conrad's words. Indeed, Vadim seemed to be reconsidering his relationship with Midas.

"What's more likely?" Conrad asked, relentless. "That Midas is going to kill you because I got away? Or because you know what he stole from the sub and where it might be?"

"Kill him," said Davies. "But get out of him what he knows."

Conrad looked at Vadim. "The only way to pull it off is like this: You have to make Midas believe you killed me before I said anything. But how is he going to believe that and keep you around? You have to make it look like I killed one of the Brits while trying to escape and that the other one came in and shot me."

"How stupid do you think I am, Dr. Yeats?" Vadim pulled out a 9mm Rook pistol of the type favored by Russian special forces and put it to Conrad's forehead.

"Quite stupid, actually," Conrad said.

Vadim shook his head, swung his arm to the side, and shot Davies in the head. Davies fell to the floor.

"Bloody hell!" screamed the other Brit, and pointed his Browning pistol at Vadim. "You killed him!"

Vadim shot the other Brit, and Conrad watched him crumple on top of his fallen comrade. Conrad, still in agony from the shock baton, kept laughing as Vadim put his gun away.

Vadim picked up the shock baton and glared at him. "You will now reveal the four-digit code, Professor Yeats."

"Look!" Conrad was staring at the bloody black hole in his thigh. "Look at what you did."

With a smile, Vadim bent over to take a closer look.

Conrad kneed him with both legs to the face, driving the protruding harpoon shard into Vadim's eye. The Russian snapped his head back with a howl. Then Conrad used his bound feet to sweep the leg of the table with the basin of water, sending it crashing to the floor.

As Vadim staggered back, his boot slipped on the water, and he lost his grip on the shock baton. Conrad watched the baton fall to the floor and lifted his feet as a blue wave of electrical light rippled across the water, electrocuting Vadim like an X-ray.

When Vadim came to a few minutes later, the yacht's "abandon ship" alarms were blaring, and Conrad was gone. In his place was a gray-green brick of C4 explosive with a timer and Davies's cut-off middle finger sticking up on top.

The display on the timer was down to one minute and twenty-three seconds. *"Chyort voz'mi!"* Vadim cursed, and scrambled topside to discover that the skeleton crew had left with the shuttle tender, leaving him no choice but to jump overboard and swim for his life.

10

Serena was alarmed to see Mercedes come up from the lower gardens alone and immediately went out on the terrace to search for Conrad, to no avail. She did, however, find Packard by the stone balustrade with a drink in his hand.

"What are you doing, Mr. Secretary?" she demanded. "Where's Conrad?"

"Elvis has apparently left the building," Packard told her. "And Midas doesn't look too happy."

Serena followed his gesture toward the statue of Apollo, where Midas seemed to be having a low-key but sharp exchange with Mercedes.

"Guess Midas just figured out that you're not the only woman here tonight who has a past with Yeats," said Packard, taking another sip of his drink. "Now, what's up in the Arctic?"

Serena tore her eyes away from Midas and looked at Packard. "Midas is prepping to mine it for the Russians."

"You sure it's for the Russians?"

"Who else?" Serena asked.

Packard finished his drink. "Your friends in the Alignment."

Serena looked out over the bay, where she could see Midas's yacht sparkling on the waters. "I have no friends in the Alignment," she told him. "Only enemies."

"But thanks to your corrupt holy order, Dominus Dei, of which you are now the head, you are by definition one of the Thirty."

Serena took a deep breath. "And as soon as I figure out who the rest are, I'll let you know."

"You were talking to one of them."

"Midas?" she said. "How do you know he's not just working for them?"

"He knows too much," Packard said. "More than you, it seems. Financial records in London show that Midas's trading firm went long on oil and gold futures this morning. If he really expected the Russians to succeed in the Arctic, he'd be shorting oil on the expectation that a new supply would depress global prices. Instead, he's betting on a spike in prices."

"Interesting," Serena said. "Midas must be anticipating a disruption in oil production."

"Or some other event that would shoot up the price of oil. Maybe a major war."

"So he knows something we don't," she said, and then she realized something. "And so does Conrad."

"You should fix that."

"Listen, I told you about Midas's operations in the Arctic. Have you given any thought to returning that celestial globe to the Vatican?"

"Have you given any thought to returning the terrestrial globe you stole?" Packard shot back.

"We've been over this, Mr. Secretary. The Masons inherited them from the Knights Templar."

"Who in turn stole them from Solomon's Temple," said Packard. "So maybe we give them both back to the Israelis."

Serena sighed. "Along with another American weapons system, perhaps? That will help the situation in the Middle East."

"The only thing you can do to help the Middle East and the rest of the world is to give us the real names and faces of the Alignment's so-called Thirty," Packard said. "Before Yeats finds out you're one of them. Get busy. Here comes Midas." Packard walked away as Midas approached her.

"Was that the former U.S. secretary of defense?" Midas asked Serena innocently enough.

"Yes," she said. "Confessing all his country's sins. Do you have any confessions you want to share?"

"Actually, I was looking for Dr. Yeats. He seems to have disappeared."

There was a feigned playfulness in Midas's voice, but his eyes were hard. He was lying, she realized. Midas knew exactly where Conrad was.

"So has Mercedes," she said, and his smile vanished.

Midas said, "She had a headache. Dr. Yeats upset her."

"He has that effect on women," Serena said when her Vertu phone rang with the song "He's a Tramp" from Disney's old *Lady and the Tramp* cartoon. "Speak of the devil."

Midas cocked his head and narrowed his eyes with suspicion as she took the call.

Conrad's voice, breathless, filled her ear: "Have Benito pick me up in front of the Andros Palace Hotel in Corfu town in two hours. I need to hitch a ride with you on your jet."

"We're all here for three more days," she said, eyeing Midas.

"I don't think these Bilderbergers like talking to police," Conrad said. "They're all going to scram before they give any statements about what they saw."

"I'm not sure I understand."

"Take a look out at the *Midas* in the bay. She sure looks like a beauty out there on the water, all lit up."

Serena glanced at Midas, then out at the water. "Yes, she does."

Suddenly, the superyacht blew up into the night sky like fireworks, drawing gasps from the crowd on the terrace. An explosion like thunder rolled over the bay. Midas crushed his glass in his fist. Wine and blood dribbled through his fingers. Serena watched his face twist into a monstrous mask of rage as the glowing debris of his beloved ship rained down upon the waters.

11

A panic-stricken Andros was waiting for Conrad at the service entrance behind his hotel. "You blew up the *Midas*!"

"Where's the head of Baron von Berg?" Conrad demanded as they hurried through the kitchen.

"In your bag in the room's closet. I couldn't stand the sight of it. Nor of you now, my friend."

They were standing at the service elevator. Conrad, his tuxedo soaked, realized he had been dripping a trail of water behind them. Two Greeks with mops were furiously following in their footsteps. The hotel's owner, Conrad had heard, was a stickler for cleanliness.

"All you have to do is smuggle me off the island, Andros," Conrad said, and pressed the elevator button again.

"I'm working on it, but the police and coast guard are everywhere now." Andros shook his head. "You've really done it this time, Conrad. Mercedes is up in your room."

"What?" Conrad stopped cold as the bell dinged and the elevator doors opened.

"She showed up just before you did." Andros nudged him inside. "You have to see her."

"But Midas sent her."

"Of course," said Andros. "Which is why you have to see her. He must hope to get something out of you."

"You mean the ice pick she'll plant in my back?"

"Maybe, but you might get something out of her. Meanwhile, give her some disinformation to take back to Midas. I'll have your ride off the island ready in twenty minutes."

"This could take longer than twenty minutes," Conrad said, knowing that Mercedes wasn't going to divulge important information to him just because he'd asked.

"Nonsense," said Andros, all business. "It took you only half as long with my cousin Katrina, and that's how you found me."

The doors closed, and Conrad rode the elevator to the top floor, where he walked down a short hallway to his room. Two security guards with earpieces were posted on either side. Conrad fished inside his pocket for his key card and realized he had lost it. That was probably how Midas and Mercedes had learned where he was staying.

"*Parakalo?*" Conrad asked a guard in Greek. "Please?"

The guard opened the door for him, and he walked

inside. The lights were dimmed, and the smooth jazz of Nina Simone was playing over the stereo speakers.

Mercedes was standing outside on the balcony, just beyond the rippling drapes, a glass of wine in her hand. It must have been at least her third glass, because the bottle in the ice bucket was almost empty. Her head tilted when the door clicked shut behind him.

He walked up beside her. Out in the bay, the Greek coast guard had spotlights over the wreckage of the *Midas*. He could hear the garble of megaphones in the wind. "What do you think we're going to do here tonight, Mercedes?"

She turned to him with her crystal-blue eyes, which were dried out and bloodshot. He had never seen her cry, and it appeared he never would. "You have no idea who Midas is and who his people are, Conrad."

"Oh, you mean the Alignment," he said, taking the glass from her hand and finishing the wine, aware of her stare. "I know. They're a sinister centuries-old group who count themselves as the heirs to the knowledge and power of Atlantis. They use the stars to wage their endless campaign to manipulate governments, armies, financial markets, and the course of human events. Their goal is a one-world government in effect if not name. In other words, ultimate power. Based on what they've already accomplished with the worldwide depression and de facto one-world central bank, I'd say they're halfway there."

She didn't appreciate his glibness. Her eyes turned into slits. "Then you know we're both dead."

"Speak for yourself, Mercedes. But I think you're better off telling Midas that your charms of old worked, that we slept together and you know I'm taking a plane out of here in the morning to Paris, where your well-heeled family can help me. Better yet, you're on that plane with me. Only we're landing in Dubai, where my well-heeled friends can help you."

She said nothing for a minute, her eyes drifting to the wine bottle and seeing it was nearly empty. "I am not a whore, Conrad."

"I didn't say you were."

"You were the one willing to prostitute yourself for the sake of your useless digs around the world," she went on. "You were willing to make love to me just to get my father to fund your stupid TV show. And you ditched me in Peru with those animals."

"I have no excuse, Mercedes. I'm sorry. And I know there's nothing I can do to make it up to you."

She put her hand on his chest and gently pressed him back toward the bedroom. "Oh, but there is, Professor," she said, regressing to her producer's "role" as his beautiful graduate assistant when he was still dividing his teaching duties between the University of California at Los Angeles and the University of Arizona.

"Two wrongs don't make a right," he told her as she began to unbutton his shirt.

"Like you and Serena? You two don't add up. You never did and never will."

"What about you and Midas?"

"He's rich and powerful. Powerful in a way you'll never understand."

"Because he's a player for the Alignment?"

"Maybe." She kissed him on the cheek.

"What did he do to make their ranks? Or did they make him?"

"I don't know," she said, moving to his ear. "Hard to tell with most of them."

"What does Midas do for the Alignment?"

"Mining and money," she said, clearly displeased to be discussing business. "His mining operations help governments, and his futures trading firm in London evens things out in the financial markets. As per Alignment protocols, his top traders use astrological charts to hedge their bets. That's why Midas Minerals & Mining is also called M3."

"And I thought M3 was my old BMW sports car."

"M3 is a constellation," she said.

Conrad perked up. "A constellation?"

"Canes Venatici. It's thought to represent the two dog stars of—"

"The herdsman in the sky, Boötes," Conrad said, unable to forget from his last run-in with the Alignment that the White House in Washington, D.C., was by design aligned to the alpha star of Boötes, Arcturus. Boötes was mythologically connected to the constellation Ursa Major—the Great Bear—from which Russia took its own identity. "I hate all this Alignment bullshit." He hated it because it reminded him of how ignorant he was of just how deep the celestial machinations and symbols of the Alignment went, and how far back—eons and eons. It was like encountering an alien race. And Mercedes had knowingly thrown in her lot with them.

It was all very suspicious, and he was already past the twenty minutes Andros had given him.

Conrad gently folded his hands around hers. "Where is Midas taking the *Flammenschwert*?" he asked.

Her face was blank. "*Flammenschwert*?"

"It was the name of a hammerhead torpedo the Nazis developed using some advanced technology. It means 'Sword of Fire.'"

"I know what *Flammenschwert* means," she told him curtly. "My German always was better than yours. But I know nothing of any *Flammenschwert*."

"Oh, you think Midas took his yacht out to deeper waters this morning simply for pleasure cruising?"

"Yes," she said, clearly irritated.

"So you never wondered why he outfitted his super-yacht with a submersible and a chopper pad?"

"I always assumed it was for effect." She sniffed.

He looked into her eyes—wide open now—and felt she was telling him the truth. It made sense to him that she'd projected onto Midas some of the foibles of her past and the men who were part of it, including him.

"Know anything about the four-digit code Midas is looking for?" he asked.

The slits returned. "How do you know about it? Did she tell you?"

By "she," Conrad figured Mercedes meant Serena.

"No," he told her, letting her read his own eyes. "You think it's for the *Flammenschwert*?"

"No," she said, and Conrad could see the light go out of her eyes as she sat on the bed. "It's for a safe deposit box."

"And Midas owns it?"

"No," she said. "You asked me if Midas has purchased anything lately. He owns the bank in Bern that holds the box. Gilbert et Clie."

Conrad wasn't sure he understood. "So he bought the bank to get to the box? That's one way to raid a tomb. What's in the box?"

"Nobody knows. It belonged to some Bavarian prince. Ludwig von Berg."

"Baron von Berg the Nazi?" He had to force himself to keep his eyes fixed on hers, to not let them drift to the closet where Andros had stashed the bag with the skull.

"Yes, yes," Mercedes said. "It's an older type of box with a chemical lining. It has a four-digit alphabet code. One wrong letter in the combination, and the contents of the box are destroyed. There's only one chance to open the box. And Midas needs whatever is inside within the next seven days."

"Seven days?" Conrad asked, realizing the world was going to be introduced to the *Flammenschwert* in short order.

"Seven days," she repeated. "Good Friday, two days before Easter."

"Is that significant to the Alignment?" Conrad asked. "Is there a connection?"

"I don't know," she said. "It's significant to me because Easter is the only Sunday of the year that I've ever gone to church."

"You're a real saint," he said. "But what's Midas doing spending three of his precious seven days with the Bilderbergers?"

"The Achillion was Baron von Berg's headquarters during the war," Mercedes said. "Midas had hoped to find some clues the baron might have left behind."

"He didn't leave any," Conrad said. "He kept everything in his head."

"I know. So I can't help you. And you can't help me."

Conrad, holding her hand, got down on one knee. "I told you, Mercedes. Come with me to Dubai and we'll figure it out."

She shook her head. "You know more than anybody else that there's no escaping the Alignment."

"Then come with me to Dubai," he told her. "Andros has the jet waiting. We'll be there in under three hours."

"And then what, Conrad?" She challenged him with her eyes. "We live happily ever after? Or you ditch me again?"

"I'm not going to ditch you, Mercedes."

"But you're going to leave me."

"I'm not going to stay with you, if that's what you mean."

"Then what's the point?"

"I want to help you," he said.

She looked at him with disdain, seemingly surprised by his naïveté. "I don't care how much money your crazy

Arab friends have, Conrad. Nobody runs away from Midas. He'll find you. And your friends will give you up in a heartbeat for less than the price of this." She held up her hand to show the glittering diamond bracelet dangling from her wrist. From the looks of it, Conrad calculated that it had cost Midas at least $1 million. A trinket for him, a handcuff for her.

"I'll give you thirty minutes before I call Midas," she said with finality. "Enough time to make it to the airport and take off."

"And you?" Conrad asked as he stood up and walked to the closet.

"I'll tell him you were asking about the *Flammenschwert* and that I offered to put you up at my apartment in Paris. Old Pierre will let you in."

Conrad pulled out his bag and slung it over his shoulder. "What happens when I don't show?"

She shrugged. "We'll all know you lied. Like you always do."

12

Vadim was parked across from the service entrance of the Andros Palace in the dark, making his calls while he waited for Mercedes to emerge. He set his 9mm Rook on the passenger seat next to his copy of *The Four-Hour Workweek.*

Despite his boasting to Yeats, his Vadimin vitamin supplements were not selling as well as he had hoped. So while Yeats was undoubtedly making love to Sir Midas's French *blyad,* Vadim was on his cell phone making calls on behalf of the collection agency Midas owned in Bangalore to shake down money from customers behind on their credit card payments. He took perverse pleasure in squeezing money from the debt-ridden pockets of Americans and their knowledge that foreigners were doing it.

A figure stepped outside the hotel—Yeats, from the looks of him at a distance—and climbed into a black BMW 7 series sedan. Vadim started his car and caught a glimpse of his own face in the mirror. He saw the patch over his eye and cursed. The BMW drove off.

Vadim pulled out and had started to follow it around front when Mercedes emerged from the hotel's main entrance and walked toward him. He stopped and let her climb in the back.

"You were supposed to kill him," Vadim said as he drove off after the BMW.

"So were you," she said sharply. "He's going to the airstrip."

Vadim looked up in the mirror. "And from there?"

"Athens, Dubai, God knows where," she said. "I invited him to my place in Paris."

Very clever, Vadim thought. She had guessed that Vadim's orders were to kill her as soon as she killed Yeats. This way she had hoped to keep herself alive a while longer. But if Yeats got off the island alive, Vadim's orders were to kill Mercedes instantly and make it appear that Yeats had done it. The time of death would be vital for the Greek coroner's report.

The car with Yeats stopped ahead. Two police cars were blocking its path. Vadim slowed down and watched as the police made the passenger step out of the limousine for inspection. Only it wasn't Yeats. It was a slightly younger man—Chris Andros III, the Greek billionaire.

"What is the meaning of this?" Andros asked.

"*Signomi, Kyrios* Andros. We thought you were somebody else."

"Obviously, you're mistaken. What do you want?"

"Where are you going?"

"My jet. I have business in Athens, as you know."

"Our apologies," the police officer said.

Vadim didn't bother to watch Andros get back in his sedan; he had already reversed course and was driving back on a small dirt road. In the mirror, he could see Mercedes getting nervous.

"Where are you taking me?" she said.

Vadim pulled to a stop and looked over his shoulder at her. She was scared. She should be. "Did you lift Dr. Yeats's fingerprints like Sir Midas requested?"

"Yes, off a bottle of wine," she said, and handed him a white card with Dr. Yeats's fingerprints trapped on clear tape. "What is Conrad supposed to have done now?"

"Killed you with this gun," said Vadim as he leveled his Rook over the seat and shot her twice in the chest.

13

At the Corfu airport, the twin turbofan Honeywell engines of Serena's private Learjet 45 hummed while she ran through the preflight checklist with the pilot and copilot. Both had more hours in the air than she did, and both were former Swiss special forces airmen she trusted with her life, let alone a short fifty-minute hop to Rome. But she hadn't heard from Conrad yet, and this took her mind off him for the moment.

"Check the thrust reverters again," she said when she was finished. "I thought I heard something."

She went back into the passenger cabin, sat down in a recliner seat, and glanced outside her window at all the private Gulfstreams lined up to go. The scene was the same in Davos, Sun Valley, San Francisco, and everywhere else she had ever seen the billionaire set meet. Her own Learjet was a hand-me-down from an American patron who had moved on to an even more expensive pair of wings. All the planes on the tarmac this morning resembled a line of luxury cars exiting a parking lot after a sporting event. Only this event—the sixtieth Bilderberg meeting—had barely begun.

Now it was over.

Conrad was right: Every European and American master of the universe was scrambling to escape the island before the police and paparazzi could question him or her. The weekend conference was in shambles, along with Sir Roman Midas's great superyacht, which no doubt was going to fire the imaginations of Bilderberg conspiracy theorists for years.

The truth, of course, was much simpler: Conrad Yeats.

Wherever he was.

The Vertu phone she was clutching in her hand vibrated. It was Marshall Packard, calling from his private jet on the other side of the runway. "You're losing your grip, girl," he barked. "Where the hell is Yeats?"

"I don't know," she said, alarmed. "What's going on?"

"Turn on the goddamn TV."

Serena clicked a small remote to turn on the cabin's TV. The local Greek channel came up first, but she didn't have to be fluent in Greek to understand the picture of Mercedes Le Roche—dead at thirty-two. She had been found at a local beach, shot in the chest.

"Oh, no," Serena said under her breath. "Conrad."

As if on cue, Conrad's picture showed up. He was the prime suspect in her death. His fingerprints had been found all over the murder weapon—a 9mm Rook.

"Conrad prefers a Glock," Serena said quickly. "He didn't kill Mercedes."

"No, he was either killed with her or is about to join her," Packard said sharply before he hung up.

Serena looked out her window to see Benito pulling up in the car, then talking to the Greek police as he stepped out. They were conducting a plane-to-plane search for Conrad Yeats. They were paying particular attention to her plane, no doubt courtesy of Midas. They needn't have worried.

Benito boarded the plane, shut the door, and sat down in the aisle across from her as the engines grew to a dull roar. They were cleared for takeoff. She held her breath while Benito solemnly fastened his seat belt and looked at her with sad, soulful eyes.

"I'm sorry to tell you, *signorina,* that once again Dr. Yeats has fooled us all."

She breathed a sigh of relief. "Thank God."

14

Conrad looked at himself in the broken mirror of his private compartment as the Czech-built diesel locomotive hauled the train clickety-clack across the Albanian countryside. He had boarded the train as a swarthy Mediterranean workman and would disembark as a Central European businessman in a dark Brooks Brothers suit, with lighter hair, goatee, and spectacles.

That was assuming the train reached the end of the line. The Mother Teresa international airport in Tirana was only an hour away, but they were going less than thirty-five miles an hour.

Conrad had escaped Corfu and crossed the Adriatic to the southern coast of Albania in under thirty minutes, all thanks to the hydrofoil Andros had provided, along with fake passports, a bag of disguises, and two untraced smartphones, a BlackBerry and an iPhone, each operating on a separate network carrier. From the beach at Durrës, he had made it to the local train station, where he first saw the news about Mercedes and his picture on all the news websites on his iPhone.

Goddamn bastards, he thought as he gave himself a final once-over in the small mirror.

He was thinking of Midas and the Alignment, Packard and the U.S., and even Serena and the Church. Everybody, in the end, was in bed with each other when they weren't killing each other. Also, it bothered him to no end to see that he had better cell phone reception in Albania than he had back in the States: He had just received his electronic boarding pass from Swissair in his bogus identity's e-mail inbox.

He put away his makeup and glared at the only other passenger in the private compartment of this secondhand railroad car: Baron von Berg. Sitting on a torn seat, the skull taunted him with its jagged grin and the secrets it once possessed.

It's all in my head.

Conrad pulled out the Glock he kept tucked inside his back waistband. Aiming the butt of the pistol like a hammer over the skull, he brought it down on the silver plate, smashing the skull to pieces. He looked at the fragments of bone scattered around the silver plate on the table.

Nothing. The skull was indeed empty.

Then he picked up the silver plate. He turned it over and held his breath. There was a glint of small engraving in the silver.

"Von Berg, you crazy bastard," Conrad said as he took a closer look at the engraving.

It was a string of eight characters—four numbers followed by four letters: 1740 ARES.

There it was: 1740 had to be the number of Baron von Berg's safe deposit box in what was now Midas's Swiss bank. And ARES had to be the combination.

This was the four-digit code Midas was looking for.

He had it and Midas didn't.

But with the Alignment, there was always more, he knew. Nothing could be taken for granted.

Ares was the name of the ancient Greek god of war. The astral projection was the constellation Aries, the first sign of the zodiac. The planet Mars, with the Roman name of the same Greek god, had entered the sign of Aries two weeks ago on March 20, the spring equinox.

A coincidence?

Not for these Alignment bastards. Every day and date had some sort of bizarre meaning for them, if for nobody else.

There was probably an astrological connection that could throw light on the baron's 1943 plans for the *Flammenschwert* and Midas's plans for it in the new millennium.

Mercedes had said something about seven more days. That would be one week from today—Good Friday for Christians around the world, according to the Gregorian calendar. There would be a full moon that night, followed the next day by the Jewish Passover and the day after that by Christian Easter.

Beyond those dates, Conrad saw nothing else of astrological or astronomical significance on the calendar while the zodiac was fixed in Aries.

Seven days.

Whatever was going to happen with the *Flammenschwert* was going to happen then. And the religious significance of the dates only further confirmed the magnitude of the Alignment's plot, whatever it was.

The train's wheels made a high-pitched screech, and Conrad looked out to see a sheer cliff as the train hugged a mountain above the Adriatic. He took the opportunity to toss the silver plate out the window and scatter the remains of the skull over the waters. Not quite a proper burial for the Baron of the Black Order, but it would have to do.

By the time the train pulled into the station in Tirana, he was all packed up and ready to step off into his new identity. He scanned the platform for any security and grabbed a cab to the Mother Teresa airport.

An hour later, he leaned back in his seat as the Swissair plane lifted off the runway and banked toward Zurich. The seat belt sign blinked off a few minutes later, and flight attendants took drink orders. He ordered two Bloody Marys, one for Serena and one for Mercedes, painfully aware that he'd just had a very close call and that this was the last free pass he'd enjoy on the journey before him.

PART TWO

Baku

15

A darkened military car carrying one American and three Azerbaijani special forces commandos rolled through the city's old town toward the harbor before dawn.

Riding shotgun in the front passenger seat with an AG36 40mm grenade launcher across her lap was the American, a knife-thin black woman in her early thirties with short hair and sharp features. Her name was Wanda Randolph, and her mission was to intercept and secure a mysterious shipment that had landed at Heydar Aliyev International Airport, sixteen miles east of Baku. The airport's advanced Antworks computer software and scanner system had tagged and tracked the crate through the cargo terminal's state-of-the-art X-rays and radiation detectors to an awaiting van. The van had taken the crate to a warehouse on the Caspian, where it was waiting to be loaded onto an oil tanker.

The operation was code-named *Feuerlöscher*—German for "fire extinguisher."

The commando raid was to be carried out jointly by American and Azerbaijani special operations forces and locals. The mission had been mounted rapidly overnight on orders from the Central Intelligence Agency and the Defense Department when the location of the crate had been confirmed. Another dozen American commandos in a specially equipped Black Hawk were ready to swoop in if the team got pinned in a gun battle.

Wanda glanced up from the glowing GPS map that General Packard had sent to her handheld computer. The ancient walls of the Palace of the Shirvanshahs, the Maiden Tower, and the Juma Mosque rose up on either side of the narrow, twisting alley. Then the car cleared the maze of buildings, and the pitch-black Caspian Sea spread out before them, marked by the lights along the waterfront.

The Caspian was called a sea because, at 143,244 square miles, it was the world's largest lake, smack between Russia to the north and Iran to the south. Azerbaijan occupied the western shores, and tonight it felt as if the city of Baku stood at the edge of the world, a world that itself was teetering on the brink of a bottomless abyss.

"Take a left," she told the driver, a young macho gun named Omar.

"Yes, ma'am," Omar said in a bogus Oklahoma accent, eliciting muffled chuckles from the other two in back. All three had been trained in a cross-cultural Oklahoma National Guard training program with the U.S. Army and loved to play the American cowboy in the new Wild West here on the Caspian. But none had ever been ordered to listen to a woman, let alone one of color, and they resisted. The election of America's first black president, it turned out, wasn't going to change human nature or much of anything else in this world.

They turned onto Neftchilar Avenue and drove along the waterfront boulevard and marina. They quickly passed the state oil company and government house and, a few minutes later, were surrounded by the oil derricks and pumps of the east harbor.

At last she could make out the warehouse where the van with the crate containing the *Flammenschwert* was parked. She directed Omar to park at the adjoining oil terminal, then led them to a communal outhouse.

"Why have we stopped?" Omar said once they were inside and could talk quietly. He was breathing through his mouth because of the stench. "The warehouse is the other way."

"Sorry to disappoint you, Omar. But we can't go storming in like Rambo if there's any chance they've got some kind of nuclear device. We've got to take them by surprise." She unfolded her schematics of the sewer tunnels. "No radios," she instructed them. "We stick to light signals until we get to the warehouse, and then it's hand motions."

She looked up and locked eyes with each man as she spoke. She wanted to make sure they understood her perfectly.

Standing around in their black-on-black Texas

Ranger baseball caps, flak jackets, and special night-vision hazmat masks, the Azerbaijanis could pass for one of her old U.S. special forces teams. Wanda had gotten her start years earlier in Tora Bora and Baghdad, crawling through caves and bunkers and sewers ahead of American troops in search of al-Qaeda terrorist leader Osama bin Laden and, later, Iraqi dictator Saddam Hussein. Bomb-sniffing dogs had the noses to find explosives, but they didn't have the eyes or sense to look out for trip wires in the dark. So she was always the first one in. Later on she was recruited by the U.S. Capitol Police to establish a special recon and tactics squad, or RATS, to police and protect the miles of utility tunnels beneath the U.S. Capitol complex. "Queen Rat," they called her.

But Omar and his friends weren't at that level of professionalism yet. They were inexperienced in these kinds of operations, a political necessity for a "joint" American-Azerbaijani mission that was anything but. Tonight was a baptism by fire.

"This outhouse is connected to an ancient sewer that pipes into the modern one under the warehouse," she told them, pointing to the map. "We come up from beneath, use a camera to get a readout, and then we hit them and secure the package."

She double-checked to make sure they had properly inserted the translucent magazines of their laser-sighted G36 machine guns. Their short-stroke gas systems enabled them to fire tens of thousands of rounds without cleaning, perfect for these guys. Then she proceeded to unbolt one of the rusty metal latrines from the concrete floor to reveal a big black hole.

Omar could only stare in horror as the mission she described on the schematic finally sank in. "This is a shithole!"

"That's what we Americans do, Omar. Climb through shitholes all over the world to make it a safer place."

He shook his head in horror. "I cannot fit through that," he said with disdain. "My shoulders are too wide."

Which was true. A man's shoulders were often the limiting factor in this kind of work. For women, it was their hips; Wanda's were unusually slim. But while women could do little to narrow their pelvis, men had other options.

"Dang, Omar, you're right. Here, let me take a look," she said, and with an open palm made a powerful thrust to Omar's right shoulder. The blow dislocated his shoulder, and it dropped like a hanging outlaw in an old western. "Oops."

"You American bitch!" he cried. "You broke it!"

"I can fix it when we get out. But now you can squeeze in."

He opened his mouth to protest, but she gave him her angry-black-woman death stare until he calmed down. She then strapped her grenade launcher to her back, slipped on her mask, pushed aside the metal latrine, and dropped into the sewer.

It was cool and dark in the tunnel as she crawled on all fours through the river of filth and oil. One spark and they'd all burn to a crisp. It had been in a crumbling, asbestos-lined tunnel much like this one that she had first met and shot at Conrad Yeats. Yeats had been America's most-wanted man at the time. Now he was Europe's most-wanted man. Or he would be once news got out that he had blown up billionaire Roman Midas's megayacht and allegedly killed his French media scion girlfriend.

But General Packard had been proved right again: The sight of Yeats had been enough for Midas to double-check his operations and, in so doing, betray the location of the package she was after. The breakthrough had come when the tail sign of Midas's twin-engine G650 was caught over the Black Sea by the cockpit cameras of an unmanned Israeli G550 AWACS, or airborne early warning aircraft, equipped with the Israeli Phalcon radar system and satellite data links. The Israeli plane's onboard SIGINT equipment then captured and analyzed the pilot's electronic transmissions and traced them to a cell phone owned by Roman Midas.

Wanda followed the schematics to reach the end point under the warehouse. She snaked a fiber-optic camera through the grating of a drain and got a visual on the van sitting on the loading dock.

She signaled her team, and they took up positions beneath the grating. It was the size of a manhole cover back in the States. She poked it with the barrel of her AG36 and found it heavy but movable. She slid it slowly across the concrete floor and climbed out into the warehouse, followed by Omar and his buddies, who looked like rats on a drowning ship coming up for air.

Omar's arm was dragging. Wanda put her slimy hand over his mask and, staring into his wide eyes, hammered his shoulder back into place while she muffled his cry. They moved out quietly, awaiting her signal.

The van sat there in the dark with a driver behind the wheel while the sound of a motorboat grew louder. She looked through her nightscope and saw two flashes from the sea. The van replied by flashing its headlights twice. A minute later, a boat pulled up, and four black-clad men jumped out.

The van door slid open to reveal the driver and a crate. The driver stepped out to meet the men but then dropped to the ground as one of the seamen slashed a knife across his throat. The killer silently kicked the body into the water and walked to the crate and hauled it over. He flashed a sign. Now four men appeared. He cracked open the box and lit a cigarette.

Wanda squeezed the trigger, and Mr. Marlboro crumpled to the ground. By the time his companions saw, it was too late. A hail of bullets from the Azerbaijanis rained down on them and riddled the van with bullets.

"Stand down!" she shouted, and ran over to the crate while the others jogged after her. "It's a miracle you didn't blow us all up!"

She broke open the crate to find a dead dolphin on a block of dry ice. The stench was rank. She heard something behind her and turned to see one of her boys puking out his last meal: lula kebab with walnuts. She was about to call this red herring in to Packard, but he had already seen everything from her head camera and was cursing loudly into her ear.

She ripped off her earpiece and looked at Omar, who had helped himself to the Marlboro of the dead man and was smiling. "You see something funny here, Omar?"

Omar started laughing.

She repeated, "I asked if you see something funny here."

"You," Omar said, pointing the cigarette at her as he blew a perfect ring of smoke. "You have shit on your face!"

16

Midas couldn't help but note all the sale items on display in the storefront windows along an empty Bond Street in the early morning as Vadim drove the Bentley toward the worldwide headquarters of Midas Minerals & Mining. The golden glass tower was designed to look like a stack of gold coins overlooking the River Thames. But the global financial depression had come into full force by the time it was finished, making it a symbol of excess from an earlier gilded age.

His beloved megayacht was another symbol of that era, and the *Times* of London had taken the liberty of printing two pictures—before and after—on the front page by the time Midas had landed after his unplanned early departure from Corfu two hours ago. Below the fold was a smaller story about the murder of Mercedes.

That goddamn American. Yeats left me no choice.

Midas hated losses, and to take them at the hands of

a two-bit pirate like Conrad Yeats was doubly humiliating. He hated feeling like he was cornered.

Now his BlackBerry smartphone was vibrating in a manner that told him Sorath was calling. Midas reached into the long trench coat he had put on upon landing—the air in London being considerably more chilly than on the tropical island of Corfu—and answered the phone.

The disembodied voice of the grandmaster of the Knights of the Alignment was chillier still, and wasted no time making accusations.

"I warned you not to attempt to kill Yeats, Midaslovich. You betrayed yourself to the Americans, and now you are brazen enough to think you can bargain with us."

Sorath sounded particularly displeased, but maybe it was just because there was a deeper bass level than usual in the harmonics of the voice scrambler that disguised his identity. For the past year Midas had tried to find a voiceprint match, all in vain. Only a face-to-face at the Rhodes summit next week would reveal the grandmaster's true identity and whether or not Midas already knew the man.

"I've done no such thing," Midas replied coolly.

"Then why, after all we've done for you, did you feel the need for extra insurance?" the voice said. "I'm speaking of the American strike inside Baku an hour ago."

"They found nothing," Midas said. "And neither did the man you had in place to relieve me of the *Flammenschwert.*"

"What have you done with it?" Sorath demanded.

Midas smiled. Sorath wasn't God, and it was pleasant to hear him admit as much. The grandmaster of the Knights of the Alignment wasn't omnipotent, and he certainly wasn't omniscient, or he would have known from the start that Midas never would have allowed himself to become expendable to anybody.

Which was why Midas had offloaded the *Flammenschwert* from the *Midas* to his second submersible while making everybody think he had sent it off by chopper. That submarine was completely undetectable as it made its way underwater until the proper time for it to surface. Meanwhile, Midas was untouchable.

"My orders were to bring the *Flammenschwert* to Uriel," he said. "And so I shall. Nothing has changed."

"Yeats changed things. Mercedes Le Roche is dead, and you're being tracked by the Americans and Scotland Yard."

Midas turned to look out the rear window and saw the unmarked police car in the distance. Two of them had been following him ever since his private jet had landed at Heathrow.

"KGB, CIA, MI5, it matters little to me," Midas said. "I've dealt with them all, and I'm happy to provide misdirection by simply going about my business as usual. I'm here in London for the weekend, then to Paris for Mercedes's funeral, and then off to Rhodes as scheduled."

There was a pause on the other end. "Did you find the code to Baron von Berg's box?"

Midas said nothing as Vadim pulled the Bentley up to the main entrance of the Midas Center.

"You know the requirements for full membership in the Thirty, Midaslovich," Sorath said. "I'd hate to have you miss our little private gathering during the Rhodes summit."

Midas heard the telltale series of beeps signaling that Sorath had hung up and their scrambled transmission was over.

Midas rode a glass elevator up from the sparkling six-story atrium of the hotel, shops, and offices into the tower of private condominiums. Few Britons knew or cared that the award-winning building, his firm's trading in precious metals, his widely publicized purchases at art auctions at Sotheby's, and even his knighthood by the queen all had been part of the Alignment's strategic branding effort to paint him as something other than another former Russian oil oligarch. Even if that was how Sorath and the Alignment preferred to treat him.

Midas walked into his bedroom and into the second of his vast walk-in wardrobe rooms. On the racks hung dozens of Savile Row suits like the one he was wearing, and on the walls hung several million-dollar paintings he had purchased at Sotheby's and later found too ugly to hang anywhere else.

He sat on one of the overstuffed chairs and unlaced his shoes, pulled off his socks, and removed every strip of clothing. He then stood before the row of mirrors and examined his sculpted physique.

He still had a six-pack abdomen, although he'd once boasted an eight-pack when he went fishing with Putin a few years back. The former Russian president always liked to remove his shirt in the great outdoors for the cameras, so the people would know their leader was virile and strong. Putin had not liked it when Midas removed his own shirt and showed him up, and Midas was never invited fishing again.

He saw his right hand trembling slightly in the mirror and closed it into a quiet fist. He opened it, and the fingers began to tremble again. With a sigh, he pushed a button, and the mirror slid open like a door to reveal a stone chamber with a glowing spa in the center. The Tank, as he called it, was his only real weakness and altar to the mysticism of the Alignment. But the reality of his long-term exposure to cyanide as a child and the resulting neurological condition had forced him to seek a cure regardless of its source. Without a cure, he would eventually suffer the same fate as the divers he had gassed in the decompression chamber aboard the *Midas*.

Lining the floor, walls, and ceiling of the chamber were bluestones from the same quarries used by the ancients centuries ago to erect the monument of Stonehenge, Britain's darkest mystery. Most archaeologists believed Stonehenge was an astronomical observatory of some kind, erected around 2500 B.C. But others long had suspected the bluestones were far older and that Stonehenge was a place of healing for pilgrims from all across Europe.

Bluestones, it seemed, were prized for their healing

properties. And it was none other than Conrad Yeats, ironically, who had used the stars to help a team of British archaeologists from Bournemouth University pinpoint the exact location in Wales from where Stonehenge's massive bluestones were quarried—Carn Menyn Mountain in the Preseli Hills of Pembrokeshire.

As for the spa in the center of the bluestone floor, Midas's mistress in London, Natalia, had filled it with kabbalah water. Her friend the American pop star Madonna had sworn by it when she purchased a flat in the tower.

Kabbalistic wisdom, Natalia had told him with a straight face, taught that water was God's medium for the creation of the world and was the essence of all life on earth. In the beginning, God's spirit moved across the face of "the deep" that was pure, positive, and healing energy. But then the "negativity" of humanity—she refused to use the word "sin"—by the time of Noah's Flood had changed the nature of water into a destructive force of floods, tsunamis, and the like. Kabbalists believed that water could be returned to its primordial state of good by infusing it with ancient blessings and meditations.

That was how kabbalah water came to fill Midas's bluestone spa, with all its miraculous powers of restoration and healing.

The Alignment, of course, had a different term for this kind of allegedly metastasized water: Tears of Atlantis. The Knights of the Alignment consumed it as a special-label drinking water courtesy of the Hellenic Bottling Company, which also distributed Coca-Cola across Europe and the Middle East.

Midas could only smile as he pictured a small team of kabbalists, all sworn to secrecy, chanting away in some obscure distillation room at the bottling plant.

On one crazy level, it made sense to him that water was a conductor of energy and that the quality of the water he took into his body impacted the information being transmitted to his nervous system. At the very least, it gave his London mistress something to do with her friend Madonna besides run off and spend his money on yet another money-losing retail store for her hideous fashion lines.

He stepped down and settled into the warm amethyst-colored waters of the spa. He reclined in the sculptured stone seat built into the bluestone basin and glided his hand past a sensor. Music piped in, and an overhead door of solid bluestone slowly slid over him and locked into place. The glass screen across the entire back of the door enabled him to surf the Internet, watch any television channel, and monitor his businesses around the world. But for now he put on his favorite screen saver of soothing light, closed his eyes, and laid his head back until only his eyes, nose, and mouth broke the surface of the water.

Kabbalah water. Bluestones with healing powers. Such articles of faith were nonsense to Midas. But these immersion experiences in the tank seemed to have arrested the progression of the neurological condition brought on by his long-term exposure to cyanide. Slowly, it was taking over his body and would eventually kill him. He had to stop it. He would do anything to live.

Even cave to the mysticism of the Alignment.

17

L ater that morning, the events of Corfu still fresh in
her psyche, Serena stared through the tinted window of her limo at the obelisk in St. Peter's Square as
Benito drove through the gates of Vatican City on the eve
of Palm Sunday and Easter week celebrations.

As she checked her Vertu phone, she couldn't shake
the memory of Conrad the night before, the hatred in his
eyes. He had left her no message. Nor any clue as to his
whereabouts. But she did have an Evite to the funeral of
Mercedes Le Roche in Paris on Monday, along with a
personal e-mail from Papa Le Roche himself, the Rupert
Murdoch of French media, begging her as a friend of the
family to attend.

"You have enough worries without him, *signorina*," said Benito, looking up in the mirror, reading her
thoughts. "He can take care of himself. You must fix your
eyes on Rhodes."

"I know, Benito," she said. "But it's different this time.
I feel it."

"It's always different, *signorina*. Every time we pass through these gates. And so it is always the same."

True, she thought as they curved along a winding drive and arrived at the entrance of the governorate. Eight years ago the pope had met her in a secret office here and given her an antediluvian map along with a holy mission to uncover ancient ruins two miles beneath the ice in Antarctica. Four years later, in that very office, the diabolical Cardinal Tucci had revealed to her the truth behind the Church's supersecret order Dominus Dei. Then he had jumped out a window to his death. Now the office was hers.

The Swiss Guards in their crimson uniforms snapped to attention as Serena walked inside. She passed a hive of offices along an obscure hallway to an old service elevator.

In normal times the elevator would take her up to the fifth floor and her suite of offices, which officially interceded on behalf of persecuted Christians in politically hostile countries and unofficially administered the work of Dominus Dei. But these were anything except normal days. She pressed her thumb to a button with no markings that scanned her biometrics, and the elevator descended to the catacombs beneath Vatican City.

She felt like a prisoner in her own castle and remembered the words of Jesus in the Book of Revelation: "Look, I'm standing at the door and knocking. If anyone listens to my voice and opens the door, I'll come in and we'll eat together." He had been talking about the door of the human heart, but He just as easily could have been talking about the Church. After all, God had called St. Paul to go beyond his Jewish world in order to bring the message of redemption through faith in Jesus Christ to the Greeks and, ultimately, to Caesar in Rome.

Perhaps it was "out there" that God had been calling her all along, beyond the walls of the Church. She had cloistered herself here, she had told herself, to protect Conrad and the Church and the world. But maybe she was doing more harm than good. After all, Jesus was more likely to be found beyond the domes and spires and walls of Vatican City, with the people He called "the least of these." Not with the rich and powerful or religious, whom she had found to be as poor and weak and worldly in spirit as anybody.

Yet here she was, locked inside the holy gates of Rome.

Serena stepped off the elevator onto a secret floor deep beneath the governorate. She walked down a long subterranean tunnel to a heavy ornate door behind which the Dei kept priceless artifacts collected from around the world and across the ages. If it were her choice, she would have returned most of them to museums in their cultures of origin. But it was not.

Indeed, her choices of late seemed to be more limited than ever.

Waiting for her inside the dimly lit chamber was a young monk from the Dei and the two otherworldly copper globes that he was guarding. Brother Lorenzo was one of the Vatican's top authenticators of antiques and therefore one of its top forgers of art. He knelt before Serena and kissed her ring with the Dominus Dei insignia.

"Your Eminence," he said. "Welcome back."

Serena, extremely uncomfortable, looked down at the top of the monk's bowed head and withdrew her hand from his clasp. The Church didn't allow female priests, let alone female cardinals. But as the head of Dominus Dei, she was automatically considered a "secret cardinal" appointed by the pope. A secret cardinal to hide the secrets of the Church. Not that the current pontiff, as traditional as they came, would ever acknowledge her as such. But to her amazement, the Vatican did secretly acknowledge the rank of her office, if not the officeholder. Her frighteningly eager underlings, hoping to gain the office for themselves someday, took every advantage to freely address her as such.

"Thank you, Brother Lorenzo. You can call me Sister Serghetti."

Lorenzo rose to his feet, but his covetous gaze was fixed on the medallion dangling from her neck. "Yes, Sister Serghetti."

As she had explained to Midas, legend had it that the ancient Roman coin in the center of the medallion was the very Tribute Penny Jesus had held up when He told His followers that they should "render unto Caesar what is Caesar's and unto God what is God's." It had been passed down through the ages from one leader of the Dei to the next. Some argued that it represented power greater than the papacy. Which no doubt explained Lorenzo's disturbing fascination with it.

Serena broke Lorenzo's trance with an order: "The globes, Lorenzo."

"This way, Sister Serghetti."

She followed Lorenzo to the small alcove showcasing the globes, one displaying the surface of the earth, the other displaying the heavens. Each sphere was eighteen inches in diameter and resembled the works of the Dutch master cartographer Willem Bleau's studio in the sixteenth century. But these had been constructed thousands of years earlier, although her attempts to date them proved inconclusive.

Both Church and Templar tradition suggested the globes once rested atop the twin columns that stood at the entrance of King Solomon's Temple. But the Knights Templar believed the globes themselves were crafted far earlier. While Noah was building his ark, other children of Lamech were engraving the globes with the lost knowledge of Atlantis and the antediluvian world so that knowledge would survive the coming destruction of the Flood. The globes, the Templars believed, contained or pointed to some pre-Genesis revelation.

The only legend that Serena had been able to authenticate with any degree of certainty, however, was that the globes had been unearthed beneath the Temple Mount in Jerusalem by the Knights Templar.

Centuries later, the Masons took them to the New

World and buried them under what would become
Washington, D.C. That was where they rested until the
twenty-first century, when Conrad Yeats dug them up
before the Alignment could.

The globes apparently worked together like some
kind of astronomical clock in a manner that Serena had
yet to figure out. But she was positive it involved a secret
code or alignment between a constellation on the celestial globe and a landmark on the terrestrial globe. After
all, Conrad's knowledge that Washington, D.C., was
aligned to the constellation of Virgo had led him to the
location of the globes. So it made sense to Serena that
the alignment of the globes themselves led to an even
greater revelation—a revelation that for centuries had
eluded the Church, the Knights Templar, the Masons, the
Americans, and everybody else.

Everybody, that is, except the Alignment, which had
ordered her to deliver the Templar globes next week to
the meeting of the Council of Thirty on the island of
Rhodes, all under the guise of the European summit on
the fate of Jerusalem.

Serena ran her hand over the smooth contours of the
continents on the terrestrial globe, marveling at its three-
dimensional, holographic look. "Now tell me what you discovered with the terrestrial globe," she said to Lorenzo.

"The terrestrial sphere is full of hidden gear wheels
that, in turn, drive the most unique surface dials I've ever
seen on an ancient astronomical clock."

"What dials?"

"The northern and southern hemispheres of the terrestrial globe are really dials," he said. "Inside the mechanism are gear trains that drive the dials. The gear trains are driven by a crank that is inserted into a tiny hole at the bottom in Antarctica."

She looked closely at the tiny hole in the ancient landmass of East Antarctica. It was in the shape of a pentagon. "How could I have missed it?"

"It is rather small." Lorenzo pulled out a tiny S-lever that he had reproduced, inserted it into the hole, and began to crank it. "It works like a keylock, moving the hidden gears within the shell."

To Serena's amazement, the surface of the terrestrial globe began to change before her eyes like some kind of high-definition animation. The continents didn't move, but the contours within them shimmered for a moment and locked into place. "What happened?" she demanded.

"This," said Lorenzo, removing the lever and inserting a penlight into the hole. Three pinpricks of light burst forth from the terrestrial globe in the locations of Antarctica, Washington, D.C., and Jerusalem.

"It's a triangle," Serena said decisively. "Just like the U.S. Capitol, the White House, and the Washington Monument. Those monuments lined up with the constellations of Boötes, Leo, and Virgo. Likewise, these three capital cities from the terrestrial globe should line up with three constellations on the celestial globe."

"The problem, of course, is that the real celestial globe is still with the Americans," Lorenzo reminded her. "And you've never seen it with your own eyes, only the terrestrial globe you stole from Dr. Yeats. He's the only person alive who has seen both globes, which puts us at a terrible disadvantage. The faux globe I've created over here is merely my attempt to mirror in astral terms the mapping I've gleaned from the terrestrial globe."

All true, unfortunately, Serena thought. Her plan had been to procure the genuine celestial globe from Marshall Packard in exchange for her intelligence on Russian mining operations in the Arctic. But that plan had gone up in flames on Corfu. So she had been forced to resort to Plan B.

"I did the best I could," Lorenzo explained weakly as he showed her the two globes side by side—the forged celestial globe and the genuine terrestrial globe.

"Oh, dear," she said, unable to hide her disappointment. The celestial knockoff looked markedly inferior next to the terrestrial globe.

"Our metallurgists, meanwhile, tell me that they've never seen anything like the copper-bronze ore from which the original globes were cast," Lorenzo said. "What you see is their best attempt to match its appearance."

Serena tried to suppress her alarm. They had but seventy-two hours to fix this disaster, and there were no second chances with the Alignment. "Give me the penlight, Lorenzo."

Lorenzo handed it to her, and she inserted it in the tiny hole at the bottom of the forged celestial globe. Three pinpricks of light appeared in the constellations of Orion,

Virgo, and Aries: the buckle star Alnilam on Orion's Belt, the alpha star Spica in Virgo, and the brightest star, Alpha Arietis, in Aries.

"I selected Orion and Virgo based on what you told me about Antarctica and D.C. And I selected Aries for Jerusalem because Aries is the cosmic Lamb and Jerusalem is where the globes are said to originate."

"I can accept that. Now we have to hope the Alignment will accept the forgery as the real thing." She looked carefully at Lorenzo's creation. "If we can't bring our celestial globe up to the quality of the terrestrial globe, then maybe we can degrade the look of the terrestrial globe without damaging it. Maybe dull it down with a coat of something or other."

"It still won't hold up to Alignment scrutiny," Lorenzo said.

"Of course it won't," she snapped. "I just need it to pass a quick visual and let the Alignment test the terrestrial globe first."

"How are you going to get them to do that?"

She didn't have an answer yet, and she didn't want to indulge Lorenzo's anxiety with an attempt. The best she could do was fool the Alignment long enough for her to unmask the rest of the Thirty. The American Twelve had been unmasked by Conrad. The remaining eighteen members were European, including her as the head of the Dei. That left seventeen more to unmask at the council meeting on Rhodes.

"That's my problem, Lorenzo. Yours is to prepare

these globes for their journey to Rhodes. You need to start working with the Greeks to get the globes through security at the EU summit. We're also going to need two custom shell crates with insulated cavities for transport."

Lorenzo nodded and left without another word, closing the heavy ornate oak door behind him.

18

It was a five-hour drive from Zurich Airport to the chic ski village of Gstaad. The A1 autobahn took Conrad and his rented BMW through the Swiss capital of Bern. He fought the temptation to drive by Midas's bank containing the secret safe deposit box of Baron von Berg and instead turned onto the A6 to Thun, where he exited on Route 11 for Gstaad.

He had one shot to break into that bank, and the only man who could help him was hopefully still holed up in these Alps.

Conrad arrived just after the runs had closed and the five-star restaurants, bars, and discos were filling up with the fashionably rich of Europe, the Americas, and the Middle East. He parked his car several blocks from Sultan's Palace and walked the rest of the way. He had exchanged plates with another BMW at a restaurant stop outside Zurich while the owner was inside eating. All the same, it would be nice to have the car buried under snow by morning.

Sultan's Palace was the grande dame of Gstaad, a multi-spired castle combining the intimacy of Aspen's Little Nell with the majesty of St. Mortiz's Badrutt's Palace. Besides its breathtaking views of mountains and crystalline lakes, it boasted five restaurants, three bars, a world-renowned spa, and the members-only Sultan's Club, infamous across the Alps for its live music performances, dancing, and endless revelry with no curfew. It was, in other words, the very embodiment of its owner, Abdil Zawas, the man Conrad had come to see.

Conrad walked a red "flying carpet" across a frozen moat and through a regal gate into the palace's elegant lobby. At the front desk, he asked for the general manager. While he waited, he looked around at the guests sharing drinks by the fireplaces.

The hotel certainly attracted an unusual quotient of celebrities and royals, he thought, starting with Abdil himself. His mother's side of the family traced itself to Egypt's deposed monarchy, the house of Mohamed Ali Pasha. His father's side of the family, however, had made Abdil first cousin to the late, great Egyptian air force colonel Ali Zawas, whose death Abdil at one time blamed on Conrad.

Come to think of it, Conrad recalled, at some point or other Abdil may have issued a fatwa against him. He hoped Abdil had remembered to rescind it after Conrad helped him out with the design of the Atlantis Palm Dubai resort and theme park. It would be just like Abdil to have forgotten that all was forgiven.

"*Guten Abend, herr,*" said a man's voice.

Conrad turned to see the hotel's middle-aged general manager looking him up and down. Apparently, the German approved of the ski outfit Conrad had swiped from an unsuspecting doppelgänger back in baggage claim in Zurich.

"Good evening," Conrad replied in English. "I'm here to see Abdil."

The manager's eyes narrowed. "You have an appointment?"

"I don't need one."

The German regarded him dubiously. "And who may I say is calling, *herr*?"

"The *herr* who did this," Conrad said, and slid the front page of the Berlin daily *Die Welt* across the desk. He had picked it up in Zurich and now tapped his finger on the photos of the *Midas.*

The manager frowned but took the page and said, "A moment, please." He disappeared into a back office. Conrad could hear the dial tone and clacking of a fax machine. This was followed by a conversation in German that was too quiet for him to make out.

The hotel manager emerged again, all smiles. "This way, *herr*," he said, and escorted Conrad across the lobby to the hotel's three elevators. "His Highness will see you now."

"How high is my friend Abdil these days?" Conrad said.

The German was not amused. "The Sultan's Palace rests

at an altitude of only thirty-two hundred feet, quite low for the Alps and just right for an undisturbed night's sleep. But our slopes are over nine thousand feet. So we always remind our guests to drink plenty of water to stay hydrated."

Conrad said, "I'm sure there will be plenty to drink with Abdil."

The doors of the middle elevator opened to reveal two security types, definitely Middle Eastern, with earpieces and bulging shoulder holsters under their expensive-looking suits.

Conrad glanced at the hotel manager, who gestured to the elevator. *"Guten Abend, herr."*

Conrad stepped inside. The doors closed, and one of the security guards slid a special card key into a slot to unlock access to the hotel's penthouse floor. He pushed a series of buttons in combination, and the elevator began its ascent to the very top of the palace.

The doors opened to reveal a spectacular two-story stone-and-glass penthouse. The last rays of sunset streamed in through the atrium windows between rock walls with waterfalls. The room's size dwarfed that of the hotel lobby, and the clusters of furniture sets, fireplaces, and marble spas were populated with women in various stages of undress.

A voice called brightly from above: "Ah, the enemy of my enemy!"

"Is your friend," Conrad said, glancing up to see Abdil, with the wild mane of a black stallion, waving from the top of the sweeping marble staircase.

The big Egyptian was in his trademark royal bathrobe and boxers, and as he descended the steps with much fanfare, Conrad could see the pearl handle of a Colt pistol tucked inside his waistband. Abdil fancied himself Lawrence of Arabia without the horses and dung, preferring to plot his next moves from the comforts of his pleasure palaces across the globe. He preferred Switzerland to Egypt in order to better tap the global financial markets—and to avoid extradition for his off-balance-sheet activities.

"Welcome, my friend," Abdil said and gave Conrad a kiss on each cheek. "Come to my private dining room."

A woman appeared on either side and helped Conrad off with his coat. He followed Abdil to a dining room with a spread of food that resembled the brunch buffet at the Four Seasons in Amman, Jordan.

"Do you know what it's like to build the world's greatest yacht only to have a Russian thug build one but a meter longer?" Abdil said, taking a seat. "I might as well have been circumcised by the Jews."

"Well, you're the . . . longest on the seas once more," Conrad said. He was tempted to add that it all would be for naught if Abdil kept walking around with a Colt jostling in his boxers. "So I was hoping you could do me a favor."

"Favor?" Abdil's eyes lit up. Conrad liked that Abdil never resented doing favors; he always trusted his negotiating skills to extract something more valuable in return. "Please tell me how I can help my friend."

"Midas owns something you were once interested in," Conrad said. "A bank in Bern called Gilbert et Clie."

Abdil nodded. "The bank of Nazis, Arabs, and other assorted terrorists," he recited sarcastically. "Slander, I tell you."

For several years, Abdil had been on the U.S. global terrorist watch list at the behest of the Saudis, who claimed that Abdil posed a greater threat to the House of Saud than Osama bin Laden. Conrad knew Abdil was no Muslim fanatic, much less a terrorist. Why blow yourself up for seventy-two virgins when you already had them at your beck and call?

Abdil's "big idea" had been to flood the Middle East with mobile phones. While the ayatollahs blew hot air in mosques and on state television, Arab boys and girls prohibited from even acknowledging the opposite sex in public could now text each other behind the backs of their parents. Abdil believed mobile networks would effectively multiply the "disruptive force" of American popular culture—the more profane and nonsensical, the better—and break the centuries-old lock of Islam's paternalistic society, upending the despots in the region with a true democratic revolution. Abdil was indeed an Arab radical of a different kind.

What had soured Abdil and the Americans on each other was the CIA's interference in his operations with cellular network carriers. The Americans wanted to operate or at least control the networks to better monitor voice and text conversations. Abdil couldn't get them to understand that this wasn't at all the point and that they were behaving no better than the despots they hoped to depose. The funds at the heart of Abdil's great Arabian youth mobilization network, held at the bank of Gilbert et Clie in Bern, were frozen. What kind of world was it, Abdil had complained, where you could own your own bank and yet not tap your own money?

Conrad looked at the giant lobster tail that had just been placed before him and asked, "Why did you let Midas buy the bank?"

"Because I saw no upside," Abdil said as he tore into his own lobster. "The rules of Swiss banking and international terrorism are such that if there were any advantage to one party owning the bank itself, then no other parties would hold their deposits there. No fun at all for me. But you obviously think Midas has some advantage?"

"There's a safe deposit box inside the bank that he wants," Conrad said. "It belonged to an SS general named Ludwig von Berg."

"The Baron of the Black Order?" Abdil's eyes grew wide.

Conrad nodded. "It's got a four-character alphabetic combination. Midas doesn't know the code. I do."

"One of the older boxes," Abdil said, leaning forward. "Is it in the seventeen or eighteen hundred series? It must be if Midas hasn't attempted to break it open."

"Yes."

"I thought so!" Abdil smiled. "Von Berg's box probably has a chemical seal that will break and destroy its contents if the combination is off by a single letter. Ha! How it must pain Midas to hold something in his hands and not be able to open it." Abdil leaned back in his chair and made a steeple with his fingers, contemplating the situation. "You think you can steal it out from under his nose if I can get you inside the bank."

"I do." Crafty minds like Abdil's always cut to the chase. That was why doing business with him was mostly straightforward—until it came time for Abdil's payback.

"Yes, yes, yes," Abdil said. "But no more words of this until the morning. The night is still young and the men too few for my girls."

"Thank you for your generosity, Abdil. But I'd really like to just climb into bed in my own room, if that's okay."

"But of course." Abdil snapped his fingers. "Layla!" A shapely young woman with an olive complexion appeared, carrying a digital clipboard. She displayed it to Abdil like a hostess showing the maître d' of a fine restaurant a map of tables.

"Suite 647 will suit our friend's tastes," Abdil said with a smile.

Ten minutes later, Conrad was shown his room. While considerably smaller than Abdil's penthouse, it didn't lack for amenities, including a young woman on his bed in nothing but a Miami Dolphins jersey.

"I'm Nichole," she said in an American accent. "What's your story?"

"Tired," he said, and decided it was best for everybody if she did the talking. "Tell me yours."

She was an American who had arrived in Gstaad a few months earlier after the Super Bowl with her boyfriend the professional football player. He'd left, she'd stayed. Blah, blah, blah.

Conrad concluded there was no way he could decline the present that Abdil had offered him. He didn't want to offend his host or make it appear that the nubile Nichole was anything less than a sexy vixen worthy of a royal harem.

"So which Dolphin am I competing against here?" he asked her.

"All of them." She giggled and pulled off her jersey.

19

Midas finally emerged from his bluestone kabbalah tank after six hours. He found Natalia in the bedroom, propped up on a pillow naked and playing with her BlackBerry. Natalia was his London mistress whenever Mercedes wasn't around, which at this point was for good.

"We have the private dining room at Roka reserved at nine o'clock," Natalia said. "I've got six friends coming. Two artists, three actors, and a fashion designer."

"We're not going anywhere tonight," Midas said flatly, and climbed into the bed.

She put the BlackBerry on the night table, revealing her full inviting breasts to him. "I'm still going to Paris, yes? I can't miss Mercedes's funeral. Every fashion icon in Europe will be there, and so will the press."

"I'm not taking you to Paris for the funeral of my official girlfriend," Midas said. "How would that look? Her father and family will be there. You can frolic with your friends another time."

Natalia seemed on the verge of pouting but thought better of it. "How long before we can go out together, just the two of us?" There was a slight demand in her voice.

"A week," he said, and she brightened considerably and kissed him voraciously. He felt himself respond in spite of his tiredness but still found himself distracted. "Tell me, have you news from any of your friends?"

Her friends were other Russian "it" girls prancing around the planet with billionaires and politicians of almost every nationality. Natalia, at twenty-six, had become a more formidable spymaster than his old superiors at the KGB.

She picked up her BlackBerry and said, "Little Nichole has a new friend in Gstaad."

An alarm rang in Midas's head, but he didn't know why. "Who's in Gstaad again?"

"Abdil Zawas. I think Nichole and the girls are stir-crazy. Like you, he doesn't get out often enough."

He ignored the displeasure in her voice. "That happens when you're on the international global terrorist watch list, like Abdil," he said. "Who is Nichole's new friend?"

"Some guy named Ludwig," she said, and showed him a picture that Nichole had sent her.

Midas sat up, grabbed the phone, and stared at the picture. He then used the phone to call Vadim, who sounded groggy when he picked up.

"I need you to get to Switzerland," Midas told him. "I've found Yeats."

20

The next morning Conrad woke up at the Sultan's Palace to find a handwritten note from Nichole on the pillow next to him. She had gone snowboarding on Videmanette Mountain and wanted to meet up at Glacier 3000 for lunch at two P.M. He looked at the clock and saw that it was already ten. He had slept over twelve hours.

There was a continental breakfast with a newspaper on the table. He put his feet into the slippers waiting at the bottom of his bed and tied on a robe. Then he poured himself some hot coffee from a silver pot and sat down at the table to look at the copy of the French daily *Le Monde*.

There was a picture of Mercedes on the front page with a headline: MONDAY SERVICES IN FRANCE FOR MERCEDES LE ROCHE, 32.

He found a smaller picture of himself on the jump on page eight. How on earth could Nichole not know he was a fugitive? He had to pray she hadn't seen it or never bothered to read a newspaper. He took comfort that the latter was more than probable.

Conrad figured Midas would have to show up at the funeral to put on a brave public face. Which gave him the perfect window: While Midas was in Paris at the funeral, Conrad would hit the bank in Bern.

Conrad put down the paper and saw that an envelope had been slipped under his door. He walked over and picked it up. Inside were architectural blueprints for the bank in Bern, marked up in French. An attached note from Abdil, written neatly in a female hand, instructed him to come up to the penthouse to meet with a Ms. Haury.

Conrad had no idea who Ms. Haury was, but he knew he had to keep moving forward and stay a step ahead of the Alignment, Interpol, and everybody else who was after him now. He had to get whatever was inside Baron von Berg's safe deposit box in Bern. It was his only bargaining chip.

He opened a closet filled with made-to-measure suits for him from Milan's Caraceni. The fabrics, fit for a prince, seemed to be cut from another world and fit perfectly.

A tailor would have had to work at gunpoint to pull this off so fast. Considering it was Abdil who had placed the order, Conrad could only wonder.

The two security guards posted outside his door escorted him down the hallway to the elevator. As they ascended to the penthouse, Conrad realized he couldn't have taken the elevator down to the lobby even if he'd wanted to.

The only way out of this palace was up.

Abdil's penthouse looked completely different in the full light of day. Conrad could have sworn it was fully refurnished, even the sculptures and art on the walls. Now it looked like a corporate boardroom of palatial proportions.

But there was no Abdil, only a curvy blonde standing next to the huge conference table, on which sat an ornate brass safe deposit box with a stainless steel door sporting four shiny brass dials and a brass keylock.

"I'm Dee Dee," the woman said, "the American CFO of Abdil's collectibles division. I understand from Mr. Zawas that you want to make a withdrawal from your box at the Gilbert et Clie bank in Bern."

"That's right," Conrad said, looking at the box with the four shiny brass dials. "I suppose it's too much to hope that this is the box in question."

"I'm afraid so," she said. "But the box you'll be opening will almost certainly be of this type. Take a seat."

Conrad sat down in a thronelike leather chair and listened to the polished Dee Dee explain the history of the box as if she were showcasing it on the Home Shopping Network.

"Any Swiss box with a number in the seventeen

hundreds at Gilbert et Clie is among the most precious antique boxes in the vault," she told him. "That's because it's a triple-lock box. Very unusual. Only a few were manufactured in 1923 by Bauer AG in Zurich. Extremely rare."

Conrad touched the brass and steel box. It was only about three inches wide, two inches high, and seven inches long. Just how big was the secret Baron von Berg hoped to hide in such a small box?

"I see only two locks on the door," he said. "The four-dial combination lock and the keylock next to it."

"That's all you're supposed to see," she told him. "The distinctive combination lock you can't miss. It has four alphabetic brass dials for a total of 234,256 possible combinations. This is a lock you never forget."

Neither did Baron von Berg, thought Conrad, already imagining himself turning the four dials in sequence to line up the letters A-R-E-S. "What about the other two locks?"

Dee Dee nodded and said, "The two other lever locks share a mechanism housed inside the box's single key-hole."

"Two locks inside one keyhole?" Conrad repeated. "How does that work?"

"With two keys, of course," she said, and placed two keys on the table. One was silver, the other gold. "One bank key and one client key. Let me show you. I'll be the bank, you be the client."

She handed him the gold client key and picked up

the silver bank key. "First things first. You need to open the combination lock. I've set the code for this box. It's OGRE."

Conrad turned the first dial to the letter "O," the second to the letter "G," the third to the letter "R," and the fourth to the letter "E," and heard an unmistakable click inside the box. "Wait a second," he said. "If the client has to open the combination lock first, before any keys are inserted, then the banker will know the combination to the client's box."

"Yes, but the client will change the combination before he closes the box," she told him. "It's like changing passwords on a computer system, only more secure." She held up the silver bank key. "Now for the tumbler-lever lock. It has seven brass levers and two different bolt levers for a total of nine levers." She inserted the silver key into the single hole. "The bank key moves the three top levers and the top bolt lever to unblock the first part of the lock." She turned the key and then removed it. "This enables you, the client, to insert your key. Go ahead."

Conrad inserted his gold key into the hole and turned it until he felt it stop.

"Your key moves the four bottom levers and the bottom bolt lever," she said. "The bottom bolt lever is connected to the door bolt and the combination lock. That's the resistance you're feeling."

"Why won't it open?"

"Each dial of the alphabetical combination lock

needs to be on the proper letter in order for you to be able to turn your key ninety degrees into a vertical position."

Conrad checked the dials again. They clearly spelled OGRE. "The dials are right. What's the problem?"

"The problem is that you're not finished yet," she told him. "Once the client key is vertical and the bolt is partially retracted, you need to scramble each dial again so your key can turn fully to the right and open the lock."

Conrad shook his head. *Von Berg, you paranoid son of a bitch*, he thought. Then again, he'd have watched his back, too, if he had worked for the world's craziest dictator.

Dee Dee seemed to feel she owed him an explanation. "Scrambling the combination before the door was opened was supposed to ensure that nobody else in the vault besides the banker could see the baron's secret combination while he was busy inspecting the contents of his safe deposit box."

"And if I make a mistake along the way somehow?"

"No second chances," Dee Dee said. "The box's chemical seal will break and destroy the contents. That's why a man as powerful as Roman Midas can own the bank and still not get to the contents of Baron von Berg's box. You have only one shot to open a box of this type. Go ahead. Give it a try."

Conrad turned the key, and the lock clicked open. He lifted the box lid and saw stacks of U.S. dollars—Ben Franklins. There had to be ten million dollars in the box. Conrad looked up to see Dee Dee lock eyes with him. "You will exchange the contents of your box for this one with Mr. Zawas after you leave the bank," she said, pausing to make sure they understood each other. Abdil Zawas didn't miss a trick; he wanted to give Conrad every incentive to come back after the job.

"I get it," Conrad said. "And if I don't show, I'm sure Mr. Zawas has a bigger box to stuff my corpse in."

"Mr. Zawas said that what you are after is not the contents of the box but the information those contents convey," Dee Dee said, and closed the box. "That being the case, he wants the contents for himself and is happy to pay you for them at this agreed-upon price."

"Fine, but there's only one problem," he told her. "I have the combination code, but I don't have a client key."

"The bank probably does," Dee Dee said. "Clients like Nazi generals who traveled to far-flung or dangerous parts of the world often allowed the banks to keep their keys because they didn't want to lose them. As long as they didn't forget their box number or combination code—or share them with anybody else—it was pretty foolproof."

"Even if I don't look like Baron von Berg's heir or, worse, I'm recognized on sight?"

"The bank's huissier will know you have business there as soon as you write down your box number, and she'll conclude from the seventeen hundred series that you're one of the bank's largest clients."

"No biometrics or anything?"

"Only in the movies," Dee Dee said. "The genius of the Swiss security system is that it's plain and transparent.

You don't have to worry about somebody hacking your computer system and accessing your data or faking your biometrics. Locks, keys, and combinations beat the computer chip any day. Like the pyramids of Egypt that you raid, Swiss boxes will survive the ages. Think of this bank as just another tomb to raid, and you'll be fine."

"And when I present the box number and the huissier promptly informs Midas that someone has come to open the box?"

"Oh, they'll let you open the box," she said. "They just won't let you walk out of the bank with it. I can't help you there. But Mr. Zawas says you have the architectural blueprints to the bank."

"Yes," Conrad said. "But I don't know how accurate they are."

"I'm afraid that's a combination I can't help you with," she told him. "No doubt Sir Roman Midas has made some modifications to the bank not reflected in your schematics."

"No doubt," Conrad said.

21

PARIS

It seemed to Serena that all of Paris had come to the church of Saint Roch to bid adieu to Mercedes Le Roche. Uniformed police held back the crowds lining Rue Saint-Honoré while office workers and residents in the buildings above leaned out their windows. All were straining to glimpse the celebrities arriving beneath a giant screen and loudspeakers broadcasting the funeral ceremony live.

Benito nudged the limousine ever closer to the hive of paparazzi ahead. Serena felt uneasy as she sank back in her seat and into the soft gray trouser suit and black trench coat that the people from Chanel had requested she wear to the funeral. A few years ago the Vatican's public relations agency had made some sort of bizarre agreement granting Chanel the right to dress Serena for affairs of state. It was an arrangement that she had always found ways to ignore. But having already packed her bags—and globes—for sunny Rhodes and not the cool rain of Paris, she'd had to reluctantly oblige this time.

The idea of a funeral as a fashion show, however, made her ill.

"Her funeral has a budget bigger than all her documentaries put together," she said. "Hardly anyone here knew her, and even fewer cared."

"It's Papa Le Roche's rank in French society that has brought out all the movie stars and other celebrities who have come to offer him their condolences," Benito said. "That would include you and President Nicolas Sarkozy."

"Where are the 'least of these' that Jesus talked about, Benito?"

"Watching the television, *signorina*."

Hopeless, she thought. Not only was she upset about what had happened to Mercedes, she was worried sick about Conrad and whether she'd ever see him again. She was also worried that she'd fail in Rhodes tomorrow. In fact, looking at the circus outside, she wondered if she and the Church had failed the world already with their complicity in this stagecraft of death. But Papa Le Roche had personally requested her presence for the family, and this was another chance to size up Roman Midas before Rhodes. Surely the grieving boyfriend would be on hand to eulogize the lover he had so ruthlessly slain.

She decided she desperately needed some fresh air. Cracking open her window just a bit, she could hear the crowds actually applauding every time a rocker or fashion designer stepped out of a limousine. As if this were some kind of award show. Which in a sense it was, she supposed, for Papa Le Roche.

"Skip the main entrance," she ordered Benito. "Take me around to the side."

They drove past the mob, turned a corner, and passed through a side gate, pulling up behind a black Volvo hearse. The hatch was up, and Serena could see Mercedes's casket in the back before the driver with an earpiece shut the door. He was going to go around the block to the crowds at the main entrance, where pallbearers would bring the casket into the church.

She was greeted at the side door by a young priest, who escorted her inside to the sanctuary. She was seated in the front row alongside a grief-stricken Papa Le Roche, a rather smug Roman Midas, and an expressionless President Sarkozy and his beautiful wife, Carla Bruni.

Serena offered her condolences to Papa Le Roche, who thanked her profusely for coming. Sarkozy and Midas looked at each other awkwardly, as if to say that today was certainly an unscheduled stop on the way to the EU peace summit on Rhodes tomorrow. Serena knew that neither had anticipated seeing the other before then. But while Sarkozy looked like he would have preferred not to be seen so close to the former Russian oligarch boyfriend of a woman who had died so violently, Midas seemed to relish his photo op next to the French president and among European society.

It was the French first lady, however, whose curious gaze after their kiss-kiss had made Serena the most uncomfortable. For some odd reason, it had prompted her to recall that she was ten years junior to Carla, who herself had been ten years junior to Sarkozy's second wife and thirteen years younger than his first. Then Serena saw the gray trouser suit beneath Carla's open black trench coat and realized that they were wearing the same outfit. Somebody at Chanel clearly hadn't cross-checked the cosmic social calendar.

Not that it bothered Serena. She was a linguist first and foremost, a nun second, and a celebrity who could raise funds for humanitarian aid a distant third. But she did feel bad for Karl Lagerfeld, the designer. He was sitting four pews behind with a row full of fashion icons, and when she glanced back to offer him a tender smile, he looked positively panic-stricken.

As the church bells tolled, six pallbearers in black Pierre Cardin suits carried Mercedes's casket into the church. They laid it feet toward the altar and then opened it to reveal a luminous Mercedes, frozen in time, with a rosary in her hands and flowers all around.

The tribute to Mercedes began with video clips of her childhood, followed by clips from her first documentary for French television. Several speakers read poems, and one played a vulgar song that was a favorite of hers. Then Midas rose to speak to his dearly departed.

Looking at Mercedes, he said, "You were a flower who faded too soon from this earth. But your sweet aroma will linger forever."

Serena wanted to gag. The duet of mourner and mourned did not go down well with her. She'd never liked eulogies staged during de facto state funerals, anyway.

Especially when the deceased wasn't much of an angel or terribly sorry about it.

But what was she supposed to do? Stand up before all the bereaved, who right now were calculating their own odds of entering the pearly gates, and speak the truth, however awful, about Mercedes? Or was she supposed to bow to social convention and assure everyone in earshot that Mercedes was in heaven? Surely anybody who knew her, even her father, doubted it. She herself doubted that eulogies even belonged in church. After all, this was supposed to be a place where self-confessed sinners gathered in the holy presence of God. Not a stage for them to pat each other on the back for their illusory virtues.

What she especially didn't like was the feeling that none of them should have been there that day. Not the French president. Not her. Not Midas. And certainly not Mercedes. She wasn't supposed to die. None of this was supposed to have happened. But it did. Why?

Conrad. He'd happened. He had shown up at the Bilderberg party and put all the wheels in motion. He had turned her life upside down, like he always did, and it was never going to be put right until he and she were right.

It was her turn to speak.

She got up and placed a wheat sheaf on the coffin and repeated the eternal rest prayer. It was the most honest thing she could say. Not in French but in Latin, the way Mercedes likely would have wanted to tweak her proud nationalist papa, who liked to believe that Jesus was really a Gaul and not a Jew and that French was the language of angels.

*Réquiem ætérnam dona ei Dómine; et lux perpétua
lúceat ei. Requiéscat in pace. Amen.*

What Serena was saying was: "Eternal rest grant
unto her, O Lord; and let perpetual light shine upon her.
May she rest in peace. Amen." She could tell that the dignitaries in the front pew didn't understand, although they
pretended they did. But several mourners in the fashion
row nodded enthusiastically.

Father Letteron, wearing white and violet vestments,
conducted the funeral Mass. There were flowers and candles all around. When it was over, Serena watched the
shroud-draped coffin float out of the church before the
hundreds of onlookers and cameras. Following behind was
Father Letteron, who sang the antiphon "In Paradisum,"
a prayer that the holy angels would bear the immortal
soul of Mercedes Le Roche to paradise.

If that meant television ratings, then perhaps
Mercedes had indeed finally found her heaven.

The show inside over, Carla Bruni and Nicolas
Sarkozy once again gave their condolences to Mercedes's
father and then wordlessly marched outside to the waiting world. Midas took Papa Le Roche's arm and guided
him out of the church. The rest of the mourners exited
wherever they'd be sure to be photographed by the
media.

Serena stood alone in the first pew, the hypocrisy of
the world around her—and her place in it—feeling like
a punch to her gut. She took a deep breath and stepped

into the aisle only to be blocked by a young French aide. He looked red-faced with shame.

"I beg your forgiveness, Sister Serghetti," he said in French.

"Is there a problem?"

He hemmed and hawed. "I don't know how to say this."

Serena's patience had worn thin over the course of the funeral. "Spit it out."

"The first lady requests that you mourn a little longer in private," the Frenchman said, barely able to form the words. "She fears there might be, eh, speculation in the press that you have, eh, upstaged her in some way with your youth and beauty."

Holy Mother of God, she thought. But then she quickly confessed her angry, inner burst to God and forced an understanding smile to the aide. She could only imagine how many times each day this poor messenger got shot while bearing his little tidings of great vanity. And this was the church where Napoleon had mowed down royalist insurgents on the front steps.

"Quite all right," she said. "I'll just exit discreetly from the side."

He made the sign of the cross and bowed his head. "Thank you."

She did her best to make it to Benito and the car outside. She had to put Paris behind her and press on to Rhodes. But halfway out, her sadness and rage at the events of the morning began to overwhelm her, and she stopped to compose herself at the freestanding holy water stoup by the side door.

As she dipped the tips of her fingers into the marble basin and crossed herself, she could see her pale reflection in the water. Suddenly, the side door flew open, and she looked up to see a camera flash in her face.

22

Conrad paid the cabdriver and walked up the steps toward the venerable private banking firm of Gilbert et Clie. The bank was an austere granite building in Bern's Old Town, its presence marked only by a discreet brass plaque set in the wall.

A porter greeted Conrad as he entered the lobby with a leather weekender bag slung over his shoulder. The porter asked Conrad to state his business and then directed him to a reception area outside the private executive offices. Here, a smiling brunette in a red cashmere sweater took his Burberry raincoat. Her pale blue eyes seemed to linger in admiration of his athletic build beneath his three-piece suit. In the most exquisite French, she informed him that Monsieur Gilbert would see him in but a moment.

Conrad took a seat and surveyed the shabby but elegant reception area. The faces of several generations of Gilberts looked down from the oil paintings on the walls. For well over a century, the bank had remained in family hands, an outgrowth of their merchandising business. Why the family had sold the bank was just another one of the secrets it kept inside its vaults. It was one of only a few private banks in Bern, as most were in Geneva, and the only one with a French surname, not German. Like the other private banks, Gilbert et Clie was unincorporated and never published its balance sheets.

The mademoiselle returned and ushered Conrad into Gilbert's office. A tall, gray-haired man, elegant in boutonniere and black suit, rose from his desk. His resemblance to the faces in the paintings was unmistakable.

"A pleasure to meet you, Monsieur von Berg," Gilbert said in German, regarding Conrad keenly. "Please sit down and make yourself comfortable."

"Thank you," Conrad replied in English, dispensing with any Bavarian pretense.

An officer of the bank, a big, bald man whom Gilbert introduced as Monsieur Guillaume, stood silently by his side. He regarded Conrad warily from under his heavy eyelids.

"And how can I help you, Monsieur von Berg?" Gilbert asked.

"I've come to recover the contents of my grandfather's box."

Gilbert raised an eyebrow. "You have the key, of course?"

"No, you do," Conrad said. "Both of them. I have the box number and combination. And that's all that's required of me for this type of box."

Gilbert nodded. "You are correct. But you will forgive us for doing our best to protect the interests of our clients. You are the first person in seventy years to open"—he had to look at his computer screen—"box number 1740."

Gilbert called in his huissier—the brunette, who answered to the name of Elise—and handed her an envelope with the number on it. "Please escort Monsieur von Berg to the vault."

"*Oui*," she replied.

If they were letting her handle him, Conrad thought, that meant their guard was down—or they wanted him to let down his own.

Elise took him to the bank's antique elevator. As the polished brass cage began its slow two-hundred-foot descent to the vault beneath the bank, Conrad noted the Venetian mirrors on the elevator walls and the gray leather benches on three sides. He also noted a tiny hook in the corner of the floor. "This is an unusual elevator," he said. "It's the original?"

"Yes," she said. "It used to go down to an even lower level beneath the vault, where a secret tunnel to a park two blocks away would allow private clients like yourself to come and go without having to enter from the street. But the new owner filled the tunnel with concrete a few years ago."

Conrad nodded. Okay, so at least one alternative exit had been cut off.

The doors split open to reveal the safe deposit vault. The massive circular steel door was open, and a security guard standing beside a small desk nodded as Conrad followed Elise inside the vault.

As they walked past rows of gleaming boxes, Conrad could only imagine how much wealth was locked away here. Truly, this was the vault of the man called Midas. Finally, when they had reached the very back of the last row, Elise stopped and announced, "Box 1740."

Conrad turned to his right and saw the numbers. The box was at eye level. "That's right."

She took her key and inserted it into the box. "I will go first and then leave you to your box. You may take it to the private consultation room over there." She gestured to a small closet door, and Conrad nodded. "Then you will return the box, lock it, and call for me."

Conrad noted that she had failed to mention that if he got the combination wrong or blew the key toggle, the box's internal chemical lining would break and destroy whatever was inside.

Conrad eyed the brass doorplate with three brass fixtures. Left to right, there were the keylock, the four brass alphabetic dials set on top of a brass circular plate, and the small rectangular number plate that read 1740.

Conrad glanced at Elise, whose eyes grew ever wider as he turned the first dial to the letter "A," the second to the letter "R," the third to the letter "E," and the fourth to the letter "S." He heard an unmistakable click inside the box. He could also hear Elise catch her breath at the simplicity of the code.

"Now it is my turn," she said, and inserted the silver bank key into the keylock, gave it a twist, and then removed it. "I will leave you now."

Conrad waited until she was gone before he inserted his gold key into the lock. He turned it halfway and stopped. He then scrambled the dials and turned his key the full ninety degrees into a vertical position and felt the lock open with a satisfying click.

He opened the door and slid the box out. It felt light in his arms as he walked to the private consultation room. He grew anxious as he entered, shut the door behind him, and placed the box on the table.

He stared at it for a moment, took a deep breath, and with one hand opened the lid. As he stared inside the box belonging to SS General Ludwig von Berg, the Baron of the Black Order, he felt a pit form in his stomach. Then he reached in and removed the only item inside the box.

It was an old Swiss wristwatch.

23

At that very moment, the prince of Egypt himself, Abdil Zawas, was driving to the bank along Bern's River Aare in his armored Mercedes Pullman Level B6 bulletproof limousine.

In addition to windows made of 42mm bulletproof, shatterproof, multiple-layer reinforced glass, the vehicle sported special fuel tanks impervious to exploding upon impact from any projectiles. The remote starting system allowed Abdil to remotely detonate any explosive charges set to go off when the vehicle ignition or door locks were activated. Just the sort of vehicle a man of Abdil's stature—and Conrad Yeats's predicament—required these days.

Abdil was en route to pick up Yeats from the bank, just in case the American archaeologist had second thoughts about coming back for his ten million dollars. Abdil's imagination was already afire with speculation as to what SS General Ludwig von Berg had secreted in Midas's bank—and the expression on Midas's face when he finally saw the contents of the box in full display aboard the new megayacht that Abdil was building to be the world's biggest.

What a moment that will be, Abdil thought with delight as the glass partition inside the limousine lowered and his driver, Bubu, said, "Police."

Abdil looked out his rear window to see a white Land Rover with orange stripes on the side and blue siren lights flashing. "See what he wants and don't make a scene," he said, and looked at his watch. He wanted to be parked outside the bank before Yeats came out.

Bubu pulled off the Aarstrasse at a riverfront park. The Land Rover parked directly in front of them. An officer stepped out in a dark raincoat and sunglasses. Abdil watched Bubu pull the registration papers from the glove compartment and lower his window.

"Yes?" asked Bubu as the officer approached the Mercedes.

The officer leaned through the open window. "The motorway pass on your windscreen is expired," he said, and shot Bubu in the head.

Instinct instantly took hold of Abdil, and he raised the glass partition in time to stop two bullets from the assassin, who removed his sunglasses to reveal an eyepatch and a face Abdil recognized as Midas's driver and bodyguard, Vadim. He knew the face from the fitness videos some of his girls used.

"You!" Abdil shouted into his two-way security intercom to the outside world for all to hear. "I am impregnable in here!" With a flourish, he picked up his phone and called his private emergency service.

A minute later, there was the comforting sound of a helicopter approaching, and Abdil started cursing Vadim, who had been patiently waiting outside. "Leave while you can, or the men jumping off that chopper will take your other eye for Bubu's sake."

Abdil heard a giant thud on the roof. The limousine lurched forward and back, then began to lift into the air. He looked out his window in time to see Vadim waving goodbye to him from the ground. Abdil started to shout as the chopper banked to the right with the entire limousine in tow, carrying him up and away.

24

Conrad frantically checked the box one more time, looking for any kind of hidden compartment or false bottom he may have missed. But there was none. There was only this damn watch.

He stared in dismay at Baron von Berg's sole piece of personal jewelry. The dial was stamped with ROLEX OYSTER and sported an unusual outer track of black-painted Roman numbers on top and Arabic numbers on the bottom. But that was all. In a vault filled with the wealth of dead Nazis, robber barons, deposed dictators, oil sheiks, and the like, why would SS General Ludwig von Berg have gone to such great lengths simply to preserve an old watch?

It felt like a bad joke.

Not only did Conrad have to get out of here in one piece, there was no way Abdil would believe that this watch was all he'd found, much less hand him millions in cash for it.

There had to be more to this watch than sentimental value to a crazy Nazi.

Just like the name of the Roman god of war carried some meaning for Baron von Berg, so, too, did the number 1740 for the box. The same had to be true of this watch, which had its hour and minute hands stopped at midnight—or noon. That was no accident. The watch didn't stop winding down at that exact minute. Von Berg had left it that way.

A crazy thought seized Conrad. Von Berg may have been insane, but he was a military man, too. Military men, as Conrad knew all too well from growing up with the Griffter, used military time. And 1740 hours meant 5:40 P.M.

Conrad carefully pulled out the watch's side-turning knob and slowly adjusted the hands until the hour hand reached the number five on the dial and the minute hand reached the number eight.

When he pushed the thumb knob down again, the watch's two-piece screw-back case fell open. A coin hit the table and rolled onto the floor.

Conrad quickly snatched it up. It was an ancient Roman coin with a Caesar's bust and an eagle on the back. It was oddly familiar; it reminded him of the Tribute Penny that Serena wore around her neck. But that medallion was one of a kind.

Or was it?

Conrad quickly inserted the coin snugly beneath the gears of the watch and replaced the back case, inside of which was stamped OYSTER WATCH CO. Then he strapped the watch to his wrist, closed the box, and stepped out into the vault with his shoulder bag. Without bothering to call for Elise, he slid the box back into its slot and walked out.

The security guard by the desk was already calling upstairs by the time Conrad stepped into the old brass elevator and let the doors close. As soon as they did, he dropped to the floor and reached into his bag to remove a knife.

He cut along the hidden seams beneath the carpet and then pulled the tiny hook in the corner he had seen to reveal a lower compartment. That was where the VIPs had entered and exited in secret from the old tunnel Midas had sealed up.

Conrad had seen this type of elevator only once before—Hitler's old Eagle's Nest retreat atop Mount Kelstein in Bavaria. The Nazis had bored a four-hundred-foot elevator shaft in the center of the mountain. That 1938 brass elevator was also a double-decker. Hitler and his important guests rode the brass-lined upper cabin to the top while his guards and supplies for the house rode unseen in the bottom cabin.

Conrad placed an explosive puck on the floor of the upper cabin and dropped into the bottom cabin and pulled the trapdoor shut. He then pulled out his hazmat gas mask and waited in the dark with a small detonator in his hand.

When the elevator stopped and the door in the top

cabin opened in the bank's lobby, he heard shouts from security guards at the sight of the empty compartment. He then pressed the button and exploded the puck containing the knockout gas sufentanil. There was more shouting, and a body dropped with a crash in the cabin above him.

It took him a minute longer than he expected to pop the trapdoor open, but then he crawled out into the lobby and stood up, hearing loud hacking coughs as he stepped over the bodies.

The porter at the front door had managed to press a silent alarm before going down, and when Conrad finally stepped outside and ripped off his mask, the sound of sirens blared.

He walked quickly down the street, turned a corner, and hailed a cab. He was opening the door when the sound of a helicopter forced him to look up. To his astonishment, he saw the screaming face of Abdil Zawas pressed against the window of his limousine before it disappeared with the chopper over the roof of the UBS building.

Conrad quickly climbed into the back of the cab and said, "American embassy."

25

Midas stood in what he considered to be his rightful place next to the French president, his wife, and Papa Le Roche at the curb outside Saint Roch as they silently watched pallbearers load Mercedes's flag-draped coffin into the back of the hearse, which would take it to the more intimate burial service at the family's tomb at Père Lachaise Cemetery.

Midas did his best to look somber before the crowds and cameras, but those next to him had more practice, and he had to work at keeping his chest from swelling with pride from his arrival at the pinnacle of European society. He'd had to buy his way in with the Brits, and even then his acceptance had felt forced. The Parisians were far more accommodating of his violent reputation, which for them only seemed to add a dash of romance to his otherwise mysterious background.

"Mercedes did love her rogues," he heard Papa Le Roche repeat outside, although the plural reference reminded Midas of Conrad Yeats, and the thought that he and Yeats had shared Mercedes disturbed him. He took comfort in the knowledge that shortly, Yeats would be joining the dearly departed in the afterlife. It was all Midas could do to keep from checking his BlackBerry for word from Vadim in Bern.

Papa Le Roche then clasped arms with Sarkozy, Carla, and Midas. To great effect, he upstaged Midas by climbing into the front of the hearse himself—there was room for only one passenger, presumably the most important man in Mercedes's life—to ride with his daughter to the cemetery.

As soon as the black Volvo hearse drove off down the Rue Saint-Honoré past the throngs of onlookers held back by police and metal fences, Midas turned to Sarkozy. "Are you going to the burial?"

The French president shook his head. "Rhodes calls. The world is a mess. Turmoil in the markets. War in the Middle East. We do what we can. I am to give the opening and closing presentations at the summit. I am but a bookend."

"I will see you there, then," said Midas, and clasped arms with Sarkozy and then enjoyed a double kiss with Carla before France's first couple climbed into their presidential limousine.

As Midas watched their motorcade drive off, led by police on motorcycles, he felt the pleasant vibration of power in the form of his BlackBerry calling. He picked up the call from Vadim. "So we are rid of Yeats once and for all?"

There was a pause on the other end. Midas didn't like it. "We got Zawas. But Yeats escaped."

Midas felt stomach acid flare up in the back of his throat. "And the contents of the box?"

"Yeats."

Midas dropped the phone and leaned on a loitering pallbearer for support. Several cameras captured the moment, confusing the expression of loss on his face to be one for Mercedes. The Rhodes summit started tomorrow, and Midas needed that coin to join the Thirty. Even the *Flammenschwert* couldn't help that. All his leverage would be gone by Friday.

Midas scanned the crowds and saw Serena making for the side entrance and her car. He took a breath, stood up, and thanked the concerned onlookers. "I'll be fine. Life goes on. Thank you."

He retreated back to the church and then broke into a run to catch Serena before she drove off.

26

The U.S. embassy in Bern was at Sulgeneckstrasse 19, and Conrad's cabdriver took his sweet time getting across the city's River Aare. Conrad clocked it on his new official Black Order Rolex: almost nine minutes to make it over a four-lane bridge, merge into the far-right lane, and reach the next intersection just in time for the light to turn red.

"What are you waiting for?" Conrad demanded. "Take a right."

"This isn't America," the Syrian driver replied rudely in English. "There is no turn on red light unless permitted by green arrow."

"I'll pay you extra."

The Syrian looked over his shoulder at him with contempt. "I am a law-abiding citizen."

Two minutes later, they turned right onto Monbijoustrasse and then took another immediate right onto Giessereiweg. Two minutes after that, the road turned into Sulgenrain, and they followed it until finally turning left onto Sulgeneckstrasse.

The street was one-way for security purposes; Conrad spotted the embassy about two hundreds yards down the street on the right. It was a white office building surrounded by an ugly security fence.

"I'll look for your picture inside," Conrad said as he paid the driver and watched him drive off.

He started walking quickly to the gate. He was half a block away and passing a paid parking area when a Swiss police Land Rover started to drive slowly alongside him. As soon as the window lowered, Conrad didn't wait for the arm to pop out with a pistol. He dove behind a parked car just in time to see Vadim's ugly face in the car's side mirror before Vadim blew the mirror off.

Conrad made a dash the opposite way up the one-way street, using the parked cars as a hedge. The Land Rover tried to back up, but oncoming traffic put a stop to that, and Vadim had to jump out and pursue on foot.

Conrad cut across the corner of Sulgeneckstrasse and Kapellenstrasse and ran downhill about three hundred yards to a blue arrow tram leaving the stop at Monbijou. He bought a ticket from the vending machine and hopped on just as Vadim ran up from behind, no doubt noting that it was Tram 9 Wabern heading for the city's train station just two stops away.

The tram began to snake beneath the storybook archways and through the arcades of old Bern. Conrad caught his breath as he stood among the tourists and commuters. The next tram was ten minutes away, so he had to assume Vadim would drive like a madman to beat him or radio someone at the end of the line.

As much as he hated the idea, he had to call Packard and ask for a secure pickup. He reached inside his pocket for the Vertu cell phone that Abdil had given him and realized that he must have lost it when he dove for cover near the embassy.

All too soon the tram stopped at Bubenbergplatz, opposite the main train terminal. Conrad had to make a run for it and hop a train out of Switzerland. Between the Swiss police, Interpol, and the Alignment, he was dead if he stayed here.

He scanned the plaza and was making a beeline for the station when he saw the Land Rover pull up and Vadim get out. He also saw legitimate police cars at the entrance and a number of patrolmen on foot talking into their radios.

In a heartbeat, he doubled back in the opposite direction to the towering Heiliggeist church. Built in the early 1700s, the Heiliggeistkirche, or Holy Spirit Church, was supposed to be the finest example of Protestant church architecture in Switzerland, with its magnificent baroque interior and encircling gallery.

The choir was rehearsing the "Easter Oratorio," as composed by Johann Sebastian Bach in 1735. Several soloists in costume sang the parts of the two Marys and the disciples who followed them to the empty tomb of Jesus. They were accompanied by three trumpets, two oboes, timpani, strings, and the church's massive organ.

The musicians were considerably younger than the choir, the church organist considerably older.

Conrad took a seat next to a young man wearing angel wings and watched the rehearsal. The angel handed him a flyer. It was in German and titled OSTER-ORATORIUM. Conrad had to think up something. *"Sprechen Sie Deutsch?"* he asked the angel.

"No, dude, I'm American," the angel said. "Semester abroad. Chicks dig this shit. So do guys. But I dig chicks. So don't dis my wings."

Perfect, Conrad thought, glancing around the vast church. He looked up at the oblong pastel ceiling high above the rows of curved wooden pews. It was held up by fourteen sandstone columns. "Do you actually have a part?"

"I get to announce the resurrection and that Jesus is alive."

"That's awesome."

"Yeah, and then I get to score with the second Mary Magdalene over there from Copenhagen."

"Never going to happen," Conrad said with an earnestness born of experience that shocked even him. "Hey, my phone battery is gone. Can I borrow yours?"

The angel handed him a Nokia and said, "Got an emergency?"

"You could say that," Conrad said. "I definitely need to call God."

"Well, you've come to a house of prayer, so pray."

"That's okay. I've got her number."

27

Benito had the engine running by the time Serena reached the limousine. Her phone rang. It was Conrad.

"Where on God's green earth are you?" she demanded as she climbed in the back.

Conrad said, "It's time we lay our cards on the table. Meet me at the Villa Feltrinelli at Lake Garda tonight at six. You're the Baroness von Berg."

"You must be joking," she said. "I'm supposed to be in Rhodes tomorrow."

"Then you better know what's on the agenda," he said, and hung up.

She met Benito's eyes in the rearview mirror and said, "What's our status on the globes?"

"Brother Lorenzo says they are prepared and will arrive separately in Rhodes as art for the exhibit at the Palace of the Grandmaster. By keeping them roped off, he feels closer inspection will wait until after the summit."

Serena's mind was racing while the engine ran in neutral and Benito waited for her signal. Lake Garda was in northern Italy, a good three hours by plane, train, or automobile. And she had duties to perform at Mercedes's grave site.

"Get me a seaplane, Benito. I'm going to fly myself to Rhodes—after an unscheduled stop. You get yourself back to the Vatican and accompany the globes to Rhodes. Don't let them out of your sight."

Benito nodded and moved the car into drive just as Serena's door opened and Midas climbed in next to her.

"What are you doing, Midas?" she nearly screamed.

Benito hit the brakes, and before she and Midas even stopped bouncing, he had a 9mm Beretta pointed over the front seat at Midas.

Midas put up his hands and said, "I needed a ride to Père Lachaise for the burial. I thought I could take the opportunity to seek your spiritual counsel. Look, I have none of my aides with me."

"You mean assailants."

"Whatever."

Serena sighed, exchanged a glance with Benito in the mirror, and nodded.

They drove slowly out the side, past a gate, and onto Rue Saint-Honoré, where the crowds had quickly dispersed and the boutiques had opened for business again, as if the orgy of stagecrafted grief had never happened.

"Conrad Yeats stole something of great value from me," Midas said firmly.

"Mercedes will be missed," Serena said calmly.

"I am speaking of the contents of a safe deposit box in Bern," Midas said. "Yeats broke into my bank and stole my box."

Serena realized that she had to meet with Conrad. "Well, you'll need to employ better security to reassure your other customers."

"No, you'll need to get it back for me and kill Yeats when he contacts you."

"Why would he do that?"

"Don't play me for a fool. Mercedes told me everything about your sordid relationship with the man. So did Sorath."

With the mention of Sorath, Midas wanted her to know that he was a member of the Alignment and that he knew she was, too.

"All the more reason for Sorath to be upset to learn of your loss. If you tell me what it is, maybe I can help you."

Midas turned his gaze from the Dei medallion dangling around her neck to the Eiffel Tower in the distance. "A few minutes ago I wondered if Sorath was Sarkozy, that pompous French prick."

"If you're asking me whether he's the Antichrist, no," Serena said. "But I'm sure a man like Sarkozy would give the position some serious consideration if it were offered to him. You, too."

"And the pope?"

"The Vatican can't be bought off like the Russian Orthodox Church."

"No, it was bought off far earlier by Constantine and the Dei," Midas snarled. "And just who do you think you are? You're a little ecclesiastical whore of the pope, a false prophet if there ever was one."

Serena let that one go and allowed silence to fill the car. They were on the Boulevard de Ménilmontant. Soon they'd reach the cemetery. "I'm sorry, you were asking me for help?"

Midas looked at her with quiet rage. "I hope for your sake you have the globes."

She retorted, "I hope for your sake you have whatever it is you think that Conrad Yeats stole from you."

"Oh, I will," Midas said. "Because you will take it from him after you kill him. Only then will your loyalty to the Alignment no longer be in question."

"And yours isn't?"

"I have leverage, Sister Serghetti," Midas said. "It is the most important tool in business. It is having something the other party wants. I have something Sorath and the Alignment not only want but desperately need."

"And what would that be?"

He smiled. "You think you have something the Alignment needs in those globes from Solomon's Temple. But here, too, I have leverage: I know you don't have both of them. The Americans still possess one. And if two globes show up in Rhodes, I will know that one of them is a fake. And then where will you be?"

Serena felt a chill. Midas had sources within the Pentagon or the Dei, maybe both. If the Pentagon, her thoughts turned to Packard; if the Dei, they immediately went to Lorenzo. Either way, her plan to unmask and ultimately thwart the Alignment was at risk—along with any future she hoped to share with Conrad in this lifetime.

"Benito, I think Sir Midas is threatening to kill me."

"*Sí, signorina.* The family will take care of him."

"The cardinals will be thanking God in their prayers once you're gone, Sister Serghetti," said Midas. "Or do they still call you Sister Pain in the Ass behind your back in Vatican City?"

"I think Benito was referring to *his* family," Serena said, then lowered her voice to a whisper for effect. "The Borgias."

The name clearly registered with Midas. The Borgias had been the Church's first crime family in the Middle Ages and included eleven cardinals, three popes, and a queen of England. They killed for power, money, and wanton pleasure. That was centuries ago, of course, and Benito's branch of the family had long left the Church to establish the Mafia.

"You crazy bitch," Midas said. "You play us all off each other. The Americans, the Russians, the Alignment, the Mob. You are the devil."

"Well, we all have our issues," she said, looking him in the eye. "I'm curious, Midas. What exactly is the Alignment promising you? You already have more money than just about anybody else in the world. And you seem to recognize what the Church has known for centuries—

that those in power are more often defined by history rather than the other way around."

"A new world order is coming," Midas said. "The old order, including the Church, will pass away."

They drove past the Métro station Philippe Auguste and through the main entrance of the Père Lachaise Cemetery, which had been established by Napoleon in 1804.

Serena took advantage of the scenery. "I've heard that before." She made a point of looking at his trembling hand and then out her window at the rows of crosses, tombstones, and burial monuments. "What good is the new world order, Midas, if you're not around to enjoy it?"

Midas smiled. "That is this thing, is it not?"

"Yes," she said as Benito parked behind the convoy of cars trailing the black Volvo hearse. "I know where I'm going when I die. So, unless there's another heaven I don't know about, where are you going to end up?"

Midas's eyes were black and shining with a secret he seemed to be dying to tell her. He leaned over. "I have news for you," he whispered. "There won't be a heaven or an afterlife."

She looked at him curiously. He seemed more certain of what he was telling her than he had seemed of anything else.

"Who knows," Midas added. "Even you might enjoy the new world order and forget all about Conrad Yeats. While you've been worrying about him, he certainly hasn't been worrying about you."

Midas pulled out his BlackBerry and played a video clip from a private file on his smartphone's memory card. The video showed Conrad frolicking in bed with a young girl in a Miami Dolphins jersey. The time stamp at the bottom of the frame showed that it was barely forty-eight hours old.

"That's enough, Midas."

"Good." Midas put away the phone in triumph. "Then we are agreed. You kill Conrad Yeats to prove your loyalty to the Alignment and bring what Yeats stole from me to Rhodes."

"Or else?" she asked.

"Or else I'll expose your sham with the globes, and it will be your funeral I'll eulogize at next week."

28

GRAND HOTEL A VILLA FELTRINELLI
LAKE GARDA, ITALY

It was half past four when Conrad's Town Car turned off the country road and onto a long private drive lined with stately palms and cypresses. The end of the gravel drive opened like a dream to reveal the majestic Villa Feltrinelli and its octagonal tower overlooking the waters of Lake Garda.

The Feltrinelli family, who made their fortune in lumber, had built the villa at the end of the nineteenth century. By the middle of the twentieth century, in the waning days of World War II, the villa became famous as the final residence of Italian dictator Benito Mussolini before his execution. In the twenty-first century, Swiss management had turned the Villa Feltrinelli into one of Europe's most private, secure, and romantic luxury hotels, an unspoiled paradise far from the cares of the outside world.

The perfect place, Conrad thought, *for a rendezvous with Serena.*

A young Swiss miss welcomed him as Baron von Berg in the grand entry hall with a bouquet of rosebuds. Conrad looked past the circular sofa and carved wooden benches to the marble staircase with tall stained-glass windows and gilded mirrors. There were twenty-one guest rooms in the main villa, including the Magnolia Suite where Mussolini had slept. For Serena's sake, Conrad had booked the private boathouse outside the main villa, away from the other guests.

A sporty Italian bellman named Gianni took Conrad's weekender bag that he had purchased in nearby Desenzano after his six-hour ride from Bern involving two trains, one passport check, and one transfer in Milan.

"*Guten Tag,* Baron von Berg," said Gianni in passable German. "Where is the baroness?"

"She has her own ride."

They walked outside the covered pergola and past the pool with ducks and terraced gardens toward the lakeside boathouse. Two couples were enjoying afternoon tea on the lawn while a third played a game of croquet. Nothing was forced, including the prosecco offered to Conrad on a floating tray. Life and love seemed to flow quite naturally here.

"We have our own yacht for cocktail cruises," Gianni told him. "You can arrange for a motor launch to take you and the baroness around the lake and even explore the medieval castle at Sirmione."

"That sounds wonderful, Gianni," Conrad said, sipping his drink.

The boathouse was spacious enough, with dark wood paneling and eggshell linens and upholstery. Its tall windows with sheer lace curtains offered a spectacular view of the lake.

Once the young bellman had closed the door on his way out, Conrad turned to find a dessert tray of lemon mousse sprinkled with fruit and edible flowers, a jasmine-scented candle burning on the nightstand, and rose petals strewn throughout the marble bathroom.

The only thing missing from this perfect romantic scene was Serena.

He looked at the antique Rolex, his gift from Baron von Berg. It was almost five o'clock, and Serena's seaplane was due to land on the lake any minute now.

Conrad removed the watch and adjusted the dial until the Roman coin fell onto the table. He then pulled out a set of two books titled *Coinage and History of the Roman Empire* that he had picked up at a rare coin shop in Desenzano. The pages were thin, the lines single-spaced, and the font small, which made reading hard, but he found what he needed.

Conrad picked up the ancient Roman coin.

It looked almost like an American quarter, with Caesar instead of George Washington on one side and an eagle on the other. But this eagle looked quite distinctive, with a club on its right and a palm frond on its left. Indeed, it looked just like the medallion Serena wore around her neck.

He took a closer look at the letters engraved around the coin's rim:

UROUIERAS KAIASULOU

Instantly, he knew the translation. He had come across it on coins during his digs beneath the Temple Mount in Jerusalem:

OF TYRE, THE HOLY AND INVIOLATE

He flipped to a page with the heading "Judas's Thirty Pieces of Silver" and a quote from the Gospel of Matthew:

> Then one of the 12, called Judas Iscariot, went
> unto the chief priests, and said unto them,
> "What will ye give me, and I will deliver him
> unto you?" And they covenanted with him for
> 30 pieces of silver.

The book said the coin was a so-called Shekel of Tyre, or temple tax coin. It was the only currency accepted at the Jerusalem temple, so it was most likely the coinage with which Judas had been paid for betraying Jesus Christ.

The bust on the front didn't belong to any Roman emperor, Conrad realized, putting away the coin books. It belonged to Melqarth, the god of the Phoenicians, with a laurel wreath around his head like Caesar's. Better known as Baal in the Old Testament. Sacrilege to Orthodox Jews, to be sure. But these coins were the only ones close enough to pure silver to be accepted at the temple. Roman coins were too debased.

He searched for a date on the coin. He found it on the reverse side, left of the eagle and just above its club.

EL

That was the year 35 c.e. on the Julian calendar—or 98 b.c., according to contemporary calendars. Well within the time of circulation during Jesus' lifetime.

It was certainly not the Tribute Penny that Jesus had used to advise followers to go ahead and give their tax money to the state but their whole hearts to God. If anything, the shekel represented quite the opposite— man-made religion that trusted not in the God of heaven but in Caesar and the power structure of this world. The penny was blessed, in short, and the shekel cursed.

Like the Dei.

Conrad's concentration was broken by the sound of a prop engine. He looked out to the lake and saw Serena flying in. Hopefully with some answers, for once.

29

Serena swung her seaplane over the treetops and came in for her final approach on the shimmering waters of Lake Garda. The breathtaking Villa Feltrinelli rose on the distant shore like a fairy castle. The sheer audacity of Conrad's selection of such a romantic locale, and this while he was on the run, amazed and angered her. A virgin like her wouldn't last the night at a place like this, especially with a man like him.

She'd flown her first high-wing Otter as a missionary in the Australian outback. Later, she'd flown in the African bush. This plane was a propeller-driven DHC-3, powered by a single six-hundred-horsepower Pratt & Whitney Wasp radial and fitted with floats, just like the type she'd used in the Andes during her work with the Aymara tribe. That was where she'd first met Conrad, on Lake Titicaca, the highest lake in the world and her personal favorite. No doubt it was an association he had hoped to evoke here.

She prayed in advance for God's wisdom and strength to do what her mission required of her. The only problem was that she had so *many* missions these days, often at cross-purposes. Her challenge here, she had to remind herself, was to steal from Conrad whatever he'd stolen from Midas, find out what else he knew, and then somehow get rid of him in such a way as to satisfy the Alignment and her own conscience.

Keeping her vows of purity, therefore, was the least of her worries.

She eased back on the throttle and put the Otter down into the water. The water was calm and gold in the late-afternoon sun, perfect to land on because of the enclosed nature of the lake. To her starboard, the hills looked like black paper cut out against twilight. *Lots of peace and quiet here,* she thought, which suited her just fine after the events of recent days and the days to come.

She taxied toward the boathouse in front of the villa. A man stood on the stone jetty with a rope tie. It wasn't Conrad. It was a porter from the villa who came along-side the Otter to tie it down.

She switched off the engine and climbed down to the plane's float. It was definitely more balmy and sensual here than in Paris at this time of year. She steadied herself for a second under the wing while she reached back into the cabin to pull out her little leather backpack. Then she took the extended hand of the young porter, who helped her step onto the jetty.

"Baroness von Berg. The baron is waiting for you."

I'm sure he is, she thought, and nodded with a smile but said nothing as she followed him down the jetty toward the villa. She could see that the Villa Feltrinelli offered everything a couple like her and the baron could want.

She looked out at the lake. If the porter knew who she was, he was saying nothing. That was one thing she had to give Conrad: Even if every member of the staff thought the holy Mother Earth had come for a secret tryst with her lover, and hazarded a guess this was her habit, nobody else would know. As much as she wanted to avoid the appearance of moral failure, this scenario was what it was, and people could think what they wanted.

He led her to the boathouse, which apparently was an even more private suite than those that occupied the main villa. *Bravo, Conrad,* she thought, and thanked the porter.

"Gianni," he offered helpfully.

She nodded. "Like the legendary soccer player Gianni Rivera?"

"Sì!" he said, eyes wide. "I was named after him."

Serena smiled. These days Rivera was a member of the European Parliament for the Uniti nell'Ulivo party. She followed Canadian hockey more closely than European football, but she knew enough about Rivera to know that he'd been the Wayne Gretzky of soccer in his day, able to instinctively know where the ball was going before it went there. It was an ability she had tried to cultivate in her own arena, where religion and politics squared off.

She switched to fluent Italian for Gianni's benefit: "We'll need his kind of passing game this year if our team is going to have a shot at the World Cup."

Gianni nodded enthusiastically as the door to the boathouse opened.

A remarkably gorgeous Conrad stepped out and handed Gianni a wad of Euros. "*Tausend dank,*" he said, and waved Gianni away.

Gianni reluctantly walked off to the main villa, glancing back every now and then as if afraid to leave the baroness in the clutches of the barbarian Baron von Berg.

"I think he's in love," Conrad told her, and looked at her with sparkling eyes. "We all are."

Without warning, he kissed her full on the lips. She threw both arms around his neck and kissed him back passionately. She felt him lift her up like a groom his bride and carry her across the threshold into their suite, where he nudged the door shut behind them and set her down.

She was breathless as they stared at each other, each waiting for the other to break the mood with some glib remark to coolly reestablish the uncrossable cosmic chasm that fate had always thrown up between them.

It's always me, she thought. *I'm always the one to push him away.*

But she didn't want to push him away. She wanted him to do it, prayed to God that he would do it. And

Conrad, who could read her soul like one of his glyphless mysteries of antiquity, obliged for her sake and not his.

"Show me yours and I'll show you mine," he said.

She blinked. "What?"

He reached up to her neck, his fingers caressing her skin ever so gently. She put her own hand to his. But then he yanked the Dei medallion off her neck, leaving a slight red burn line.

"Conrad!" she yelled, and gripped her throat while he dangled the medallion in front of her face, his eyes on fire.

"So what's Her Holiness of the Roman Catholic Church doing holding the face of Baal between her breasts?" he demanded.

"I know." She swallowed hard. "It's not the Tribute Penny of Jesus."

"No, it's a Shekel of Tyre. Just like one of those thirty goddamn pieces of silver Judas took to betray *your* Lord and Savior."

"No, Conrad," she gasped, trying to catch her breath. "It *is* one of the Judas coins."

30

Conrad looked at Serena across the table outside the boathouse. She was clearly enjoying the lakeside dinner personally prepared for them by Chef Stefano Baiocco: fish soup with tiny squids, Parma ham with prawns and artichoke hearts, Lake Garda white fish called corégone, and homemade tagliolini with pesto. All paired with the most amazing wines.

When all the plates were cleared and the sun had finally set, Conrad sat back and listened to her telling him everything.

According to the New Testament gospels, Judas had sold out Jesus to the ruling religious council of the Jews, the Sanhedrin, for thirty pieces of silver. Those shekels came out of their temple tax coffers. After the Sanhedrin turned Jesus over to the Romans and it was clear that the Romans were going to kill Jesus by crucifixion, Judas was filled with remorse and hanged himself. Before he did, however, he returned to the temple and threw his money at the priests. The priests, recognizing at this point that the shekels were blood money, couldn't deposit them back into the holy temple treasury. So they used the money for charity. They bought some land and turned it into a cemetery for paupers who couldn't afford a proper burial.

"That much I know," Conrad said. "Go on."

According to the tradition of Dominus Dei, Serena told him, the man who sold his land to the Sanhedrin used the thirty pieces of silver to purchase another piece of land. This land he purchased from St. Matthew, the former tax collector and disciple of Jesus who wrote the authoritative gospel account of Judas's coins. The land Matthew sold, moreover, was land that Judas had purchased for himself with money he had stolen from the disciples' slush fund.

Conrad knew that apocryphal traditions were hard to authenticate and too often served the agendas of those who propagated them, so he was suspicious. "Why would Matthew even want that money?" he asked her. "What did he do with it?"

"Church tradition doesn't really speculate on what happened to Matthew, but somehow the coins got to Rome," she told him. "The Dei were established in the courts of Caesar well before St. Paul arrived in Rome and was beheaded by the emperor Nero. They were the secret Christians among Caesar's staff and praetorian guard that Paul referred to in his last letters from prison before his execution."

"So they just watched Paul's head roll down the palace steps?" Conrad asked dubiously. "Nice friends there, Serena.

But I guess you have to save your own ass before you save the world. Is that what Jesus said? No, I guess not."

"I'm not excusing the Dei, Conrad. I'm just telling you their history. Because the Roman emperors established themselves as gods, any Christian who claimed to serve another god faced death. So instead of using the old codes of crosses and fishes, which Rome's imperial intelligence services had cracked, they used the silver shekels to identify themselves to each other."

"And how long did that work?" Conrad asked.

Serena gave him a funny look. "For about three hundred years, at which point the emperor Constantine converted to Christianity and it became the official religion of the Roman Empire."

"And completely corrupted by power," Conrad added. "At some point these coins stopped being heirlooms passed along after death. They became objects to be possessed by killing their owners in order to move up in the ranks of the Alignment."

"I don't know when it started, exactly," she said. "Maybe with the Knights Templar."

"What the hell are *you* doing with these people, Serena? That's what I want to know. Especially after you pledged your undying love to me under the Mall in Washington, D.C., only to ditch me and steal that terrestrial globe."

She seemed to visibly tense up at the mention of the globe, and Conrad was glad to see it was still a sore point with her, too.

"The Alignment had targeted the U.S. ever since its founding and was on the verge of taking over the American republic from within until you stopped it," she began. "But when you left me alone there under L'Enfant Plaza with the globe, the secret seal of the United States, and those creepy Houdon busts of America's 'other' founding fathers, I didn't know if you were going to succeed in stopping the Alignment and come back for me."

"So you stole the globe."

"If the Alignment had succeeded in taking over the federal government, they would have had both globes, Conrad. I couldn't take the risk, especially after I recognized the face of one of those busts. The family resemblance, together with my knowledge of his history, led me to realize that Cardinal Tucci of Dominus Dei was a member of the Alignment. I had no idea that the Dei itself was an organ of the Alignment until after Tucci's suicide and his passing of the mantle, or rather medallion, to me."

It took an incredible amount of willpower, but Conrad maintained an even tone of voice. "You didn't have to stay."

"I was just supposed to run off with you, make love, have babies, and let the world go to hell?"

"Yeah, if the alternative is hooking up with the devil."

"Sometimes you have to join them to lick them, Conrad. The Dei is just one thread of the Alignment, the ecclesiastical thread, represented by one coin—mine.

Destroying my cell would do little to hurt the larger organization. You know the Alignment traces itself much further back than the Church, to before the Egyptians and even Atlantis. They use empires and religions and new world orders like locusts consuming one host after the other. Now these coins are in the hands of the world's most powerful political, financial, and cultural leaders."

Conrad sighed. There was no way she was going to bed with him tonight. "So you want to put names to faces."

"No, I want to put faces to the names I've got."

She explained that the Alignment had organized itself along the ranks of angels. There was the grandmaster at the top, surrounded by a council of thirty "knights." In addition to possessing one of the original Judas coins, each knight had a divine name that described his or her nature and role within the organization.

"Sorath is the name of the grandmaster," she told him. "Sorath is a fallen angel whose number, Rome believes, is 666. I have no idea who he is, but I assume he will be in Rhodes, where the Council of Thirty will be gathered for the first time in three hundred years."

"Why now?" Conrad asked, although he knew that the recovery of the legendary technology of Atlantis in the *Flammenschwert* was certainly one factor. But he suspected it wasn't the deciding factor.

Serena shrugged. "I guess I'll find out when I get there."

There was something she wasn't telling him, but he

couldn't put his finger on it. "What about you, Serena? What's your name?"

"Naamah," she said, looking down. "The fallen angel of prostitution who is more pleasing to men than to God."

Conrad decided he didn't want to go there in this discussion. She was already scaring the hell out of him. "And Midas?"

"Well, he's clearly inherited Baron von Berg's rank," she said. "His name is Xaphan—the fallen angel who keeps the fires of hell burning at full blast."

"You got that right," he said, and decided to tell her all about Baron von Berg's lost submarine and the *Flammenschwert*.

She looked stunned, as if everything made sense to her now. "I know the legend of Greek fire and its use during the Crusades, but I never imagined that the Nazis had found a way to tap Atlantean technology."

"Apparently, they did. I've seen the technology up close and personal."

He could see she was lost in thought when something like a flash of lightning flickered across her soft brown eyes. "And what about Baron von Berg's safe deposit box in Bern?" she asked. "What did you find inside?"

"This," he said, and slapped down the Shekel of Tyre on the table. "See, I've got one, too."

31

Serena stared at the coin on the table and fully grasped Midas's predicament and her own. Midas had been claiming some sort of provisional status within the Thirty based on his control over Baron von Berg's box, with the assumption that somehow, someday, he would possess its contents. Now Conrad had the coin and, technically, membership in the Alignment.

Until somebody like Midas or herself killed him for it.

"How did you get this?" she asked. "And why couldn't Midas?"

Conrad explained the code in the metal plate from Baron von Berg's skull, the self-destruct box in Bern, and how he'd circumvented all the security and escaped. He smiled and said, "So I guess we're going to Rhodes."

Serena was shaking inside. "I don't think so, Conrad."

"Names and faces, Serena. Names and faces. And, I'll bet you, the designated target for the *Flammenschwert*."

She couldn't let it happen, she realized. But she didn't want to fight him now. "We'll need a plan," she said. "A good one."

"How about this one?" he said, and produced a long tube he had been keeping under the table. It was a roll file, and inside were architectural drawings of a massive fortress. He spread them across the table. "Look familiar?"

"The Palace of the Grandmaster," she said. "Where did you get these?"

"Beneath the floorboards in the Magnolia Suite of the main villa."

"Seriously, Conrad."

"Seriously," he told her. "This was the last residence of Mussolini before he was executed. Rhodes belonged to the Italians back then, and Il Duce had grand plans for his Palace of the Grandmaster."

"It wasn't his," Serena said. "It was built by the Knights of St. John of Jerusalem in the seventh century."

"True, but that palace was pretty much demolished by the explosion of Turkish gunpowder centuries later. Mussolini restored and modified it between 1937 and 1940. These are the plans of the architect Vittorio Mesturino."

Serena didn't like the direction of this conversation and had to change it, put Conrad back on his heels. "How could you possibly know there were blueprints beneath the floorboards in the Magnolia Suite?"

"I didn't," he said. "But the hotel staff told me that was the suite Mussolini slept in, and I knew from his other residences where he liked to hide documents."

"Everybody missed it during the hotel's renovation?"

"The beauty of preservation," he explained. "The charm of this place is that most everything is as it was. Now look at the blueprint. There's a secret council chamber under the palace that's not shown in any contemporary floor plans. It's directly beneath the large courtyard in the center of the palace. That's where the Knights of the Alignment are going to meet."

Serena stared at the blueprint and then looked up at Conrad, who was studying the schematics and clearly making plans in his head. Yet again his genius genuinely frightened her. She was a careful strategist, but Conrad was opportunistic to a fault, able to find an opening when all doors seemed closed and bullets were raining down. That wasn't going to save him on Rhodes, though. Nothing would, if he actually stepped foot on the island.

"I think we should look it over after dessert," she said. "I'm going to shower and change first. It's been a very long day, and the week ahead is looking longer still."

She excused herself and walked into the boathouse. It was lavishly appointed, and she half believed she was capable of going to bed with Conrad that night. It could be their last chance ever. She picked up her backpack from the bed and went into the marble bathroom with flower petals everywhere. She splashed water on her face, feeling the queasiness of betrayal.

She pulled out her Vertu phone from her backpack and placed a call. The voice on the other end said, "Well?"

"I've got him," she said. "He's yours."

32

Conrad sat on the bed, anxiously waiting for Serena to emerge from the bathroom and wondering exactly what he'd see. There wasn't a lot of room in her little backpack for a change of clothes or a nightgown. But in every previous do-or-die moment of physical intimacy between them, she'd always managed to surprise him and leave him wanting.

"Conrad?" she called from the bathroom. "How did you find out which box was von Berg's?"

"It was etched beneath the metal plate in his skull."

"What was the code?"

"ARES, the god of war."

"Makes sense," she called out. "And the box number?"

"1740."

There was no response.

Conrad paused, wondering if he should say anything. Then he looked up to see Serena step out of the bathroom wearing only his white dress shirt, which managed to both hide and highlight her irresistible figure. He swallowed hard and stood up as she approached him.

She stood barely an inch away from his face, looking up at him. Their bodies did not touch, but he felt an unmistakable exchange of sexual energy between them.

"Do you really think it's a weapon forged from the technology of Atlantis?" she asked.

"I think it really turns water to fire on some molecular level, and that von Berg had a connection to Antarctica, which might have a connection with Atlantis."

"You're the one with the DNA of angels, Conrad. The Alignment and Americans both think you've got traces of Nephilim blood."

The Nephilim, according to the sixth chapter of Genesis, were the offspring of the mysterious "sons of God"—fallen angels, according to some theologians—who bred with women. Their civilization was wiped off the face of the earth by the Great Flood, which the Bible said was God's wrath upon a corrupted humanity.

"You say Nephilim and I say Atlantean," Conrad said. "But at the end of the day, we all share the same ancestral DNA."

"Some more than others."

Conrad shrugged. "Hasn't helped me yet."

"But it helped me back in D.C.," she reminded him. "Your blood provided the vaccine that saved me from the Alignment's military-grade flu virus."

"Oh, right," he said. "We've already swapped bodily fluids."

Serena's warm gaze embraced him even as she maintained her one-inch distance. It was all Conrad could do to keep from grabbing her.

"Why did you come back, Conrad?" she asked him. "After what I did to you?"

"I knew there were other forces at work, Serena," he told her. "I had to find out what they were."

Her face looked sad, defeated. "And then what?" she pressed him. "What were your plans for our future—if we had one?"

"You mean if you weren't a member of the Alignment? Or a nun?"

"Technically, I'm not a nun. I had to give up my role with the Carmelites for the Dei. And since the Dei doesn't recognize women as such, I'm pretty much a lay leader in the Church."

Conrad felt a glimmer of hope. "That's wonderful," he blurted, grasping her hand. "The best news yet."

"So how many children do you want, Conrad?" she asked, obviously trying to scare him. She was no wallflower. "You'll have to take care of them, you know."

"Me?" he asked.

"Just because I'm not a nun doesn't mean I'll be giving up the Lord's work traveling to the farthest corners of the earth to help the helpless."

"Okay with me," he said, playing along. "The ruins I

explore tend to be in the same places. You can just strap the little guys to your back and swing from trees all you want."

"What's wrong with little girls, Conrad?"

"Nothing," he said. "But biologically, aren't I the one to decide that? Guess there's only one way to find out." He gently pulled her closer to him, and his voice turned tender. "You're the only thing I have to show for my life, Serena. Everything else is dust. That Hebrew slave settlement I found by the pyramids in Giza. Gone. Atlantis in Antarctica. Gone. The only thing I ever recovered were the globes, and you and Uncle Sam stole them from me."

"I'm so sorry, Conrad. I really am."

"No, you don't understand, Serena. I'm okay with it. I don't need to make any great discoveries. We can make our own. You're what I've been searching for all my life. I knew it the moment I saw you. And I don't ever want to lose you."

Her eyes sparkled with tears. She threw her arms around his neck and turned her lovely mouth up to his and kissed him.

His whole body and spirit seemed to come alive as they embraced. He couldn't believe this was about to happen.

"Please forgive me, Conrad, for all I've done to you," she said, kissing him again. "For what I'm going to do to you."

His head was swimming in ecstasy. Or was it something else? He opened his eyes and saw the room spinning behind Serena's blurred face.

"I hate you," he groaned as whatever drug she had applied to her lips took hold of his body.

"Forgive me," she whispered as she kissed him generously, passionately, until he blacked out.

33

1740!" Conrad shouted, and bolted upright in bed.

He opened his eyes. He was inside an Airstream trailer with a loud but familiar hum around him. The air was cold, and there was a woman sitting next to him, but it wasn't Serena. It was Wanda Randolph, the former U.S. Capitol Police officer who had taken shots at him in the tunnels beneath the U.S. Capitol.

"Where am I?" he asked.

"You're on U.S. soil now, so to speak," she said, and smiled. "Everything's okay."

He looked at the wires and electrodes attached to his body. "The hell it is," he said, and with his right arm struck Wanda in the head and knocked her against the Airstream's wall. He pulled off the wires, opened the trailer door, ran out into a cavernous hangar, and looked for an exit.

"Stop!" Wanda shouted, running up behind with a gun pointed at him.

He ran past a chopper and a tank to a large door and

found the button to open it. Warning lights flashed and an alarm sounded. As the door slowly opened from the top down, Conrad realized where he was even before he saw the curvature of the Mediterranean Sea thirty thousand feet below.

There were more shouts and the thunder of boots on the metal flooring, and Conrad turned to see a team of U.S. airmen surround him with their guns drawn.

"Step away from the panel, sir," an airman ordered.

Conrad knew he was going nowhere and stepped away.

The airmen holstered their guns and closed the door as Wanda escorted him back to the Airstream trailer, where Marshall Packard was waiting with some files.

"Good, you're up," Packard said.

"Where's Serena?" Conrad demanded.

"On her way to Rhodes," Packard said. "She exchanged you for our celestial globe. She was actually going to attempt to slip a forgery past the Alignment, which never would have worked. Now she can deliver the goods at the EU summit and be our eyes and ears inside the Alignment."

Conrad shook his head. "You don't need me, Packard. Why did you do it?"

"Your girl said she needed you off the playing field to convince the Alignment you're dead, like she promised, and she had some bizarre notion that you might not play along," Packard said. "So we'll keep an eye on you."

"Not a chance," said Conrad. "You know she's dead meat once she turns over those globes."

"That's a risk she's willing to take to identify the remaining officers of the Alignment. Meanwhile, we've already seen both globes and know what the Alignment is getting. So there's no downside for us."

"You're idiots," Conrad said. "The globes work together. You have no idea what the Alignment has."

"Enlighten me."

"The number of Baron von Berg's safe deposit box was for the date 1740."

"Yeah, yeah, we're ahead of you, son," Packard said. "The only thing that popped up in history for that year was the death in Rome of Pope Clement XII, who had forbidden Roman Catholics from belonging to Masonic lodges on pain of excommunication. Von Berg's joke. Ha, ha."

"Joke's on you, Packard. That was also the year that the Masons in Berlin established the Royal Mother Lodge of the Three Globes. I don't know why I didn't see it before. I guess I needed Baron von Berg and his box number to finally make the connection."

The color drained from Packard's face. "Three globes?"

"That's right," Conrad said. "There were three of them all along. The Masons must have kept one in Europe and let the other two go to the New World. How much you want to bet that the Alignment has had the third globe all along? Now Serena is about to hand them the other two."

"But for what purpose?" Packard demanded. "What the hell do three globes do that two globes can't?"

"Reveal the target and timetable for detonating the *Flammenschwert*, that's what," Conrad said.

PART THREE

Rhodes

34

The early-morning sun glinted off the calm waters of Mandraki Harbor as Midas's yacht, the *Mercedes,* motored past the long breakwater with its three wind-mills toward the medieval city of Rhodes. There, atop its highest point, its massive fortress walls dwarfing the city below, was the Palace of the Grandmaster.

At least the *Mercedes* could enjoy the intimacy of the harbor with its pleasure craft and seaside cafés, Midas thought as they entered the mouth of the harbor. The *Midas* would have required them to anchor farther away.

Much smaller than the *Midas,* the *Mercedes* was a mere 250-footer that he picked up in Cyprus the day after Mercedes's funeral in Paris. He had planned to arrive in Rhodes in the *Midas.* It had taken two days to acquire a yacht large enough to take in a submersible. Midas had contacted his rogue submersible that had been roaming the deep with the *Flammenschwert* all this time. As soon as the captain emerged after five days underwater, Midas rewarded him with a bullet to the brain and dumped him overboard.

Now the *Mercedes* passed between the two defensive stone towers where the Colossus of Rhodes was said to have straddled the harbor. The giant statue had been one of the seven wonders of the ancient world before an earthquake in 226 B.C. brought it down into the sea a century after it was erected.

Midas left the deck and entered his stateroom to admire the magnificent sculpture in the center of the room—a bust of Aphrodite, the ancient Greek goddess of love. The cover was brilliant. As an act of goodwill, Midas would be returning to the Greeks the bronze head of Aphrodite from the British Museum, which he had managed to exchange for several works of art he had purchased at auction from Sotheby's on Bond Street. It had taken months of negotiations with the museum's Department of Greek and Roman Antiquities, but he needed this particular bust to both house the warhead and bring as a gift for the Greeks at the summit.

The beauty of the head of Aphrodite was that it was a sculptural mask of the Greek goddess of love, so the back was missing. That enabled Midas to fit the *Flammenschwert* warhead neatly inside. The fitted plaster piece on the back of the mask would be tossed once the transfer of the warhead had been made, and the mask could be handed off to the Greeks for display in the exhibition halls of the palace.

Midas ran his finger down the face of the serene mask. The deeply set eyes had come from a complete statue and dated back to the second or first century B.C. It was seventeen inches high, twelve inches wide, and eleven inches deep. The warhead was only six inches in diameter, inside of which were two pounds of Semtex plastic explosive and an initiator device. The detonator would explode the Semtex and ignite the metallic fire pellets of the *Flammenschwert*. The fire pellets, in turn, would ignite any water around it.

Midas looked at his watch. He was due to deliver the mask to the Palace of the Grandmaster in twenty minutes.

Vadim was waiting on the dock with the limousine and a police motorcycle escort. They placed the packing crate with the Aphrodite mask in the back and then made their way to the palace.

"Where's the bitch?" Midas asked.

"At the convention center," Vadim said.

Midas sighed. He felt vulnerable without his membership coin. His deal with the Alignment had been that he would recover Baron von Berg's coin and the *Flammenschwert* from the baron's sub in exchange for a seat on the Council of Thirty. But then Conrad Yeats had ruined everything. Fortunately, Yeats was out of the picture now, and the coin would soon be in Midas's hands.

They drove along the harbor toward the Old City. The medieval town of Rhodes was surrounded and defined by a triple circuit of walls, which looked to Midas to be in very good condition. The fortress city seemed to have it all: moats, towers, bridges, and seven gates.

Vadim pulled the limousine up to the security checkpoint at the Eleftherias Gate, or the Gate of Liberty. Only permanent residents of the Old City were allowed to drive on the narrow cobblestone streets. But today dignitaries were allowed through with a police escort.

They followed the stone-paved streets past the third-century temple of Aphrodite and turned onto the main drag, the Odos Ippoton, or the Street of Knights, named for the Knights of St. John, who had established themselves on the island in the fourteenth century and who Midas was convinced must have been a front for the Alignment at one point. At the entrance was the fifteenth-century Knights Hospital, and at the end of the street, opposite the Church of St. John, stood the imposing Palace of the Grandmaster with its spherical towers.

They drove past the massive round towers flanking the main entrance to the palace—where Greek *Evzones* in uniform stood on either side of the sharp arch—and went around to the west entrance by the square tower, where a Greek cultural attaché welcomed Midas and the Aphrodite mask into the grand reception hall. This was the regal backdrop where the opening and closing ceremonies were staged for the cameras, while the sessions and breakout panels took place in the ballrooms, conference centers, and suites at the Rodos Palace hotel and international convention center ten minutes away.

"On behalf of the people of Greece, I thank you for returning to us the Aphrodite head from the British Museum," the attaché said.

"It is my pleasure," Midas said. "And I was told I could spend a moment alone with my dear Aphrodite before I handed it over."

"Yes," said the attaché. An armed Greek *Evzone* with an earpiece appeared and led Midas past a Medusa mosaic down a large vaulted corridor. There were 158 rooms in the palace, all bedecked with antique furniture, exquisite polychrome marbles, sculptures, and icons. Only twenty-four of those rooms were open to the public on any given day.

But the room to which Midas was escorted wasn't in any of the tourist guides or public blueprints registered with Greece; it was even closed to the VIPs of the summit. It was a chamber constructed beneath the palace. Closed to all but members of the Alignment, it was known as the Hall of Knights council room.

Midas entered the hall and waited for his escort to leave. Then a door slid open, and he walked into the adjoining chamber with the Aphrodite mask, prepared to hand the *Flammenschwert* to Uriel.

But Uriel wasn't there—only a single copper globe, split open, resting on a stand on top of a large round table. Inside the globe was an envelope, and next to the round table was a fireplace with a fire burning.

No surprise here, really. Midas had known the identity of Uriel, and vice versa, all along. They weren't supposed to be seen together in public, a rule Midas had violated at the disastrous Bilderberg party. But as this handoff was private, he hadn't been sure what to expect.

He looked at the globe. It was the first time he had seen one of them.

So this is the delivery device.

Not a missile. Not a warplane. But this old globe.

If it had been his choice, Midas would have held on to the *Flammenschwert* until its detonation. He certainly wouldn't have left it alone here. But the holier-than-thou Uriel didn't want to see the *Flammenschwert,* much less touch it. And Uriel was the only one who could get it into position and leave the dirty work of pulling the trigger to Midas.

He opened the envelope, read the handwritten note, tossed it into the fireplace, and watched it burn to ashes.

He removed the plaster back of the bronze Aphrodite mask and tossed it into the fireplace, too. Then he put his hand behind the sphere containing the *Flammenschwert* and turned the mask over until the sphere rested heavily in his hand. He lifted the mask with the other hand and placed it on the table. With both hands, he carefully placed the sphere containing the *Flammenschwert* inside the globe, where it fit snugly. He sealed the globe shut like a skin over the warhead sphere. The seam along the 40th parallel seemed to disappear.

The door on the other side of the chamber magically opened. He picked up Aphrodite's head, brushed it off, and walked out.

35

Conrad watched another F-16 take off from the tarmac and walked back up the rear ramp of the C-17 to Packard's office inside the "silver bullet." Packard had been on the phone ever since they'd landed on Crete. The Greek air base was home to the Hellenic Air Force's 115th Combat Wing, but the U.S. Naval Support Activity Souda Bay occupied over a hundred acres on the north side to support Sixth Fleet operations in the eastern Mediterranean and Middle East. Conrad was waiting to hear if he would get any of that support now.

Packard, still on the phone, frowned at him and slid across his desk the leather binder containing Conrad's hastily prepared but well-documented report on the Three Globes Society and their relationship to the Freemasons of colonial America, the Nazis, and the contemporary Alignment. Conrad picked up the binder and saw Packard's notations in the margins. The most frequent words were "insane," "crazy," "speculation," and "aha."

There were no comments on Conrad's outline of possible origins of the globes and whether they were originally housed in King Solomon's Temple, or perhaps some place older still.

Packard hung up the phone and looked at him. "It's going to take a few hours, but I think we can clear you with Interpol so that police everywhere will stop shooting at you on sight."

"You can't do that," Conrad said. "Midas would know that Serena lied to him about my demise. That alone would put her loyalty in doubt with the Alignment. I need an alias with ID to get me through all zones of security."

Packard sighed. "That's going to make it easier to nab the globes?"

"I don't need to steal anything. That's the beauty of it. I just need to see the three globes for myself. In and out."

"Because you think they'll reveal where and possibly when the Alignment will detonate the *Flammenschwert*?" Packard asked skeptically. "I'm not sure I'm ready to make that assumption."

Conrad said, "I think the leadership of the Alignment will use the message of the globes as some sort of mystical directive for their mystical weapon, even if they manipulate the meaning to suit their ends. So that message is invaluable regardless."

"Serena's whip-smart, son. What makes you think she can't figure it out for herself?"

"Not on the spot, she can't. She hasn't had the time

I've had with both globes. And she's a linguist, not an astro-archaeologist. She won't be able to figure out the celestial-terrestrial alignments between the globes, let alone translate them to real-world coordinates. Even if she could, you know they're not going to let her leave Rhodes alive once she's delivered the only leverage she's ever had with the Alignment."

Packard licked a finger and flipped through the report again, clearly still agitated with himself and his analysts for having missed the possibility of the existence of a third globe. "So let me get this straight: You think all three used to be in Solomon's Temple and were later buried beneath the Temple Mount when the Babylonians destroyed the First Temple. Furthermore, you think they may have been the Holy Grail that the Knights Templar were after when they started digging up the Temple Mount looking for Solomon's treasures during the Crusades."

"I think they worked to pinpoint a location of some great treasure, but it may not have been gold."

"Then what the hell else could it have been? And don't tell me the Ark of the Covenant."

"Obviously, something of great value. In ancient Egypt and Tiahuanaco and Atlantis, that meant the secrets of First Time or the End Times."

"The Alignment already has the secret of the End Times, son, and it's called the *Flammenschwert*. That's how they're going to end things for all of us. And that's why we need to find that weapon." Packard's face reddened, and he threw the report down. "I traded the globe for you and got nothing."

There was something just a little too forced in Packard's voice, and Conrad suddenly understood.

"You bastard," he said. "You weren't that desperate to get me. You just wanted to give Serena the globe and make her think she worked for it. What did you do to it?"

Packard sighed. "It's got a tracker."

Conrad slapped his hand on the table, furious. "Like the Alignment's not going to find it and kill her? Then they'll have the globes as well as the *Flammenschwert*, and you'll still have nothing."

"I told you, son, she's our girl at this EU summit. Both she and Midas are invited. You and Uncle Sam aren't. Security is going to be extremely tight, and the Alignment is supposed to think you're dead. Anybody recognizes you, she's dead."

"She's dead already."

Packard seemed to be going back and forth in his head, weighing the risks and rewards. "Well, I can't send U.S. troops, even Randolph, into this theater," he said, as if thinking aloud. "And when it comes to European summits, trust me, it's always theater."

"So I'm in."

"Hey, it's your head and hers," Packard said. "This doesn't come back to Uncle Sam. Just stay out of sight, if that's possible, and report as soon as you know anything."

"I told you, I can do this without being seen, even by Serena. But I'll be watching her."

"As will everybody else. So watch yourself."

Ten minutes later, the twin engines and four blades of the Super Puma Eurocopter were winding up for take-off as Wanda Randolph walked Conrad across the tarmac and gave him his identification badges.

"Your name is Firat Kayda, a military liaison with us in Turkey, and you're working the EU summit for the delegation from Ankara. It'll take you about an hour in the air from here to there."

Conrad looked at the four Greek airmen in the chopper. They already seemed to be glaring at him, the Turk. "Packard is truly determined to make everybody in this world hate me, isn't he?"

"Well, he tries," said Wanda. "At least this way, the Greeks won't be asking you too many questions on the way over."

36

Serena stepped off her seaplane in Mandraki Harbor at Rhodes and felt like she had stepped back in time to the Crusades. The Palace of the Grandmaster, the fifteenth-century Tower of St. Nicholas, and the Mosque of Sultan completely overwhelmed the contemporary seaside cafés, chic shops, and sleek yachts lining the harbor.

Brother Lorenzo of the Dei, his mouth agape in astonishment, was waiting for her by a silver Mercedes-Benz G55 AMG sport-utility vehicle as she walked toward him, holding the celestial globe from the Americans against her belly and looking like a pregnant woman about to give birth.

She felt naked without the full escort of Swiss Guards she normally had at her disposal. But this was not official Vatican business, and if any agents of the Alignment were watching from rooftops through scopes, it was probably for her protection until she delivered the globes. There was no reason for any sort of smash-and-grab attack.

"The genuine celestial globe," Lorenzo said reverently as he helped her load it into the back. He had no clue where she had gone between Paris and Rhodes and was clearly impressed with her acquisition. "But how?"

She certainly wasn't going to tell him. "Where's Benito?"

"At the convention center with the terrestrial globe and the fake celestial globe."

"Let's go, then."

The Rodos Palace hotel and convention center sat on a hill overlooking Ialyssos Bay and billed itself as Greece's finest and largest convention resort, specially built to host the European heads of state. Serena could see from all the armored vehicles and police outside that this was certainly the case today. Some twenty-seven ministers of the European nations and all their security had descended on the peace summit to discuss and possibly reach some sort of international resolution on the fate of Jerusalem, which they had deemed the key to establishing an independent Palestinian state and peace in the Middle East.

Lorenzo bypassed the main entrance to the complex on Trianton Avenue and rounded the corner to the vehicle inspection point in front of the drop-off lane at the VIP entrance. He popped the rear hatch, lowered his window, and handed to a police officer his license and registration, along with their summit ID badges. Serena watched the officer slide the badges through a card reader while four soldiers surrounded the SUV and passed mirrors under the chassis in search of explosives.

A couple of the soldiers had gathered around the globe and asked that she and Lorenzo step out and explain while the interior cabin of the SUV could be examined.

"It's part of the art for one of the exhibitions at the summit," she said. "We're not even taking it inside. We're picking up another globe at the loading dock outside the Jupiter Ballroom and then taking both of them to the Palace of the Grandmaster for viewing."

"Of course, Sister Serghetti," the officer said. "I am sorry for the inconvenience."

She climbed back inside the SUV, and Lorenzo got behind the wheel and started it up again. Then he drove them all of fifty yards down to the loading entrance outside the Jupiter Ballroom.

In the ballroom, Serena found the EU heads of state seated in front of their national flags around a pentagon of tables beneath Murano crystal chandeliers. Around the leaders was a much larger ring of tables packed with diplomatic staff, international press, and banks of equipment for audiovisual and simultaneous interpretation.

She made her way behind the press area, glancing up now and then to see the image of a talking head flash across the large screen over the stage. She could only guess how many of those faces belonged to the Thirty. Whoever her counterparts of the Alignment turned out to be, Serena was convinced that the message of the Templar globes and this EU summit were connected symbiotically. The origins of the globes had been traced to King Solomon's

Temple in Jerusalem, after all, and it was the future of that city under discussion in this ballroom.

She found Benito backstage with the globes, which were disregarded by all the technical people moving to and fro as mere set pieces and part of the show, somebody else's responsibility.

Midas was there, too, and he wasted no time. "You have something for me?"

Serena removed the Shekel of Tyre from her pocket and handed it to him.

He didn't take her word for it and took out some sort of pocket-sized device to shine an infrared light on it. "The ancients used some kind of polymer material on the coins. The effect is like an invisible UV stamp. See?" he said. He showed her the coin under the light, and to her amazement, she saw four arrowlike markers emblazoned at the cardinal points around the bust of Baal. They made a cross, and she recognized it as the adopted flag of the island's Knights of St. John.

Midas held up his infrared device and said accusingly, "I used this on your celestial globe here, too. It's a fake."

"I have the real one in my car outside. You were to give me further instructions?"

Midas seemed pleased. "You are to take the globes to the west entrance of the Palace of the Grandmaster at three o'clock, where you will be met by a nameless Greek attaché and directed to a chamber where you will present the globes to Uriel," he told her. "You have ten minutes."

She left Lorenzo and the faux celestial globe at the

convention center and climbed into the back of the SUV with the two genuine globes. Benito pulled onto the access drive, and the police waved them through the exit gate.

Uriel, she thought. Serena had never heard that name among the Thirty. But she knew that Uriel was the name of the angel in Genesis who guarded the gate to the Garden of Eden with a flaming sword after God kicked Adam and Eve out of paradise. Conrad's information about the *Flammenschwert* weapon was beginning to make sense, and she was eager to find out who this Uriel could be.

As they drove toward the Palace of the Grandmaster, she could tell Benito was impressed with her acquisition of the genuine celestial globe but concerned all the same.

"And *Signor* Yeats?" he asked, glancing at her in the rearview mirror.

"With the Americans," she answered.

Benito bit his tongue, but Serena could read his eyes: *That man will hate you for the rest of your life, you cold, heartless bitch.* Well, he wouldn't say that. Benito didn't swear, and he knew more than anybody else what was necessary. He seemed sad all the same, though.

But she had come to Rhodes to unmask the Alignment. In a few minutes she would deliver the globes, as promised. In a few hours she would attend tonight's Council Meeting of the Thirty. Then everything she had worked for and sacrificed—including a life with Conrad—would pay off once and for all.

37

The Greek pilot brought the Super Puma Eurocopter over Rhodes at nine hundred feet, steering clear of the EU summit's security red zones below and following an alternative glide path to the airstrip. The skies were clear and offered Conrad a spectacular view of the island below.

"Security zones?" Conrad asked in broken English with the best Turkish accent he could make up. His attempt was so bad it actually worked, cracking up one of the Greeks. Another, named Koulos, decided to help the confused Turk get a lay of the land.

"The red inner-security zones are around the Palace of the Grandmaster in the Old Town down there, and the Rodos Palace hotel and convention center are in New Town over there," Koulos shouted in English above the whir of the rotor blades. "They are linked by the harbor drive. Only authorized personnel or security assigned to those zones can pass through the checkpoints."

Conrad nodded.

"The walls of Old Town outside the Palace of the Grandmaster are the perimeter of the yellow outer-security zone. No vehicles without proper registration and full inspection are allowed through the gates."

Conrad pulled out the military BlackBerry Packard had given him with the GPS tracking program. He called up the satellite map of Rhodes from Google Earth and tried to find the pulsing blue dot that represented the celestial globe Packard had given Serena. The glare from the sun outside the chopper windows made it too difficult to read the screen until they landed and he jumped off onto the tarmac.

That was when he got the fix: The globe was in the red zone at the convention center, hopefully with the other two.

Conrad signed for his police motorcycle as Firat Kayda. Though the bike belonged to the police department, it wasn't an official police motorcycle and had no siren. When he reached the convention center, his ID badge worked beautifully, and he was able to glide through the checkpoint to the main entrance of the hotel, allegedly to meet his Turkish superiors.

He followed the GPS signal through the hotel atrium and into the airy exhibition area where all kinds of "green" technology companies promised to turn the Middle East into a tropical paradise for investment and generate fat profits to European investors. "More than oil" seemed to be the theme, highlighting the commercial benefits of peace in the region.

The bright sunlight provided him with the perfect excuse to keep his sunglasses on, like many others, and look nondescript as he passed a spectacular circular staircase toward the Delphi Amphitheater.

He stopped outside the door and put away his BlackBerry. The security guard glanced at his badge and nodded.

Conrad slipped into the back of the three-level amphitheater, which was packed with almost six hundred delegates. Up on the stage, speaking from the podium before an impressive array of flat-panel screens flashing all sorts of logos and graphics, was Roman Midas.

What does he have to say that any of these people want to hear? Conrad unconsciously shrank back against the wall with a group of bystanders who couldn't find seats. He felt like a convict in a police lineup for Midas to pick out. But all the lights and attention were on Midas now, and Conrad doubted the man could see anyone beyond the front row.

"It's the new alchemy," Midas proclaimed. "Water springing forth from the desert."

High-definition graphics showed how the same deep-mining technology that Midas Minerals & Mining had used to extract oil from the "world's most difficult to reach substrata" could now be harnessed to extract water from the hidden rivers and aquifers of the Sinai Peninsula.

Midas said, "The dust bowl becomes the bread basket of the Middle East, freeing the region from dependence on foreign agriculture and offering local populations the opportunity to grow and export more than oil."

The names of various Israeli and Arab partners popped up on the screens to underscore the international cooperation of this "consortium of leading industries" to "rid the Middle East of its dependence on oil."

Well, that's a new one, Conrad thought as he slowly made his way along the curving back wall of the room. He suspected he would come upon a door leading to a projection booth or control room of some kind, which was probably as obscure a place as any to store the globes until they could be moved. He couldn't imagine them alone without armed security. But the only door that appeared was the other rear exit.

He stepped out of the amphitheater into the bar reception area and saw the celestial globe standing there like some piece of art with a young man in a suit and collar—a priest's collar.

Worse, the priest had recognized him.

Damn, Conrad thought as he marched up to the priest.

The priest began, "Dr. Yeats—"

"Shut up," Conrad said quietly, and glanced around. "What the hell is going on?"

"You needn't worry," the priest said drily. "This isn't the globe you gave her. This is a fake. She took the real one with her after she removed the tracker and put it inside this one."

"Where is she . . . Lorenzo?" Conrad said, reading the priest's ID badge.

Lorenzo had suddenly taken a vow of silence.

Conrad pressed him. "She's in danger."

The priest screwed up his eyes at Conrad. "From whom?"

"Last time, Lorenzo."

"She's at her three o'clock appointment," Lorenzo said. "Do I need to call security?"

"No, but I'm taking this." Conrad took the globe off its pedestal and walked off with it, leaving an open-mouthed Lorenzo behind.

Outside, Conrad opened the globe, tossed the tracker, and strapped the globe to the back of his motorcycle. Then he pulled out his BlackBerry and called Wanda Randolph.

"Report," said Wanda.

"Tell Packard she found the tracker. But she's still with the packages. I need you to hack the security system here and see when was the last time her ID badge was scanned."

"Copy that," Wanda said.

Conrad looked at his watch. It was 3:05. He was worried he was too late.

Wanda rang him back two minutes later. "She passed through the checkpoint at Liberty Gate in the Old Town. She's going to the Palace of the Grandmaster with two packages. They're listed only as 'art' on the system."

But Conrad had hung up at "Grandmaster," kick-started his bike, and roared off toward the fortress.

38

Back at the hotel and convention center, Lorenzo crossed the atrium lobby and approached the commanding officer at the security desk. He was an ambitious priest, and Dr. Yeats had given him a golden opportunity to accelerate his rise within the Dei even as he attempted to protect his superiors.

"I just saw the fugitive who murdered Mercedes Le Roche," Lorenzo said breathlessly. "Conrad Yeats the American. He is here at the summit."

The Greek looked at Lorenzo's badge and collar and decided to take the report seriously enough to ask further questions. "Was he wearing a badge, Father?"

"Yes," said Lorenzo helpfully. "The name was Firat Kayda, and it had a red security stripe for access to the inner zones. Holy Mother of God, maybe this American killed Kayda and has taken his place to kill someone here!"

"Please, Father. Do not repeat this. We will investigate."

Lorenzo detected a dismissive tone in the Greek official's voice. "You're not going to do any such thing, are you?"

The officer picked up a phone. "Firat Kayda," he said, and hung up.

"That's all?" Lorenzo said.

"Please wait, Father."

The officer attended to some papers with the other officers while Lorenzo watched, burning with anger. A minute later, the Greek saw his frown and looked at a computer terminal. "Here it is," he said, looking at a time-stamped video clip of the moment Kayda had passed through the hotel checkpoint. A concerned expression took hold on the Greek's face as the facial-recognition program kicked in. "There is a high degree of probability that you are correct."

"At last," Lorenzo said.

The Greek started typing furiously. "I am flagging his name and attaching the video for when he presents himself at a checkpoint. He'll be refused entry and arrested immediately."

"Don't forget that he is armed and dangerous, Officer. He has killed and may kill again."

The Greek looked up warily. "Thank you very much, Father. You have been most helpful."

Lorenzo made the sign of the cross and walked away.

39

Vadim was sitting inside the Peugeot parked opposite the Palace of the Grandmaster. He looked past the vehicle ID badge dangling from his rearview mirror to see the silver Mercedes SUV drive through.

He reached back and pulled down the rear seat to access the trunk. Squirming next to the blocks of C4 plastic explosives was a bound, gagged, and badly beaten Abdil Zawas. Vadim had brought the Egyptian to Rhodes directly from Bern hours before the security checkpoints had been set up. Since this car had been registered to a resident for several years, the security forces sweeping the Old Town yellow zone hadn't opened its trunk.

Abdil was waking up a little sooner than Vadim wanted. The streets were so narrow and cars so few that he couldn't afford to have somebody walk by while Abdil banged his head and feet to draw attention.

"Siesta isn't over," Vadim said, and removed an injection pen from his pocket. "We have to keep you alive long enough for the coroner to pronounce your proper cause of death as a martyr for Allah." He delighted at the look of horror in Abdil's eyes. The pen was filled only with a concentrated dose of trazodone to put him to sleep. Nothing painful, unfortunately, and it was a shame to think that the Egyptian wouldn't be awake for his final moments.

"Don't you wonder how many of your little sluts will miss you when you're gone?" Vadim asked, injecting the trazodone into Abdil's thick neck. "I think you'll miss them more where you're going."

Abdil's eyes rolled around in panic even as his eyelids grew heavy. In a few minutes it would all be over for the late, great Abdil Zawas.

"I'm going to make you famous, Abdil," Vadim told the Egyptian. "You're about to open a new front on the war against Jews and Crusaders. Look at this clip that's about to be posted on YouTube. Recognize yourself?"

Vadim was about to play the video on his BlackBerry when the device began to ring. It was Midas.

"Security says Yeats is alive and on Rhodes," Midas barked. "She has betrayed the Alignment."

"You seem surprised," Vadim said. "Your plan was always to kill her as soon as she delivered the globes. She knows too much. More than I do. Nothing has changed. Yeats won't make it in time to interfere."

"Is everything set?"

"Yes," Vadim said. "The only street into or out of the Palace of the Grandmaster is the Street of Knights. I'll take care of her as soon as she leaves the palace."

"She must not have even a moment to contact any-body with information about what she may have learned from Uriel or figured out for herself," Midas said, and then there was a pause. "Remember, Vadim. She will be the second car. I repeat: the second car. Not the first. Everything is lost if you mistake the two."

Vadim said, "I won't."

"See that you don't," Midas said. "It must look like the first car was the target but that Zawas hit Serghetti's car instead and blew himself up in the process."

"Yes," said Vadim, looking at Abdil's limp body in the mirror. "I understand."

40

All the way down the Street of Knights toward the Palace of the Grandmaster, Serena wondered who Uriel could possibly be. If his role within the Alignment was true to his name, then Uriel could be the one who ultimately possessed the *Flammenschwert*. That pointed to Midas, however, and she braced herself to see his ugly smile waiting for her with the third globe.

"I wish I could join you inside, *signorina*," Benito said as he pulled the G55 SUV up to the west tower entrance.

"Me, too," she said.

The Greek attaché Midas had told her about was already waiting with two aides and a cart. Benito opened the rear door, and the aides placed the two steel boxes containing the copper globes on the cart. Serena followed through the entrance.

Inside, they walked past the Medusa mosaic and down a large vaulted corridor to the lower level. It was right out of the blueprints Conrad had shown her back at the lake in Italy. And when they entered the Hall of Knights and left her alone with the globes, nobody had to tell her what room she stood in. Its scale and decor announced itself in a sinister way.

Then the small wooden door on the side opened by itself, and she saw the adjoining chamber and the reflection of a fire bouncing off what could only be the third globe. She pushed the cart inside, next to the round table, and beheld the globe on top.

The third globe.

She stood in silence, staring at it. It was magnificent, like something forged from the depths of a volcano or the mountain copper ore of Atlantis. It closely resembled its celestial and terrestrial cousins and was clearly part of the family. But the dials carved across the surface of this globe marked it as an armillary, built to predict the cycles of the sun, moon, and planets. It was the third element of time that Brother Lorenzo had correctly suspected was missing from their calculations back at the Vatican.

The door opened, and she looked up to see General Gellar, the Israeli defense minister, looking her up and down in surprise.

The feeling is mutual, she thought. "You're Uriel?" They had been acquaintances for quite some time, and suddenly, they both looked at each other in a very different way. "What do you want with these globes?" she asked.

"You have to ask?" Gellar sounded offended. "They're ours. They belong to Israel. You took them."

"We took them?"

"The Knights Templar stole them from under the Temple Mount along with whatever else they could pillage to fund their wars, increase their powers, and persecute the Jews."

Serena took it in, trying to figure this all out. "Well, on behalf of the Roman Catholic Church, I certainly plead guilty. And the pope has made official apologies for all that. I wasn't around at the time, of course. But if I had been, I'm sure that I, too, would have engaged in anti-Semitic behavior."

Gellar seemed to realize he was being ridiculous—although he clearly regarded the Dei medallion hanging around her neck as if it were a Nazi death's-head badge.

"You're not one of the Thirty, General, are you?"

"No," he said.

"But you'd do business with them."

"You mean with you? Yes. If Israel had relations only with its friends, we wouldn't be a country."

Serena wanted to say "Hey, I'm not Alignment," but that wouldn't carry much water here beneath the bowels of the Palace of the Grandmaster, built by the Knights of St. John, a military unit itself and cousin to the Knights Templar. All the same, she had to find out the purpose of the globes and why the Alignment would give them to the Israelis. "You're going to take these with you back to Jersualem?" she asked.

"To the place where they belong."

Serena stared at him. "You're going to rebuild the temple. You've just needed to get all the pieces together."

"Yes." Gellar was almost defiant.

"To do that, you need to remove the Dome of the Rock mosque."

"Yes."

"That would start a war with the Arabs."

"Yes."

"And you would defend yourselves, naturally."

"No," Gellar said. "You and Europe will defend us if America chooses to sit this one out. And if not, God will protect us."

"When is all this supposed to happen?"

Gellar smiled. "You had two of the globes and are the great linguist. Could you not interpret the signs?"

Serena realized she could not, but she couldn't let Gellar slip away without giving her something more. She remembered what Conrad had told her about why he'd given up his dig in Jerusalem: He couldn't figure out the astronomical alignments of the temple. Without them, he hadn't known where to dig.

"The alignments of the stars on the celestial globe don't mirror the landmarks on the terrestrial globe," she told him. "For example, there's no star on the celestial globe that mirrors Jerusalem."

"Not yet," Gellar told her with a hint of a smile. "That's why the third globe is necessary. The Hebrew prophets believed that God used the planets to give them a sign that something important was about to happen.

Look closely at this globe, and you'll notice that we're in the midst of an extraordinary alignment of two symmetrical triangles formed in the sky by six planets. Do you recognize this alignment?"

"Oh my God," said Serena, seeing it clearly. "It's the Star of David."

"This is the star you were looking for over Jerusalem, Sister Serghetti," Gellar told her. "It's not a comet or a nova or a so-called star of Bethlehem. This star is the conjunction of planets that the prophet Jeremiah predicted would appear in these last days at the coming of the Messiah. It is this star to which we will align the Third Temple."

The exit door opened, and Gellar pointed the way out to her. "Thank you for returning the globes to the people of Israel, Sister Serghetti. I will take good care of them."

She stepped out of the chamber, and as soon as it closed behind her, she knew there was no turning back. A minute later, she climbed into the G55 SUV outside.

"General Gellar is Uriel," she told Benito, whose face in the mirror registered shock. "The globes are going to the Temple Mount. Surely this means war. Gellar thinks he's getting a new Jerusalem. But the Alignment is clearly betting on a new Crusade that will see them picking up all the oil and whatever else is left of the Middle East. A new Roman Empire. And that is in nobody's interest."

41

Conrad waited behind three cars in line at the Liberty Gate to Old Town. Two armored trucks flanked the gate while Greek *Evzones* in tights with submachine guns inspected every vehicle entering the fortress.

He looked at his watch: it was already three-fifteen. By now Serena had probably delivered the globes, blowing his chance to see them. Worse, he had been seen by that Dei disciple of hers, who may have warned her to exit through a different gate.

A soldier waved him up to the gate, and he handed over his license and registration slip. While the soldier ran them through a card reader, a police officer asked him questions. "Where are you going?"

"Church of St. John," Conrad lied, referring to the church across the Street of Knights from the Palace of the Grandmaster. "I'm delivering this to the icon exhibit." He glanced over his shoulder at the globe strapped precariously to the back of his seat.

"You call that an icon?" the officer said gruffly.

Conrad recovered quickly and smiled. "A replica of an icon."

The officer was still grim. "I call that an accident if it fell off your bike onto the road."

"But it didn't," Conrad said when the soldier came back with his ID.

"Firat Kayda?" the soldier said as four others circled him with their machine guns.

"Yes," Conrad said quietly.

"You're under arrest."

Conrad thought quickly as he saw a car approaching from the opposite side of the gate. "I didn't mean to steal it," he said, reaching back to the icon as he heard more than one bolt click. "I just wanted to bring it back."

He pulled the string, and the icon fell to the ground and cracked open. "Oh no!" he said.

While all eyes were diverted to the ground for a moment, he twisted the accelerator and burst through the open gate and took a sharp left behind the tower.

There were shouts and the squeal of brakes and then a delayed spray of bullets that raked the tower. Conrad hit the straightaway down the Street of Knights but saw trouble up ahead: a black S-class Mercedes sedan coming his way, leaving him little room to maneuver on either side. He'd have to cut down one of the two hundred narrow cobblestone streets and lose the police without getting lost himself.

But then he saw a second car—a silver Mercedes G-class SUV—turning out from a gate at the Palace of the Grandmaster and onto the street toward him. As it turned, he saw her in the backseat.

Serena!

Sirens blared behind him, and he glanced at his mirror to see the lights of a police car flashing from behind.

He looked back up the Street of Knights in time to swerve away from the oncoming black Mercedes, taking out the driver's-side mirror as he whooshed by.

Dead ahead was the silver Mercedes SUV. Conrad could glimpse Benito's astonished face as it passed a parked Peugeot in front of the Inn of Provence. Everything seemed to go slow-motion as Conrad considered the police behind him, the silver Mercedes ahead of him, and the parked Peugeot.

It didn't belong there.

And before he could warn Benito, the Peugeot exploded in a ball of fire and blew the Mercedes apart.

"Serena!" he shouted before the shock wave sent him flying through the air.

42

Serena found herself on her hands and knees on the street. The SUV had been split open. She tried to get up but couldn't. As she crouched there, numb from shock, she could see Benito barely moving on the other side of the burning wreck.

"Oh my God. Benito!"

She crawled on all fours toward him. Half his face was burned off, but his arm was moving. Then she saw his insides spilling out. "Oh God." She reached toward him but was still several feet away.

Benito knew he was dying and struggled for breath. "Do not be afraid, *signorina,* for he will take care of you now."

Just then a shadow fell across Benito's face, and Serena looked up to see a twisted face with an eyepatch standing over her. She screamed as the man pointed a gun at her.

"Last rites," he said in a Russian accent, and pulled the trigger.

She heard the shot but felt nothing. The assassin fell facedown in front of her. She stared in shock and heard her name.

"Serena!"

It was Conrad driving up through the smoke on a motorcycle, like a demon from hell. Behind him were the police, chasing him like the Furies.

He braked to a halt and pulled her up to her feet. "Come on."

She couldn't leave Benito. "I can't."

"Hurry," Conrad said, and dragged her by the arms and plopped her on the back of his bike. He slid in front of her and took her slack arms and wrapped them around his waist. "Please, Serena, hold on."

"I told you not to come, Conrad," she said breathlessly, bitterly, and started crying. "I told you."

"This was set up long before I got here, Serena, long before you got here." He kick-started the bike, and she could feel it roar to life beneath them. He was going to carry her away, and her work wasn't done yet.

"The council meeting tonight. I have to stay."

"I'm sorry, Serena," she heard him say as the rear tire squealed and they drove off.

43

Conrad squinted at the setting sun as he raced out the west end of the Street of Knights into Kleovoulou Square, the police close behind. He could feel Serena's heart pounding as she barely held on. He turned onto the wide, shady Orpheos Street and, to the right, spotted the wall linking the interior wall and the main wall of Old Town. He found what he was looking for—the Gate of St. Anthony—and rode up the ramparts, leaving the police cars blocked below him.

He flew past the iron benches and artists drawing portraits of tourists, scattering easels and eliciting shouts and curses. Then he turned left into a dark tunnel.

A moment later, he burst out of Old Town through the impressive d'Amboise Gate. Two policemen started shooting as he drove across the arched bridge and over the dry moat into New Town. He cut right onto Makariou Street and thundered down toward the harbor.

"I've got a seaplane by the windmills at the breakwater," Serena said, coming to life.

"I've got a boat, I think. One of Andros's."

"I'll fly us out," she said.

There were sirens growing louder from all directions. All at once the street opened up into Kyprou Square, and he could see two triangular traffic islands in the middle of an intersection of seven streets from seven angles. There were no traffic lights, and most of the cars whizzing through were police or driven by Greek citizens.

"Hang left!" Serena shouted.

"Right," he said.

"Left as in straight ahead!"

"I know!" he shouted, and drove in the channel between the two islands to the other side, barely clearing two cars that hit their brakes.

Conrad could hear the squealing and then the crash of metal and horns behind him. In his mirror, he saw that three police cars had locked fenders.

He turned right and slowed down as he passed Starbucks and the post office and vanished into the early-evening shadows that had fallen across the seaside cafés.

At the breakwater front by the secluded windmills, Conrad could see Brother Lorenzo waiting by the Otter seaplane. The priest started to shake at the sight of him. Conrad drove up the stone pier to the edge of the water.

"They're saying a roadside bomb went off in the Knights' Quarter," Lorenzo said breathlessly as he helped Serena off the bike. "Two bodies were found."

"Benito," she told him.

Lorenzo looked at Conrad. "They said that the Israeli defense minister was the target and that the Egyptian terrorist behind it, Abdil Zawas, accidentally blew himself up. Your picture is on the television as one of his associates."

"Point that bony finger at me and I'll break it off," Conrad snapped. "What the hell are you doing here?"

Serena stopped him with a weak hand. "His instructions were always to fall back here if we ran into trouble," she said, and climbed on board and started the props.

Conrad glared at Lorenzo, who quickly followed Serena into the Otter and frantically waved him in.

Conrad rolled the motorcycle into the water, climbed into the plane, and pulled up the door behind him. Soon they lifted off into the evening sky and banked to the east as Conrad looked down to see flashing lights descend on the harbor below.

44

It was almost ten o'clock that night on Rhodes when a triumphant Roman Midas walked out onto the steps of the Palace of the Grandmaster with assorted European leaders and waited for his limousine. He was in a tuxedo after a spectacular black-tie concert outdoors in the courtyard, made all the more poignant by the violence of that afternoon's car bombing.

"Gellar and the Israelis were bloody lucky," he had heard the British prime minister tell the German chancellor before the concert. "A tragic loss for Sister Serghetti, however. Good drivers are hard to find."

"Oui" was all he heard from the French president afterward, who could understand why she'd chosen to skip the concert. "But I'm more troubled by intelligence reports that this YouTube video from Zawas signals an imminent attack on a much bigger target."

All of them had enjoyed the concert.

Some, Midas knew, more than others. While most of

the dignitaries sat in chairs under the stars and listened to the Berlin Philharmonic, seventeen of them sat in chairs under the courtyard, in the Hall of Knights, and listened to Sorath lay out the plan for world peace.

None of the faces were ones he had expected, and yet by the end of the meeting, he couldn't possibly imagine anybody else qualified to carry out the plan.

As for the plan itself, it left him in awe.

The Solomon globes were back in the hands of the Jews after so many centuries. Now General Gellar and his ultra-Orthodox friends possessed their final puzzle piece to begin construction of a Third Temple. Only the Al-Aqsa Mosque stood in their way, and Gellar was all too willing to let the Alignment do the dirty work for him and call it an act of God. All Gellar had to do was use the globes to transport the *Flammenschwert* into place beneath the Temple Mount.

There would be an uprising from the Palestinians, of course, quite likely igniting a wider war. When all reasonable avenues of diplomacy had been exhausted, which was always the case in the Arab world, the international "peace process" that Gellar had bound Israel to at this EU summit would come into play—too late for Gellar to realize that he had betrayed his country for his religion. Not that there would be room for either in the new world order. Jerusalem would be occupied by international peacekeepers, and the new temple would become the throne of the Alignment to control the Middle East.

Most amazing of all, by bringing the three Solomon

globes to their final resting place, Gellar would essentially activate them at their point of origin, revealing the real prize beneath the Temple Mount that Midas and the Alignment were after. It was a revelation greater than anything found in Judaism, Christianity, or Islam, and the foundation of a master civilization that would supplant anything that had come before in human history.

History itself would be history.

In under twenty-four hours, Midas marveled, the Jews once again would be betrayed by thirty pieces of silver. A final Crusade would be unleashed on the Middle East that would ensure lasting world peace and the rise of a new Roman Empire in the twenty-first century. All it would take was a little piece of Atlantean technology tweaked by the Nazis.

If that wasn't the final solution, Midas thought, what was?

Everything, mostly, was following the plan. Midas almost allowed himself to smile. Then he saw Vadim pull up in the limousine. Well, almost everything.

"You look like shit, Vadim," Midas said as they drove out of the town and into the hills toward the airstrip. "I'm amazed security let you through. Did you get the bullet out?"

"No," Vadim grunted, clearly in pain. "But the bleeding stopped."

"We'll take care of it after Jerusalem," Midas said. "At least you had enough presence of mind to get out of the street after you failed to kill Serghetti."

"The Inn of Provence is about the only one on the street with a side door," Vadim explained. "No problem, what with the smoke and confusion caused by Abdil's explosion."

Midas said nothing and turned on the television to watch the BBC.

"Despite the terrorist attack on Rhodes today, the twenty-seven European foreign ministers unanimously agreed to intensify their dialogue with Israel on diplomatic issues," the big-haired anchor said. "Vice Prime Minister and Minister of Foreign Affairs Tzipi Livni said that this is a meaningful achievement for Israeli diplomacy, opening a new chapter in Israel's diplomatic relations with EU states. Israel intends to use the intensified dialogue to convince Europe to increase pressure on the Palestinians over the fate of Jerusalem and ensure that Israel's strategic interests are protected in the Middle East peace process."

Midas turned off the TV and checked his messages on his BlackBerry. He was still bothered by Vadim's failure. He'd have to get rid of Vadim as soon as he had fulfilled his purposes, two of which were still out there somewhere.

Then he saw the text from the Alignment spy code-named Dantanian.

It read: I'VE GOT THEM.

Midas smiled. It was turning out to be an even better night than he could have imagined.

45

Serena set the Otter on autopilot so she could collect herself after the devastating loss of Benito and before whatever end-of-the-world madness she and Conrad would have to deal with now. They would need to land on the water near the coast of Israel and find some way in, if they didn't get shot down first. But that was for Conrad to figure out, because she could barely think at all.

She looked over at Conrad in the copilot's seat. The entire flight, she felt him keeping one eye on her and one on Lorenzo, who was fast asleep in the rear of the cabin.

"It doesn't stop, does it, Conrad?" she asked him. "The death, the violence, the evil in this world?" She couldn't hold back anymore, and she burst into tears. "He was like a brother to me. My only real family." She started weeping uncontrollably in a way she hadn't for years. She knew Conrad had never seen her like this because *she* had never seen herself like this. Not even in her private moments. But it was as if something had broken inside.

"I can't do it, Conrad," she said. "I'm all used up. I have nothing left."

Conrad held her in his arms as best he could with their seating arrangement and brushed the wet hair away from her eyes. "What matters is what's required of us," he told her softly. "I need to know what Gellar told you."

"I told you what he told me," Serena said sharply, realizing that she wouldn't get much more in sympathy and that Conrad was right. "He wants to build a Third Temple and seems to think he's going to start very soon. The only place to build it, according to Orthodox Jews, is on the Dome of the Rock."

"Which is considered Islam's third-holiest shrine and where Al-Aqsa Mosque sits," said Conrad. "You destroy the mosque, and all hell breaks loose. I get it. Gellar gets what he wants, and the Alignment ultimately gets what it wants. But tell me about this whole Uriel thing."

"That's what doesn't make sense," she said. "In the Bible, there's an angel who guards the gate back to Eden with a flaming sword. Some traditions specifically reveal the angel's name to be Uriel."

Conrad nodded. "So you figured that Midas was bringing the *Flammenschwert* to Uriel."

"But it doesn't make sense with Gellar," she said. "He wants to destroy the Dome of the Rock and build a Third Temple for the Jews. The *Flammenschwert* turns water to fire. But there's no water in Jerusalem. No lakes, no rivers, nothing. The ancient Jews depended on precipitation from the skies, collecting rainwater in tanks and cisterns."

He looked at her and said, "You're forgetting the Gihon Spring and the network of tunnels beneath the Temple Mount."

She knew where he was going and liked to see him enthusiastic, but this wasn't realistic. "The Gihon Spring isn't really a river. That's why they call it a spring."

"It could be enough," he told her. "Back at the EU summit, Midas was pitching his mining technology as a means to extract water from the desert. Some kind of tracing technology that could reveal underground rivers and aquifers with thermal imaging."

Suddenly she saw it all. "There's going to be plenty of thermal energy after he sets off the *Flammenschwert*."

"The Temple Mount is honeycombed with well shafts, including one I've seen directly under the Dome of the Rock," Conrad told her. "All you have to do is position the *Flammenschwert* somewhere in that underground spring system, and boom—you destroy the mosque on the surface and maintain the integrity of the Temple Mount foundations. It's like a neutron bomb."

Serena said, "I suppose it would almost look like divine judgment. It's brilliant, really."

Conrad nodded. "Gellar gets his Third Temple. The Alignment gets its Crusade when it rises to defend Israel against the Arabs. And Midas gets the water and technology rights." Then he looked her in the eye. "How much do you want to bet that the warhead from the *Flammenschwert* is inside one of the globes Gellar took back to Israel? He's probably placing those globes inside some secret chamber under the Temple Mount right now."

Serena switched off the autopilot and took the steering column. "We have to warn the Israelis."

"Which Israelis?" Conrad asked her. "We could be warning the very people who are perpetrating the plan, like Gellar. We need to know for certain who's *not* Alignment, and right now, except for me and you—actually, just me—we don't even know that. We need to get to Jerusalem on our own."

"I have friends in Gaza," she said. "Catholics who helped me run food relief supplies through the blockades the Israeli coast guard set up. They could get us official work permits and fake IDs and smuggle us into Israel. I'll have to splash down within a few miles of shore, though."

"Now you're talking," he told her as she leveled off and prepared for their descent.

Then a voice from behind said, "No water landing, Sister Serghetti. You will take us to Tel Aviv."

She looked over her shoulder at Lorenzo, who had a gun pointed at her head and was glaring at Conrad.

"Now the weasel shows his true colors," Conrad said, unusually calm. "You gave me up to the police on Rhodes, didn't you? Told Midas I came so he could go and kill Serena and you could take her precious medallion?"

Serena stiffened as she felt the barrel of the gun at the back of her neck. "Lorenzo, tell me this is a moment of fear overwhelming your faith—that what Conrad said isn't true."

"Tel Aviv," Lorenzo said, waving the gun between her and Conrad. "Then you will hand me the Dei medallion before General Gellar's men take care of both of you."

"I think you should stick with your vow of silence," Conrad said.

Lorenzo pointed the gun at Conrad, pulled the trigger, and heard the click of an empty cartridge. Lorenzo frantically searched his pockets.

"I've got your bullets in here," Conrad said as he pulled out his Glock from under his shirt and shot Lorenzo in the head.

Serena didn't scream as she gripped the steering column tightly with both hands to keep herself and the Otter steady. But she shivered as she felt Lorenzo's body slide to the floor of the cockpit next to her. And the smell from Conrad's discharged Glock made her ill.

"Looks like the Dei wants you dead, Serena. You should think twice before going back to Rome."

She couldn't look at him. At either of them. She focused on bringing the Otter down for a safe landing off the waters of Gaza.

Conrad, however, was already on his phone. "Andros, it's me."

She could hear the voice on the other end shout, "Mother of God! Where are you?"

Conrad glanced at her while he talked. "I'm a few miles off the coast of Gaza. I need to get in."

"Why?" asked Andros.

Conrad said, "You see that explosion at the EU summit?"

"I told you not to come back to Greece, my friend," Andros said.

"Well, at least I got out," Conrad answered. "Now I need a ride into Gaza. You must have ships making runs here."

She couldn't make out what Andros was saying.

"Jaffa's no good," Conrad said. "Gaza. You must know someone in these waters. Someone who can meet us and take us ashore. Someone you can trust." After a minute, Conrad said, "Fine."

"Well?" she asked him when he hung up.

"Andros says he has just the man for the job. He'll meet us one kilometer due west of the breakwater at the beach north of the port."

Two hours after they splashed down, the twelve-year-old Palestinian shipowner Andros had promised finally arrived in his yellow wooden sardine boat and brought them ashore. His white T-shirt said: TODAY GAZA . . . TOMORROW THE WEST BANK AND JERUSALEM.

PART FOUR

Jerusalem

46

The catering truck pulled up behind Ohel Yitzhak, or the Tent of Isaac, synagogue in the Muslim quarter of Jerusalem's Old City. General Gellar stepped out in a caterer's uniform, glanced both ways, and then gave the signal. The caterers brought out three food cases, each containing one of Solomon's three globes, and wheeled the cases on carts into the kitchen.

The elegant synagogue had been blown up by the Jordanian army in 1948. After Israel captured the Old City in the 1967 Middle East War and annexed East Jerusalem, it was finally rebuilt and rededicated in 2008. One particular modification was a secret underground passage that connected the synagogue to the Temple Mount.

The passageway was supposed to be part of a large underground complex attesting to Jewish heritage in the contested city. It was funded by the semi-governmental organization known as the Western Wall Heritage

Foundation, which had signed an agreement with Jewish-American donors to maintain the Ohel Yitzhak synagogue and the areas beneath it. Those donors had been active for decades in settling ultra-nationalist Jews in Arab areas of Jerusalem.

But General Gellar, who was on the board of the foundation, had never shared his purpose for the new passageway with his donors or submitted the final plans to the Israel Antiquities Authority for approval.

The passageway linked the synagogue with the Western Wall tunnels in the Jewish quarter. And those tunnels beneath the Western Wall in turn linked to a more ancient network unknown to either Muslims or Jews. As such, it violated Israel's promise to stop digging within the Al-Aqsa compound. After all, the last time an Israeli prime minister had opened an archaeological tunnel near the holy sites, more than eighty people had been killed in three days of Palestinian riots.

Gellar could only imagine the reaction in a few short hours when the scourge of the Temple Mount would be wiped clean by a pillar of fire that would reveal the power of the one true God.

47

Israeli troops armed with assault rifles guarded the Via Dolorosa, or the Way of Sorrows, as thousands of Christian pilgrims from around the world crowded the narrow cobblestone streets of Jerusalem's walled Old City for the traditional Good Friday procession. Some Christians even carried large wooden crosses on their shoulders along the route that Jesus was believed to have taken to His crucifixion.

Ridiculous, thought Midas, watching from the curb. He turned to Vadim, standing beside him, and said, "With the beating you've taken, you look like you could be one of the actors here."

Vadim said nothing.

"At least you're still alive." Midas looked at his BlackBerry. "It appears the Israeli coast guard found an Otter seaplane four kilometers off the coast of Gaza this morning with a dead priest inside. Bullet to the head. The Israelis say it was drug smuggling gone bad. The local rabble-rousing Catholic bishop in Gaza City says it was the trigger-happy Israeli coast guard. I say it was Yeats."

The Good Friday procession ended at the Church of the Holy Sepulcher, where tradition said Jesus was crucified and His body laid in a tomb. It was there, on Easter Sunday, that Christians would celebrate His resurrection.

Or so they believed.

The thought that the world would change in minutes, and that there was little Conrad Yeats could do about it, prompted a smile to replace Roman Midas's impatient expression as he and Vadim made their way out the Damascus Gate.

They followed the north wall of the Old City toward Herod's Gate and found an iron gate at the base of the wall. It was the cave entrance to Solomon's Quarries, a huge subterranean cavern that extended beneath the city in the direction of the Temple Mount. Inside the quarries was a secret entrance to the Temple Mount, where General Gellar would meet them.

Midas looked at his watch. It was two-thirty P.M. The first in a series of gates was about to open before him.

The cave was an official tourist site, open to the public, and a couple of Israeli policemen were outside the entrance. But today, by design, it was sealed off for a private event. It was a semiannual ceremony hosted by the Grand Lodge of the State of Israel for the benefit of Masons visiting Jerusalem during Holy Week. Non-

Masons were not allowed, which kept the Good Friday crowds away.

Midas and Vadim showed the policemen their identification cards issued by the Supreme Grand Royal Arch Chapter of Israel and were allowed to step into the cave.

Midas followed a well-lit path for a hundred yards as the floor sloped down about thirty feet and opened into a cavern the size of an American football field. It was known as Freemasons' Hall, and the Masonic ceremony that Midas had hoped to avoid was under way in Hebrew and English. Twenty older gentlemen of various nationalities stood in their Masonic aprons as the Mark Master degree ceremony recounted the tale of an irregular rejected stone hewn from these very quarries that had turned out to be the capstone of the entrance to the temple.

But Midas already knew that. Ancient tradition said that the stones for King Solomon's First Temple were quarried here. The cavern was especially rich in white Melekeh, or royal, limestone, used in all the royal buildings. Some caves had been created by water erosion, but most had been cut by Solomon's masons.

Midas glanced up at the imposing ceiling of rock that was held up by limestone pillars just like the kind he used to make in the mines. It felt damp, and he could see beads of water trickling down the rough walls.

"Zedekiah's tears," he was told by an old Scot standing next to him. "He was the last king of Judah and tried to escape here before he was captured and carted off to

Babylon. But the water comes from springs hidden all around us."

Midas and Vadim nodded, then broke away from the gathering to follow an illuminated walkway out of the cavern into one of the inner chambers separated by broad columns of limestone. There, Midas found the royal arch carved into the wall they were looking for and waited. A moment later, there was a faint tap. Midas tapped back twice. The outlines of an arched doorway appeared more prominently, and the stone slid open to reveal Gellar.

The only way to enter the secret tunnel, Gellar had told him, was from the inside. The irony was that Gellar was so ultra-Orthodox and regarded the Temple Mount as so holy that he refused to enter its lower chambers himself. That left the dirty job of setting off the *Flammenschwert* to Midas and Vadim.

48

From his small office near the Western Wall Plaza, Commander Sam Deker could look up and see the Dome of the Rock without the banks of monitors that helped him police the goings-on around the Temple Mount. For Jews, it was the rock on which Abraham had nearly sacrificed his son Isaac before God intervened, and later, the Holy of Holies within Solomon's Temple where the Ark of the Covenant rested. For Muslims, it was where the Prophet Muhammad had put his foot down before he ascended to heaven. For Deker, it was like the pin of a grenade placed in his hand with orders not to blow up the world.

Especially today, Good Friday.

Three weeks ago, a Palestinian construction worker had plowed a bulldozer into a crowd of young Israelis. Two weeks ago, Israeli archaeologists had accused Muslims of destroying First Temple artifacts in an attempt to erase any traces of Jewish settlements on the Temple Mount. One week ago, Christian monks had broken into a brawl at the

Church of the Holy Sepulcher in advance of today's celebration.

It was always something.

A secular Jew who had grown up in Los Angeles and served with the U.S. armed forces as a demolitions specialist in the wars in Afghanistan and Iraq, Deker had been recruited by the former head of Israel's internal security service, Yuval Diskin, to work for the Shin Bet. A man who specialized in the destruction of major structures, Diskin told him, was uniquely qualified to protect one such as the Temple Mount. However, Deker quickly gathered that his chief qualification was that he was Jewish but not a real Jew, if that was possible.

For some time the Shin Bet had been concerned that Jewish extremists could attack the Temple Mount in an attempt to foil peace moves with Palestinians. It had happened before, with the assassination of Prime Minister Yitzhak Rabin, and the Shin Bet didn't want to see it again.

"The Shin Bet sees in the group we're talking about on the extreme right a willingness to use firearms in order to halt diplomatic processes and harm political leaders," Diskin told him.

Ironically, that group Deker had been warned about for so long included Israel's current defense minister, Michael Gellar, who had made a surprise appearance at the office and now stood before him.

"You saw what happened on Rhodes?" Gellar demanded. "It was intended for me."

Deker had seen it. The Egyptian Abdil Zawas had managed to blow himself up while trying to wire a roadside bomb at the European peace summit. The man wasn't a bomb maker, and it all sounded fishy to Deker. But then Zawas was always trying to outdo the ghost of his late crazy military cousin Ali, and it wouldn't surprise Deker if the Egyptian playboy had gotten in so over his head that he'd lost it.

"Greek police found evidence in the car that Abdil's real target today is the Temple Mount. Analysis of his video claiming responsibility for the attempt on my life suggests that it was an attack code to his associates in Jerusalem to detonate a nuclear device."

Deker blinked. "Today?"

"You need to seal the Temple Mount."

"You want me to seal off the Temple Mount on Good Friday and the eve of Passover?"

"Yes."

"But that means closing off the Western Wall to worshippers, ticking off both Jews and Christians. That's on top of the Arabs, who are always mad."

"I know what it means, Deker." General Gellar was pulling rank. "You need to check all access points and your informants. Things the security feeds don't pick up."

Deker nodded, typed an alert on his BlackBerry, and then put it away.

"What did you just do?" Gellar demanded.

"I sent a quick 140-character text through Twitter to my network."

"Is that secure?"

"Yes and no."

The BlackBerry chirped, and Deker looked at the feeds and frowned. The guide at the Gihon Springs was reporting that a man and woman had gone into Hezekiah's Tunnel but never emerged from the tunnel exit at the Siloam Pool.

He called up the video, and as he watched the monitor, he watched Gellar. The blood from the general's face drained.

"That's Conrad Yeats and Serena Serghetti. Abdil's associates."

Yeats, maybe, thought Deker, who had heard plenty of stories in his days with the armed forces. Sister Serghetti, Mother Earth herself, never. Perhaps Yeats had abducted her at gunpoint and forced her to help.

Deker radioed Elezar, who was monitoring Warren's Shaft near Hezekiah's Tunnel. "Anything on the intruders?"

The radio crackled. "They're in the tunnels," Elezar reported. "Under the Temple Mount."

"Tell the Yamam unit to assemble in the Map Room right away." Deker turned to Gellar. "Too late to seal the Temple Mount now."

49

Hezekiah's Tunnel
Jewish Quarter

Serena knew that ancient cities couldn't exist without a water source, and Jerusalem was no exception. The City of David had developed around the only real water source in the area, the Gihon Spring, which ran through the bottom of the Kidron Valley. During the Assyrian and Babylonian attacks, King Hezekiah had constructed an aqueduct through which the waters could be hidden inside the city, an extraordinary engineering feat at the time.

It was through this tunnel that Serena followed Conrad through waist-high water in the dark with only one flashlight to guide them. It was all their driver from Gaza had on hand. They had been greeted at the beach north of Al Gaddafi by a van from the local Catholic church, which drove them up Salahadeen Road to the Erez industrial zone and the border gate with Israel. The Israeli official at the checkpoint had looked over their bogus work permits, which Serena had insisted would give them a better chance of getting into Israel than the underground smuggling tunnels, which Israeli warplanes bombed almost daily. A long minute later, the soldiers had waved them through. They had crossed the 1950 Armistice Line into Israel and driven toward Jerusalem, only forty-eight miles away.

The drive from Gaza had ended in Silwan, a poor Arab village of cinder-block houses crumbling down the hillsides to the Gihon Spring at the bottom of the Kidron. There, Serena found the Fountain of the Virgin and the church commemorating the spot where Mary once drew water to wash the clothes of Jesus. It was almost one P.M. and a Friday, so the caretaker was about to close the gate. But Conrad gave him a tip, and he let them descend the stone steps into the spring's cave.

It was here that Serena's expertise was exhausted and she had to trust Conrad's knowledge of Jerusalem's underbelly. But sloshing through the ever rising water, she was beginning to have doubts.

Hezekiah's Tunnel was a third of a mile long, mostly under three feet wide, and in some places, under five feet high. The caretaker at the entrance had warned them that the water was knee-high today and the walk would take them about forty minutes before they exited at the Pool of Siloam. Conrad, however, told her that they would be exiting halfway through, at the point where the tunnel took an odd S-shaped course through the rock. This was where Hezekiah's Tunnel branched from the tunnel leading from the Gihon Spring to the bottom of Warren's Shaft.

The tunnel had narrowed, and the dirty water was now waist-high. Serena bumped her head against the ceiling of the tunnel, which had started to slope sharply. The water was now up to her neck.

"The ceiling is lowest here, under five feet high, and the water level highest," Conrad told her. "So you'll have to hold your breath."

He took her by the hand, and they walked forward until their heads were underwater. They walked about three feet before the tunnel ceiling started to rise and their heads surfaced.

They were in a different tunnel, the water level dropping rapidly, and they soon reached a stone platform on the edge of a giant precipice. Serena felt chilled to the bone and wrung her dripping hair like a towel to squeeze out the water. When she looked down, she saw what looked like a giant subway tunnel with wide white limestone steps descending into the depths of the earth. She said, "This looks like the grand gallery of the Great Pyramid in Egypt."

Conrad nodded. "Why do you think Solomon married all those Egyptian princesses? To gain access to the sand hydraulic technology that built the pyramids. Except what he did here was amazing. He inverted the design so that everything you know is upside down."

That's crazy, she thought. But now that he mentioned it, the tunnel made sense.

Conrad said, "You know that shaft I was telling you about under the Dome of the Rock?"

She craned her head up and saw the opening in the ceiling overhead. It appeared to go all the way up to the top of the Temple Mount. "I thought I felt a draft."

"Back when the First Temple was up there, the top of the shaft was capped with a platform on which the Ark of the Covenant could be lowered during a siege," he told her. "Here, take this."

She looked down in her palm and saw a brick of C4 explosive. "Where on earth did you get this?"

"From the driver of your Sunday-school van in Gaza," he told her. "Now climb up on my shoulders and stick this inside the mouth of the shaft. We need to close it off in case we fail to stop the *Flammenschwert*. Otherwise, a geyser of fire is going to incinerate that mosque."

She took his hand, put a boot on his knee, and stepped onto his shoulders until her head was inside the bottom of the shaft. She planted the C4 on the wall of the shaft and jumped back down onto the stone platform.

She said, "You gave us only twenty minutes on the fuse."

"Insurance that we close the shaft to the surface before the *Flammenschwert* goes off," he explained. "The important thing is to make sure the mosque is still standing on the surface. Without Arab uprisings in the streets, Gellar can't justify the disproportionate Israeli response that will ignite a wider war. Whatever happens down below here is, well, secondary."

She looked down into the great gallery below. "The King's Chamber is down at the bottom, isn't it?"

"Right." He pulled out his Glock, the one he had killed Lorenzo with, and checked the clip. "So are the globes, the *Flammenschwert,* and God knows what else."

50

With a full-blown national emergency under way, Commander Sam Deker of the Israeli Shin Bet had no trouble assembling the elite five-member counterterrorism unit known as the Yamam. They were beneath the temple in under six minutes.

They gathered inside the top-secret Map Room, itself a national secret. The chamber looked like a flight briefing room, with theater-style seating for six in front of computer consoles and a nine-by-twenty-four-foot curved screen with 160-degree views. Each officer carried the standard M4 assault rifle with a Glock 21 .45 sidearm.

"We all follow the plan used in the Taibe raid a few years ago," Deker told them. "We're to capture or kill an armed group hidden in the tunnels below us and secure a device that may be nuclear in nature before it goes off. I cannot overemphasize how grave this threat is to the Temple Mount and the very existence of Israel."

High-definition three-dimensional images of the tunnel system filled the screen. In addition to live security feeds, the computer models used military flight-simulator technology to enable virtual remote viewing around the tunnels. Gellar in particular preferred a remote hookup. Being Orthodox, he refused to walk the holy limestone tunnels himself, leaving it to impure types like Deker.

"Four security zones make up the Temple Mount in descending order: this Map Room, Solomon's Hall, the King's Chamber, and the four River Gates region. We pair in three teams of two. Team One stations itself here. Team Two stations itself in the King's Chamber and monitors access to the River Gates. Team Three patrols the tunnels. Shoot to kill anybody who is not in this room. Should you exit the tunnels alive, you will not speak of this again."

The faces he saw understood him perfectly. Yamam forces specialized in both hostage-rescue operations and offensive takeover raids against targets in civilian areas such as the Temple Mount. Most of their activities were classified, and their success was credited to other units. Most important to Deker, they answered to the civilian Israeli police forces rather than the military, although most came exclusively from Israeli special forces units.

"Let's go," Deker said.

As the unit prepared to disperse, the officer who had been paired with Deker called him over to his console. "There's something you should see, sir," he said.

Apparently, the officer had been curious enough to

research the construction of the Map Room and had called up the names of the A-list experts who had consulted on the project with the Israel Antiquities Authority and the UCLA Urban Simulation Team in the United States.

The top archaeologist on the list was Conrad Yeats.

"Looks like Yeats kept or cut a tunnel or two for himself," Deker said, red-faced. "If it's not on the map, it's not on the camera. We're going to have to move out with the others."

"There's more, sir," the officer said. "The shaft plugs to secure the tunnels were manufactured by an Israeli company based at the Tefen Industrial Park. It's a subsidiary of Midas Minerals & Mining."

Deker frowned. "The Midas conglomerate?"

"Yes, sir. And it appears that General Gellar has an interest in the Tefen subsidiary. What does it mean?"

Deker heard a thud and turned to see two Yamam on the floor and the rest gasping for breath. He smelled almonds in the air and realized it was cyanide gas. The door to the chamber was closing from the top down, and Deker knew that anybody trapped inside would die.

"Gellar has betrayed us!" Deker shouted, and made a flying leap for it.

51

The *Flammenschwert* was gone.

Conrad stood with Serena inside the King's Chamber—an expansive vault in the shape of a perfect one-by-two rectangle, its height of forty cubits exactly half the length of its eighty-cubic floor diagonal. In the center of the stone floor stood the three globes, but the armillary globe was split open like an empty womb. On each of the chamber's four walls was a towering archway, each leading down its own tunnel.

Four tunnels, two people, little time, Conrad thought. The *Flammenschwert* could have been taken down any one of the four shafts.

But Serena was already ahead of him, reading the ancient Hebrew letters over the archways, trying to figure out which tunnel to take, because they'd only have one shot.

"This is incredible," she said. "Do you know what these say?"

"I have my suspicions," he told her. "The star shafts of an inverted pyramid obviously can't point to the heavens. So I figured there weren't any beneath the Temple Mount. These are well shafts."

"Each one leads to a different river," she said. "Their names are written in some kind of Proto-Semitic language. It's practically pre-Atlantean. That door says Tigris, that one says Euphrates, that one over there says Pishon, and this one here says—"

"Gihon," Conrad said. "The four rivers of Eden. So Uriel is the angel with the flaming sword at the gate of Eden after all."

Serena said, "But Eden was in Mesopotamia, where the ancient Babylonian civilization originated."

Eden was like Atlantis, Conrad knew. Everybody had a different idea about where it could be, and archaeological evidence to back it up. But Jewish legend pinpointed the land of Israel as one distinct possibility. What seemed to throw off most archaeologists was the second chapter of Genesis, which described four separate rivers in the Land of Eden that shared a common headwater source. Only two were ever found—the Tigris and the Euphrates. Nobody had discovered the rivers Pishon or Gihon. But Genesis never said all four rivers were aboveground.

"Mesopotamia is just where the Tigris and Euphrates empty out," Conrad told her. "Their headwater source could be down here somewhere, along with the underground waterways of the Pishon and the Gihon."

"Genesis does refer to underground waterways providing water to the surface," she said, the linguist in her apparently rising to the surface. "The original Hebrew word is 'springs.' Genesis says the springs came up from the earth and watered the whole surface of the ground. And the Book of Revelation says that at the end of time, those four rivers will flow out from the temple."

Conrad closed the armillary globe and locked its two hemispheres in place. He could feel Serena's stare as he began to adjust the dial that controlled a tiny marker in the spiral groove representing the motion of the sun.

"This works just like the observatory deck at the Temple of the Water Bearer in Atlantis and the west patio of the U.S. Capitol," he said. "The only difference is that this deck is underground. You can't look at the skies with your naked eye to mark the position of the sun in relation to the stars. You have to use these globes."

"Gellar said the armillary uses planetary geometry," Serena said.

"It does," he said. "The planets align to form the Star of David. Which was how the Israelis got their national symbol in the first place. It's astrologically derived, just like the fish symbol of the early Church in the age of Pisces. Anyway, the trick is to follow the path of the sun across the alignment until X marks the spot. In this case, it's a location beneath the Temple Mount."

"Uriel's Gate," Serena said all of a sudden. "The gate to paradise. That's where Midas has taken the *Flammenschwert*."

"Eureka." Conrad checked the clip in his Glock again and rammed it back in. The click broke Serena's trance; she stared at the gun and at him. Which was what he'd intended. "The sun marker points to the Gihon shaft to reach Uriel's Gate," he said.

"You have to be sure, Conrad."

"This isn't a panel discussion at some conference. Look around you. We're in an ancient chamber deep beneath the Temple Mount with three globes and four doorways. The Gihon Spring of Jerusalem obviously has its source in the same Gihon River of Eden."

He stopped and stared at the gateway marked Gihon.

"That's it, Serena. That's the revelation of the globes: The Temple Mount guards the gate to Eden."

"The River of Life," Serena said. "The properties in the water contain the building blocks of life on earth."

Conrad nodded. "This is what Midas was after all along, what all the money in the world can't buy him: life. He's using the *Flammenschwert* to light the Gihon ablaze and trace it back to its headwater source."

"And at the same time destroy the Dome of the Rock," Serena said.

Conrad heard another click of a Glock, but it wasn't his. He looked up at Serena, who was staring over his shoulder, and then heard a voice say, "Hands up, Yeats."

Slowly, Conrad turned to see an Israeli soldier pointing a gun at him—Sam Deker. Conrad knew him from his earlier digs at the Temple Mount. A good if humorless man.

"It's your boss you should be after, Deker," Conrad said.

Deker kept the gun trained on him. "What makes you sure Gellar is involved?"

"Because he told me," Serena said when a bullet struck Deker in the shoulder.

Conrad turned to see Vadim pop up from the entry of the Gihon Gate. He made a grab for Serena, and she screamed as he pulled her down into the hellhole.

"Serena!" Conrad shouted and ran over to the tunnel as a flurry of bullets flew up at him from the dark. He dove for cover. Breathing hard, he realized that Midas and Vadim were one step ahead of him—the final step. They must have removed the *Flammenschwert* from its globe and were preparing to detonate it at the source of the Gihon below. And now they had Serena.

"There's another way down to the Gihon," said Deker, who was sitting up against another wall, his hand on his shoulder, blood seeping through his fingers.

"Oh, so now you're convinced that I'm not with Gellar?"

"Just tell me what you're really after, Yeats."

Conrad said, "Stopping Armageddon. Midas has an incendiary weapon that's about to ignite the Gihon and everything on the surface. I have to stop it, and you have to go back up and stop Gellar if I fail."

"You know how to dispose of a nuclear device? Because that's what I do," Deker said. "Maybe I should go down and you go back up."

"It's not exactly a nuke, but I can disarm it," Conrad said. "But I can't disarm Gellar if I go up. Or stop your government from overreacting after the Arabs overreact if the Dome of the Rock blows."

Deker nodded to the Pishon Gate on the other wall. "You can take that shaft down to the end and turn right. Follow the riverbank, and it will lead you to the two pillars by the Gihon."

Conrad helped Deker to his feet and then made his way to the Pishon Gate. He looked back inside the King's Chamber. Deker had already disappeared back up to Solomon's Stairway, and Conrad realized that he had forgotten to tell Deker about the C4 under the Dome of the Rock well shaft.

No matter, Conrad thought as he started down the shaft. Deker had as much chance of reaching the surface as Conrad had in reaching the *Flammenschwert* in time to stop it.

52

Midas was with the *Flammenschwert* at the banks of the Gihon River when Vadim and Serena emerged from the two pillars that guarded the entrance of the tunnel back up into the Temple Mount.

"Behold the Gihon," Midas told her with a sweeping gesture across the vast subterranean cavern. He made a show of punching in the activation code on the instrument panel. The display lit up as the *Flammenschwert* came to life.

The timer counted down from 6:00 . . . 5:59 . . . 5:58 . . .

Midas let out a sigh of relief. He had done it. He had obtained the Sword of Fire. He had found the gate to Eden and the primordial waters of life on earth, the waters that could heal his fatal neurological condition and let him live forever. The very River of Life that had scared even the God of Genesis. Now Midas would blow it open and restore paradise on earth.

The old order would pass. The old religions would be

swept away in the cleansing fire of Armageddon. Then the cool water of the new world order would come. And he would control it. He, the Water Bearer. Truly, this would be the Age of Aquarius. The age of Pisces and the Church was over.

"Vadim," he called. "It's time." He motioned Vadim over to the *Flammenschwert* and watched him take it to the water.

"It's going to work like this, Sister Serghetti," Midas said, digging his gun into her side. "The *Flammenschwert* will ignite the water. The heat will force it to rise like a coil through the well shaft you just emerged from, gather steam from the chambers above, and ultimately spew out fire like a geyser, destroying everything topside. It could alter geography significantly. In fact, I think that's what this whole complex was built to do, like some sort of geo-thermal machine."

"I know how it works, Midas. I've seen it before."

Midas said nothing for a moment, making sure Vadim launched the *Flammenschwert* into the water correctly. The casing assembly floated by itself, an amber light blinking six times before burning a steady red.

Serena said, "Hope you've got a place to hide when this blows, Midas, because you're going to fry when it does."

"As a matter of fact, I do," Midas said, then barked his final order to Vadim. "You stay with the *Flammenschwert* until the two-minute mark. Then you can join us in the Map Room. It should be clear by now."

Vadim looked unsure about staying behind but nodded.

Midas could feel Serena shaking as he pushed her back toward a stone stairway she hadn't seen before. "The Map Room, above the King's Chamber, is separated from the main line and closed off. We'll ride out the chaos for a few days and then emerge into a new world."

Midas knew Serena was smart enough to accept that he was going to kill her, but she would go along with him in the vain hope that her beloved Conrad Yeats would come to the rescue. Midas doubted that. But just in case, he would keep her close.

"I see what Gellar thinks he's going to get out of this, Midas," she said as they began to ascend the narrow stairwell. "And I see what the Alignment is sure it will get out of this. But I don't see what you get out of blowing up the Dome of the Rock."

"That's not what I'm blowing up, Sister Serghetti. I'm blowing up what is at the other end of the Gihon River, buried deep beneath us. The very Gate to Eden. The primordial waters of life itself. If you can live forever, you don't need heaven. You don't need God. Because you are a god."

"You know, Lucifer had that problem. He confused himself with the Creator."

Midas laughed, but then the steps started to shake from an explosion high above. He felt an elbow in his gut as Serena tried to push him down the steps. He recovered swiftly and gave her a blow across the face with his gun. She cried out in pain.

"I'm in control," he hissed in her ear. "Soon the world will know it."

She said nothing in the dark, but he could hear her breathing.

He was pushing her forward when he heard a gunshot back at the Gihon. Then the voice of Conrad Yeats rang out.

"Vadim bit the big vitamin, Midas. I've got a deal for you: the *Flammenschwert* for Serena."

53

URIEL'S GATE

Conrad stood dripping wet by the banks of the underground river. The *Flammenschwert* warhead he had retrieved from the water was on the stone platform next to Vadim's body. The timer was down to three minutes and counting.

How the hell am I going to deactivate this thing? he wondered as he began to unscrew the casing of the sphere with the blade of his knife. Then he thought better of it and stopped. *Maybe all I have to do is keep this out of the water when it explodes.*

He folded his knife, picked up his gun, and stood up as Midas emerged with Serena from a tunnel. Midas had one hand wrapped around Serena's throat and the other pointing a gun at her chest, using her like a shield.

"Drop the gun," Midas said. "Or I kill her."

"Don't do it, Conrad. Shoot me and Midas both. Save the Temple Mount."

Conrad saw the strength in her eyes. She was ready

to die. But *he* wasn't ready for her to die. "I can't lose you again."

Midas smiled. "Then you'll drop it."

Conrad put his gun on the ground, reminding himself that all he had to do was keep Serena alive and the *Flammenschwert* out of the water.

"Kick the gun into the water," Midas ordered.

Conrad gave it a swipe with his foot and it skidded to the edge of the river and stopped.

That was good enough for Midas, who said, "Take the *Flammenschwert* and set it back into the water where it belongs. Hurry."

"No, Conrad!" Serena shouted. "If you do what Midas wants, you can kiss any hope of peace in the Middle East goodbye. Me, too. Let me go and save the world—for me."

Conrad hesitated. Something had changed in her eyes.

"I understand, Conrad," Serena said calmly as she put her hand on top of Midas's gun. "Let me help you."

She forced Midas's hand, and the gun exploded. She collapsed, exposing a stunned Midas as he staggered back a step and raised his gun to shoot Conrad.

"No!" Conrad shouted, diving for his gun and shooting Midas between the eyes. The bullet blew Midas's skull against the stone wall, killing him instantly.

Conrad ran to Serena. Her shirt was soaked in blood. It was pumping out of her chest.

"Oh, God, no." He ripped the shirt open to see the bullet hole above her left breast. Right above her heart. "No!"

He put his hands on the wound to try and stop the bleeding. Then he felt her hand on his and looked into her eyes. The light in them was fading.

"Take Uriel's sword, Conrad. Back to the King's Chamber. It can't explode in the water."

"There's water seeping through the stones all over this place, Serena. Every chamber is like an empty oil drum. You can't tell me that it still won't ignite this river."

"No, but the impact might not be so bad if it's not immersed."

"I can't leave you."

She shook her head. "No time . . ."

"Serena," he said, trying to lift her, but even more blood came out. "I can't."

"What's the clock say?"

He looked at the readout. "Ninety seconds."

"You know the Book of Revelation?" she said.

"I know," he said. "You read the ending. The Church wins."

"No," she said. "God wins. There is no Church in the New Jerusalem. No temples or mosques, either. Just God and his people."

"That's great," said Conrad. "But what do I do in the meantime without you?"

She didn't answer. Her body was limp.

"Serena!" he said, shaking her. "Serena!"

He looked at the timer on the *Flammenschwert*: 57 seconds . . . 56 seconds . . .

He wiped his hands, lifted the device, and then took off with it for the shaft. At the bottom of the steps, he looked back and saw Serena's lifeless body on the floor of the river cave.

Four granite slab doors inside the King's Chamber were already beginning to drop by the time Conrad reached the armillary globe and placed the *Flammenschwert* inside. He barely slipped under the falling slab into the Gihon shaft before it shut. Then he ran back down the steps to Uriel's Gate. The timer started to beep at the thirty-second count . . . 29 seconds . . . 28 seconds . . .

He burst past the pillars into the cave. Serena's body lay on the banks where he'd left her. He collapsed next to her, pulling her into his arms.

"I stopped him," he told her, though he knew she couldn't hear him. He looked at the hole above her blood-soaked breast and wept. "Oh, God, no. Please, no."

He lifted her into his arms and carried her to the torrent, the beeping of the timer counting down audibly to zero. A terrific quake shook the entire Temple Mount as the *Flammenschwert* exploded in the upper chamber. Chunks of rock began to fall around him, making huge splashes in the river.

Holding Serena in his arms, he jumped into the rushing waters as flames burst out of the Gihon shaft. Sheets of fire flickered like waves in the air above the river, illuminating Serena's face as if she were an angel beneath the surface.

As the current carried them both away, Conrad kissed her goodbye with his last breath. The river sucked them down a dark tunnel. He tried to hold on to her, but her hand slipped away. He shouted out to her in the water, but then his head hit a rock and everything went black.

54

It was just after three o'clock, and General Gellar was praying at the Western Wall, his head covered with his yarmulke and his shoulders draped with his silk tallith, when the explosion rocked the Temple Mount.

There were screams and shouts, and he looked up at the Dome of the Rock to behold the pillar of fire he had dreamed of for so long. But it didn't come, and the shaking began to die down like a small earthquake. There were no aftershocks.

Confused and disturbed by what this could mean, he slowly made his way across the crowds in the plaza who were engaged in animated discussion over what had just happened.

As he approached the curb, a white van pulled up and a door slid open to reveal a bleeding Commander Sam Deker and several armed Yamam. Gellar tried to turn but felt something prick his neck as he blacked out.

*　*　*

Several hours later, Deker and his team stormed the labs of the Israeli subsidiary of Midas Minerals & Mining at the Tefen Industrial Park near the Lebanese border. After the raid, he met with his U.S. counterparts in one of the theaters on the corporate campus. Marshall Packard was sitting on a chair on the stage, reading over a report with a tall, thin woman who introduced herself as Wanda Randolph.

"Hell, Deker, this month alone they had engineers from Intel, Siemens, Exxon, and MIT visiting the R & D center to learn about this new water detection and extraction technology," Packard told him. "How could the Israelis not know Gellar had an ownership interest in the company?"

"Many members of the government and military have similar arrangements with the companies here."

Packard frowned. "You secured the rest of those metal pellets in the labs?"

"Destroyed." Deker held his ground. "I trusted neither my superiors nor you to properly dispose of them."

"That's unfortunate," Packard said. "Just one of those little fire beads could have unlocked Atlantean technology."

Deker said nothing.

"What are you going to say about Gellar in your report to the Israeli prime minister?"

"That he died a hero of Israel, preventing what could

have been a debilitating strike on the Temple Mount. Had it succeeded, it would have triggered a war in which Israel would have prevailed, of course, but at the cost of many lives."

"What about the globes? I don't suppose they could have possibly survived."

"If they did, I wouldn't tell you," Deker said. "I'm more concerned about Yeats and Serghetti. Any word on their fate?"

Packard looked somber. "No," he said. "But wherever they are, I think it's time we finally leave them the hell alone."

That evening Deker returned to the Western Wall and looked for the slip of paper with the prayer on it that Gellar had inserted between the massive rocks. It was taboo, but Deker wasn't much of a devout Jew.

Using what he had seen from the surveillance footage, he found what he was reasonably certain was the prayer.

Come let us go up the mountain of
the Lord, that we may walk the
paths of the Most High.
And we shall beat our swords into ploughshares,
and our spears into pruning hooks.
Nation shall not lift up sword against nation—
Neither shall they learn war any more.
And none shall be afraid, for the mouth of the
Lord of Hosts has spoken.

It was a good prayer, Deker thought. He was sure he had heard it somewhere before in his childhood. Seeing the Jews and Christians around him praying, and hearing the distant call of the minaret for Muslims to pray as well, he decided to repeat that prayer as his way of saying kaddish for the souls of Conrad Yeats and Serena Serghetti.

55

It was already hot at ten A.M. on Easter Sunday when Reka Bressler, a grad student from Hebrew University's Orion Center for the Study of Dead Sea Scrolls, led her American tour group past a stone marker that said SEA LEVEL to the rocks of the Dead Sea over four hundred yards below.

The desolate area was the lowest point on earth, an otherworldly landscape of sheer cliffs, caves, and rocks around the waters. It was believed to be the site of several biblical cities, including Sodom and Gomorrah, or rather, what was left of them. Indeed, it looked like the aftermath of a nuclear explosion, and the smell of sulfur didn't help.

But the water of the Dead Sea was supposed to possess therapeutic powers. Already a couple from her group had jumped in to test the salty sea's legendary buoyancy. One American, settling comfortably in the water, looked like he was reclining on an invisible lawn chair as he scanned the *Jerusalem Post*.

That was when Reka saw the body of a fully clothed man washed up on the beach. He was clearly no tourist. She cursed and ran down the shore to him and turned him over.

His face was caked with blood. His head must have struck a rock somewhere. She bent down, placed two fingers on his neck, and felt a faint pulse. She pressed on his stomach, and he spat up water. She was about to give him mouth-to-mouth when she felt a hand on her shoulder.

"That's okay, I've got him."

Reka rose and saw a woman in torn clothes with a scorched medallion on her chest. There was something familiar and ethereal about her. But the footprints behind her proved that she was just as flesh-and-blood as her companion. "But you look worse than he does," Reka said.

The woman smiled. "I'll be sure to tell him. He'll like that. You may want to get back to your group. I think there's a man under that hand waving a newspaper above the surface of the water."

"*Harah*," Reka muttered, and started running down the beach.

Serena held Conrad's head in her arms as he coughed, blinked his eyes open, and looked at her and then at the seemingly godforsaken place around them.

"This can't be hell, because you're here," he said.

She saw him staring at the scorched medallion hanging from her neck. Her Shekel of Tyre had been sheared in half by the bullet it had deflected, searing her chest with a cauterized flesh wound in the shape of a crescent moon. "River of Life, Conrad."

He sat up and wrapped his arms around her. "Thank you, God."

She wiped the tears from her eyes, and then she removed the medallion from her neck. "Well, I'm not returning to Rome."

Conrad looked at her. "Where are you going?"

"Wherever you go, Conrad."

"You sure you want to do this?"

"I do."

"And then?"

"We can love God, serve others, be fruitful, and multiply."

"Well, let's not be disobedient, then," he said, and kissed her under the beating sun.

ACKNOWLEDGMENTS

Special thanks to my amazing editor, Emily Bestler, and my unflinching agent, Simon Lipskar, for their insight and support. To my publisher, Judith Curr, at Atria for her enthusiasm and genius, and to Sarah Branham and Laura Stern for keeping everything running on time—even me. Thanks also to Louise Burke, Lisa Keim, and the world-class team at Pocket responsible for getting my books out to the farthest corners of the earth.

I'm incredibly fortunate to have the marketing support of such creative individuals from Simon & Schuster as Kathleen Schmidt, David Brown, Christine Duplessis, and Natalie White. Also Doug Stambaugh at S&S Digital, Tom Spain at S&S Audio, and Kate-Lyall Grnat in the UK. Thank you all.

I owe a debt of gratitude to those individuals within the intelligence communities of the United States, Europe, and the Middle East who plied me with Mojitos in hopes I'd forget certain parts of our conversations and their real names. Done. Thank you for generously sharing your unique perspectives on world peace.

Thanks, finally, to the Israel Antiquities Authority, the Jordanian Waqf, and members of certain nongovernmental organizations on either side of the Temple Mount divide in Jerusalem who share a passion for the protection of the holy places.

ATRIA BOOKS
PROUDLY PRESENTS

THE PROMISED WAR

THOMAS GREANIAS

Available in hardcover from Atria Books

Turn the page for a preview of *The Promised War.* . . .

1

The Dome of the Rock mosque rose like the moon behind the towering wall that surrounded the Temple Mount. Sam Deker cleared the top of the wall and dropped into the gardens below, a wraith in the night. He glanced at the illuminated hands of his Krav Maga watch. Seven minutes to three. He had told Stern fourteen minutes back at the van. He had used up six. Time was running out.

Deker reached into his combat pack and pulled out a brick of C-4. He had enough bricks to take out half of the thirty-five-acre complex. If he had any doubts about this mission, now was the moment to turn back. He slipped the C-4 back into his pack and moved through the maze of trees and shrubs.

The Temple Mount was the most contested religious site in the world. For Muslims, the eight-sided, golden-capped Dome of the Rock mosque protected the "noble rock" that they believed to be the foundation stone of the earth and the place from which the prophet Muhammad ascended to heaven.

But religious Jews believed the rock was the place from which God gathered the dust to create the first man, Adam, as well as the site of King Solomon's Temple. According to Jewish prophecy, it was also where a new temple would be built—once the Dome of the Rock was gone. Many of these Jews, like Deker's fanatical superior officer Uri Elezar, refused to set foot on such holy ground.

None of this was a problem for Deker. He couldn't care less. Deker had been recruited by Israel's internal security service, the Shin Bet, precisely because he was a secular American Jew who had served with the U.S. Marines in Iraq and Afghanistan as a demolitions officer. Who better to protect the Temple Mount, he was told, than a twenty-six-year-old who specialized in the destruction of major structures and equally offended both sides of the religious divide?

Deker followed the route he had planned well in advance, timing his steps with the movements of the Palestinian security guards of the Islamic Waqf, or religious trust.

For almost a thousand years the Waqf had served as the protectors of the Temple Mount, even after Israel captured Jerusalem in the 1967 Arab-Israeli War. Such was their status as the true guardians of Islam—and allegedly above the petty political interests of the modern Palestinian Authority, which claimed it had sovereignty over the site.

Deker, however, knew the Waqf to be as political as any Muslim organization; it simply saw the Arab-Israeli struggle in terms of centuries, not decades. So far as the Waqf was concerned, Israel's resurrection as a modern state in 1948 after three thousand years of exile was but a foul blot on the long scroll of history. Israel, meanwhile, decided it best to prevent unnecessary provocations by its own more zealous citizens. So not only did it allow the Waqf to continue to manage the Temple Mount, it even enforced a controversial ban on Jewish prayers there.

When Deker finally reached the east wall of the Dome of the Rock mosque, he pressed his back against the blue ceramic tiles of the outer wall. He peered around the corner. A Waqf guard was making his way across the vast plaza toward the other mosque on the Mount, the silver-capped Al-Aqsa. Deker waited until the guard passed under the ma'avzin arches and disappeared down the steps to the lower plaza. Then without hesitation he darted across the colonnaded entrance of the mosque and ducked inside.

The Waqf officer in charge that night was rounding one of the titanic marble columns that supported the dome twenty meters overhead when Deker entered the mosque. The Palestinian managed to grab his radio, but before he could engage the device to transmit even a sound, Deker gave him a chop to the throat. He crumpled to the floor.

Deker made sure the guard still had a pulse before he turned to his right and followed the plush ruby carpet to the steps that led down to a cave dedicated to King Solomon. A relic of the Crusades, the cave had been carved out by the Order of the Knights Templar after they had converted the Dome of the Rock into their Templum Domini, or "Temple of Our Lord."

Medieval maps marked the cave as the "center of the world," and the "Well of Souls" beneath it was said to have once served as the resting place of the legendary lost Ark of the Covenant. According to the ancient biblical account, the sacred Ark—an ornate box made of shittim-wood and coated with gold—contained the original Ten Commandments, the tablets that God gave to Moses at Mount Sinai as the ancient Israelites wandered the desert in search of the Promised Land. Deker thought God—Yahweh to the Israelites—should have simply given Moses a map. It would have saved the Israelites forty years and countless lives.

But the Knights Templar couldn't hold the Temple Mount for long. A few years later it was back in the hands of the Muslim Waqf, where it had remained that past millennium.

Recently, the Waqf had quietly begun a massive subterranean tunneling operation. The Israeli Defense Forces, or IDF, feared that the Waqf was on the verge of discovering an ancient network of chambers and corridors deep beneath the mount that predated even the First and Second Jewish Temples. The front door to that network was none other than the Well of Souls beneath the Dome of the Rock.

Adjan Husseini, the Palestinian head of the Waqf in

Jerusalem, was kneeling facedown in prayer when Deker entered the cave. At the sound of Deker's footsteps, he lifted his head and started at the sight of the C-4 brick Deker removed from his pack.

Looking Husseini in the eye, Deker held the brick up and said, "Boom."

"Commander Deker." Husseini rose to his feet. "Go ahead. Take the shot."

Deker put the C-4 brick back into his pack and took out his BlackBerry. Draping one arm around Husseini's neck, he extended the other and snapped a photo with his phone's camera. He then e-mailed it to Colonel Elezar.

"It's time-stamped," Deker said, putting the phone away. "I copied you too."

But Husseini, eyes wide, was staring at the explosives and blinking LED displays inside Deker's open pack, catching on that the C-4 charges were real. "You could have blown us all to bits!"

Deker said, "I promised you that I would expose loopholes in your security in the hopes you'd finally relent and let us put up the electronic surveillance net."

"So you can spy on us."

"So we can better defend the Dome of the Rock from the ultra-Orthodox Jews who want to destroy it so that they can erect a Third Temple. Or from radical Palestinians who would pin the blame on Orthodox Jews. You've seen the intel. The threat's real and it's imminent."

Husseini said nothing for a moment. A hole in the six-foot rock ceiling allowed a shaft of light from the mosque above to illuminate several small altars and prayer niches around the chamber. Deker could see Husseini's eyes study him with bitter resentment through the haze of incense and flickering candlelight.

"You knew from the start that we'd never agree to Israeli surveillance," Husseini said. "Yet, you proceeded to pull this dangerous stunt only to humiliate us."

Husseini was baiting him now, stalling. Deker sensed a trap and realized he had no idea where the Waqf guards outside were at the moment. He thought of Stern back at the van. It was time to leave.

"This security test isn't nearly as dangerous as the weapons cache you've been stockpiling in the southeast corner under Solomon's Stables," Deker said.

Surprise registered on Husseini's face, although Deker wasn't sure if it was real or manufactured by the man.

"Oh, yes, we know about that," Deker told him. "And that tunnel you've been digging right under this cave. If anyone is going to start the fire, it's going to be you."

Husseini picked up a bronze candelabrum and brought it down heavily onto the floor's marble slab. It gave out a hollow thud, revealing the existence of a lower chamber known as the Well of Souls. His face was an unreadable mask again.

"Is that really your concern here tonight, Commander Deker? Or are you afraid we might find something that Israel has been hiding from the world? Wise men have long believed that a cosmic portal exists here, a tunnel through space and time that leads to paradise."

Deker paused. "Or maybe it's the gate to hell."

Husseini was angry now. The expression on his face didn't show it, and his voice was steady and subdued. But his words were bitter and sharp.

"You think you're so special, Deker, better than the rest of us. That you're the human pin in a live grenade, standing alone between old Arabs like me and Jews like your Colonel Elezar. But know this: the Jews won't stop until they have destroyed the dome above us. Armageddon is inevitable. It's a time bomb that will go off. You can't stop it. Just like you couldn't prevent your girlfriend from blowing herself up with an explosive made by your own hands."

Deker felt the world give way under his feet at the thought of his Rachel. But he stood firm, emotionless in his expression, and turned to face Husseini, who picked up a ceremonial washbowl with a candle from the altar.

"I'm told it looked something like this," Husseini said, stroking the red-and-black ceramic pattern. "You and your IDF masters intended to assassinate a Hamas militant inside the home of a Palestinian government official. But by some mystery known only to Allah, your bowl ended up in the hands of your beloved as she prepared to light her Shabbat candles to celebrate the first night of the Passover at the Western Wall. Mercifully, she perished the instant you hit your remote detonator. News reports said the six injured Jews around her took several hours to die."

In that second, Deker wanted to reach out and rip out

Husseini's throat. And he would have, if he didn't know that's exactly what Husseini wanted him to attempt.

"The grief must torment you every waking hour and haunt you in your sleep," Husseini went on, the corners of his mouth turning into a slight smile at having gotten even the suppression of a reaction out of him. "Perhaps that's why you can't leave this place. To you it was always a holy pile of rubbish, but to her it was her faith and life. Now it's her tombstone and you are a ghost stumbling in the graveyard of history. But it's impossible to bring her back. We can't change the past any more than we can change the future."

"That hasn't stopped you from trying." Deker produced a pottery shard he had found in an open trench at the base of the eastern wall. He pointed it like a dagger at Husseini's chest. "Your bulldozers are destroying ancient First and Second Temple artifacts. As if you can erase Israel from history."

Husseini's eyes flickered in fear for the first time that night as he looked at the shard in Deker's hand, clenched so tight that Deker didn't know he had cut himself until he felt a trickle of blood through his fingers. The Palestinian seemed to realize he had pushed Deker too far, but he stood defiant.

"Keeping your dead lover's memory alive doesn't change the fact that Jerusalem has always been an Arab and Islamic city," Husseini said, sticking with the party line to the end. "This is a plant. No Jewish temple ever stood here."

"Right," Deker said, placing the bloodstained shard on the small altar as a souvenir of this encounter. "Neither did I."

"Would that were true," Husseini told him. "But a man at war with himself can't keep the peace forever."

Deker wiped his bloodied hand on his trouser leg, gave him a slight bow and turned toward the cave entrance. He then vanished up the steps, leaving Husseini to his prayers.

Three minutes later—and six minutes later than he had promised Stern—Deker rappelled over the eastern wall and landed on the roof of a yellow Caterpillar backhoe loader parked against the base. He jumped off and raced down the slope of the Muslim graveyard abutting the wall, weaving his way through the tombstones toward the parked Gihon Water and Sewage Company service van.

He stopped the second he saw the cracked windshield and unmistakable bullet hole.

Deker whipped out his Jericho 9mm pistol from his pack and rushed to the driver's side of the van, aiming his Jericho through the window with one hand as he threw open the door with the other. Stern was slumped over the wheel, motionless. Deker felt sick with rage. He pushed Stern's head with the steel nose of his gun. The head rolled to the side, without the resistance of life, revealing a hole in the temple, blood pooling heavily inside the ear.

A flash in the driver's-side mirror caught Deker's eye and he glanced back to see a black van barreling up from behind. In the same motion, Deker jumped into the Gihon van, pushed Stern's corpse away and slid behind the wheel. He heard the squeal of brakes and the crash of boots on the ground. As he turned the ignition and shifted gears, the glass behind him shattered.

He felt a prick in the back of his neck and he lurched forward into the dashboard. His head hanging down, everything spinning, he saw Stern's twisted face staring at him before everything exploded in a burst of light.

36995271R00197

Made in the USA
Middletown, DE
16 November 2016